OECD-FAO
Agricultural Outlook
2008-2017

OECD

ORGANISATION FOR ECONOMIC
CO-OPERATION AND DEVELOPMENT

FOOD AND AGRICULTURE ORGANIZATION
OF THE UNITED NATIONS

ORGANISATION FOR ECONOMIC CO-OPERATION AND DEVELOPMENT

The OECD is a unique forum where the governments of 30 democracies work together to address the economic, social and environmental challenges of globalisation. The OECD is also at the forefront of efforts to understand and to help governments respond to new developments and concerns, such as corporate governance, the information economy and the challenges of an ageing population. The Organisation provides a setting where governments can compare policy experiences, seek answers to common problems, identify good practice and work to co-ordinate domestic and international policies.

The OECD member countries are: Australia, Austria, Belgium, Canada, the Czech Republic, Denmark, Finland, France, Germany, Greece, Hungary, Iceland, Ireland, Italy, Japan, Korea, Luxembourg, Mexico, the Netherlands, New Zealand, Norway, Poland, Portugal, the Slovak Republic, Spain, Sweden, Switzerland, Turkey, the United Kingdom and the United States. The Commission of the European Communities takes part in the work of the OECD.

OECD Publishing disseminates widely the results of the Organisation's statistics gathering and research on economic, social and environmental issues, as well as the conventions, guidelines and standards agreed by its members.

THE FOOD AND AGRICULTURE ORGANIZATION (FAO) OF THE UNITED NATIONS

The Food and Agriculture Organization of the United Nations leads international efforts to defeat hunger. FAO's mandate is to raise levels of nutrition, improve agricultural productivity, better the lives of rural populations and contribute to the growth of the world economy. Serving both developed and developing countries, FAO acts as a neutral forum where all nations meet as equals to negotiate agreements and debate policy. FAO is also a source of knowledge providing access to information in print and electronic format. We help developing countries and countries in transition modernize and improve agriculture, forestry and fisheries practices and ensure good nutrition for all. Since our founding in 1945, we have focused special attention on developing rural areas, home to 70 per cent of the world's poor and hungry people. FAO's activities comprise four main areas: putting information within reach; sharing policy expertise; providing a meeting place for nations; bringing knowledge to the field.

Also available in French under the title:
Perspectives agricoles de l'OCDE et de la FAO 2008-2017

Foreword

*T*his is the fourth time that the Agricultural Outlook report has been prepared jointly by the Organisation for Economic Co-operation and Development (OECD) and the Food and Agriculture Organization (FAO) of the United Nations. The report draws on the commodity, policy and country expertise of both Organisations in providing a longer-term assessment of future prospects in the major world agricultural commodity markets.

The report is published annually, as part of a continuing effort to promote informed discussion of emerging market and policy issues. This edition of the Agricultural Outlook offers an assessment of agricultural markets covering cereals, oilseeds, sugar, meats, milk and dairy products over the period 2008 to 2017. For the first time, it also includes an analysis of and projections for global biofuel markets for bioethanol and biodiesel, facilitating the discussion of interactions between these markets and those for the main agricultural feedstocks used in their production. The market assessments for all the commodities are based on a set of projections that are conditional on specific assumptions regarding macroeconomic factors, agricultural and trade policies and production technologies; they also assume average weather conditions and longer-term productivity trends. Using the underlying assumptions, the Agricultural Outlook presents a plausible scenario for the evolution of agricultural markets over the next decade and provides a benchmark for the analysis of agricultural market outcomes that would result from alternative economic or policy assumptions.

This year's Outlook is set against a backdrop of exceptional increases in prices for many agricultural commodities, and this has posed a considerable challenge in preparing the projections and assessing the "durability" of the various influences shaping these prices. That is, which of the factors that are driving up prices are temporary and which will prove to be more permanent influences? How will they individually and collectively affect price levels, price trends and price volatility in the future? How will markets react to currently high prices and a more uncertain price outlook? What are the appropriate policy responses? This report comes at a very timely moment and provides important information, with a view to enlightening the discussion on food-price increases, their causes and their likely consequences for agricultural markets as well as for the policy-formulation process.

The projections and assessments provided in this report are the result of close co-operation between the OECD and the FAO Secretariats and national experts in member and some non-member countries, and thus reflect the combined knowledge and expertise of this wide group of participants. A jointly developed modelling system, based on the OECD's Aglink and FAO's Cosimo models, facilitated the assurance of consistency in the projections. The fully documented Outlook database, including historical data and projections, is available through the OECD-FAO joint Internet site www.agri-outlook.org. Within the OECD, this publication is prepared by the Trade and Agriculture Directorate, while at FAO, the Trade and Markets Division was responsible for the report.

Acknowledgements. This Agricultural Outlook was prepared by the following staff members of the OECD and FAO Secretariats:

At the OECD, the team of economic and market analysts of the OECD Trade and Agriculture Directorate that contributed to this report consisted of Loek BOONEKAMP (team leader), Marcel ADENAUER, Céline GINER, Alexis FOURNIER, Franziska JUNKER, Garry SMITH, Pavel VAVRA (outlook co-ordinator) and Martin VON LAMPE.

Research and statistical assistance were provided by Armelle ELASRI, Alexis FOURNIER, Claude NENERT and Nicolas RUIZ. Secretarial services and co-ordination in report preparation was provided by Christine CAMERON, Nina DHUMAL, Anita LARI and Stéfanie MILOWSKI. Technical assistance in the preparation of the Outlook database was provided by Frano ILICIC. Many other colleagues in the OECD Secretariat and member country delegations furnished useful comments on earlier drafts of the report. The contribution of Joe DEWBRE in reviewing and editing Chapter 2 of this report and Linda FULPONI in drafting Box 2.1 in that chapter is particularly acknowledged.

At FAO, the team of economists and commodity officers from the Commodities and Trade Division contributing to this edition consisted of Abdolreza ABBASSIAN, El Mamoun AMROUK Concepcion CALPE, Kaison CHANG, Merritt CLUFF (team leader), Piero CONFORTI, Cheng FANG, Holger MATTHEY (baseline co-ordinator), Adam PRAKASH, Grégoire TALLARD, Peter THOENES, Koji YANAGISHIMA, and Carola FABI from the Statistics Division. AliArslan GURKAN and Alexander SARRIS initiated support for FAO's Cosimo modelling project.

Research assistance and database preparation was provided by Claudio CERQUILINI, Berardina FORZINETTI, John HEINE, Marco MILO, and Barbara SENFTER. Secretarial services were provided by Rita ASHTON.

Chapter 2 of this report was drafted by Wyatt THOMPSON (University of Missouri) elaborating on and analysing input from the OECD and FAO Secretariats, Pierre CHARLEBOIS (Agriculture and Agrifood Canada), Frank ROSE (Lewis University, formerly CBOT) and Pat Westhoff (University of Missouri).

Finally, the assistance of the Executive Director of the International Sugar Organisation, Peter Baron and his staff in reviewing the sugar projections is gratefully acknowledged.

Table of Contents

Figures

OECD-FAO AGRICULTURAL OUTLOOK 2008-2017 – ISBN 978-92-64-04590-3 – © OECD/FAO 2008

Acronyms and Abbreviations

ACP	African, Caribbean and Pacific countries
AMAD	Agricultural Market Access Database
AUSFTA	Australia and United States Free Trade Agreement
AI	Avian Influenza
BNGY	Billion gallons per year
BNLY	Billion litres per year
BSE	Bovine Spongiform Encephalopathy
Bt	Billion tonnes
BTL	Biomass to liquid
CAFTA	Central American Free Trade Agreement
CAP	Common Agricultural Policy (EU)
CCC	Commodity Credit Corporation
CET	Common External Tariff
CIS	Commonwealth of Independent States
CPI	Consumer Price Index
CRP	Conservation Reserve Program of the United States
CMO	Common Market Organisation for sugar (EU)
Cts/lb	Cents per pound
cwe	Carcass weight equivalent
DBES	Date-based Export Scheme
DDA	Doha Development Agenda
DDG	Dried Distiller's Grains
dw	Dressed weight
EBA	Everything-But-Arms Initiative (EU)
ECOWAP	West Africa Regional Agricultural Policy
ECOWAS	Economic Community of West African States
EISA Act	Energy Independence and Security Act of 2007 (US)
EPAs	Economic Partnership Agreements (between EU and ACP countries)
ERS	Economic Research Service of the US Department for Agriculture
est	Estimate
E85	Blends of biofuel in transport fuel that represent 85 percent of the fuel volume
EU	European Union
EU-15	Fifteen member states of the European Union
EU-10	Ten new member states of the European Union from May 2004
EU-27	Twenty seven member states of the European Union (including Bulgaria and Romania from 2007)
FAO	Food and Agriculture Organization of the United Nations

FMD	Foot and Mouth Disease
FOB	Free on board (export price)
FR	Federal Reserve (US central bank)
FSRI ACT	Farm Security and Rural Investment Act (US) of 2002
FTA	Free Trade Agreement
GDP	Gross Domestic Product
G-10	Group of 10 countries (see Glossary)
G-20	Group of 20 developing countries (see Glossary)
GDPD	Gross Domestic Product Deflator
GHG	Green House Gases
GMO	Genetically modified organism
HFCS	High Fructose Corn Syrup
HS	Harmonised Commodity Description and Coding System
IEA	International Energy Agency
kt	Thousand tonnes
LAC	Latin America and the Caribbean
La Niña	Climatic condition associated with temperature of major sea currents
LDC's	Least Developed Countries
LICONSA	Leche Industralizada
lw	Live weight
MERCOSUR	Common Market of the South
MFN	Most Favoured Nation
Mha	Million hectares
MPS	Market Price Support
Mt	Million tonnes
MTBE	Methyl Tertiary Butyl Ether
NAFTA	North American Free Trade Agreement
OECD	Organisation for Economic Co-operation and Development
OIE	World Organisation for Animal Health
PCE	Private Consumption Expenditure
PIK	Payment in kind programme (US)
PROCAMPO	Mexican Farmers Direct Support Programme
PPP	Purchasing Power Parity
PRRS	Porcine Reproductive and Respiratory Syndrome
PSE	Producer Support Estimate
pw	Product weight
R&D	Research and Development
rse	Raw sugar equivalent
rtc	Ready to cook
RFS	Renewable Fuels Standard in the US, which is part of the Energy Policy Act of 2005
rwt	Retail weight
SEAC	Spongiform Encephalopathy Advisory Committee
SFP	Single Farm Payment scheme (EU)
SMP	Skim milk powder
SPS	Sanitary and Phytosanitary measures
STRV	Short Tons Raw Value

OECD-FAO AGRICULTURAL OUTLOOK 2008-2017 – ISBN 978-92-64-04590-3 – © OECD/FAO 2008

t	Tonnes
t/ha	Tonnes/hectare
TRQ	Tariff rate quota
UK	United Kingdom
UN	The United Nations
URAA	Uruguay Round Agreement on Agriculture
UNCTAD	United Nations Conference on Trade and Development
US	United States of America
USDA	United States Department of Agriculture
VAT	Value added tax
v-CJD	New Creutzfeld-Jakob-Disease
WAEMU	West African Economic and Monetary Union
WMP	Whole milk powder
WTO	World Trade Organisation

Symbols

AUD	Dollars (Australia)	KRW	Korean won
ARS	Pesos (Argentina)	lb	Pound
Bn	Billion	Mn	Million
BRL	Real (Brazil)	MXN	Mexican pesos
CAD	Dollars (Canada)	NZD	Dollars (New Zealand)
CNY	Yuan (China)	p.a	Per annum
EUR	Euro (Europe)	RUR	Ruble (Russia)
gal	Gallons	THB	Thai baht
Ha	Hectare	USD	Dollars (United States)
hl	Hectolitre	ZAR	South African rand
INR	Indian rupees		

THE OUTLOOK IN BRIEF

- World reference prices in nominal terms for almost all agricultural commodities covered in this report are at or above previous record levels (see Fig. 2.1). This will not last and prices will gradually come down because of the transitory nature of some of the factors that are behind the recent hikes. But there is strong reason to believe that there are now also permanent factors underpinning prices that will work to keep them both at higher average levels than in the past and reduce the long-term decline in real terms. Whether transitory or permanent, appropriate policy action for agricultural development and for addressing the needs of the hungry and the poor needs to take account of both these characteristics.

- The dramatic increase in prices since 2005/06 is partly the result of adverse weather conditions in major grain-producing regions in the world, with spill-over effects on crops and livestock that compete for the same land. In a context of low global stocks, these developments alone would have triggered strong price reactions. These conditions are not new; they have happened in the past and prices have come down once more normal conditions prevail and supply responds over time. The Outlook sees no reason to believe that this will not recur over the next few years.

- Once they have fallen from their current peaks, however, prices will remain at higher average levels over the medium term than in the past decade. But the underlying forces that drive agricultural product supply (by and large productivity gains) will eventually outweigh the forces that determine stronger demand, both for food and feed as well as for industrial demand, most notably for biofuel production. Consequently, prices will resume their decline in real terms, though possibly not by quite as much as in the past (see Figures 1.1, 1.4 and 1.5 in the Overview section).

- On the supply side, the Outlook expects continued yield growth for crops to be more important than new areas brought into cultivation in determining crop supply. Slowly increasing dairy and livestock yields also support the increase in milk and meat production. A key assumption in the Outlook is some strengthening of the US dollar against most currencies. In the countries affected by this change, this will reinforce domestic price incentives to increase production. These factors combine to sustain the growth of global agricultural production, although some of that impetus is abated by the supply-reducing effect of high oil prices that raise production costs.

- On the demand side, changing diets, urbanisation, economic growth and expanding populations are driving food and feed demand in developing countries. Globally, and in absolute terms, food and feed remain the largest sources of demand growth in agriculture. But stacked on top of this is now the fast-growing demand for feedstock to fuel a growing bioenergy sector. While smaller than the increase in food and feed use, biofuel demand is the largest source of new demand in decades and a strong factor underpinning the upward shift in agricultural commodity prices.

- As a result of these dynamics in supply and demand, the Outlook suggests that commodity prices – in nominal terms – over the medium term will average substantially above the levels that prevailed in the past 10 years. When the average for 2008 to 2017 is compared with that over 1998 to 2007, beef and pork prices may be some 20% higher; raw and white sugar around 30%; wheat, maize and skim milk powder 40 to 60%; butter and oilseeds more than 60% and vegetable oils over 80%. Over the Outlook period, prices will resume their decline in real terms, albeit at a slower rate. However, the impact of various supply and demand factors on prices will differ across commodities.

- In addition, prices may also be more volatile than in the past: stock levels are not expected to be replenished substantially over the Outlook; demand is becoming less sensitive to price changes at the farm level as the commodity share in the final food bill falls and as industrial demand grows; weather conditions and agricultural product supply may become more variable with climate change; and speculative non-commercial investment funds enter or leave agricultural futures markets as profit opportunities dictate.

- Within this overall context, the epicentre of global agriculture will further shift from the OECD towards developing countries. Both consumption and production are growing faster in developing countries for all products except wheat. By 2017, these countries are expected to dominate production and consumption of most commodities, with the exception of coarse grains, cheese, and skim-milk powder.

- Corresponding shifts are also occurring in global trade patterns. Imports are growing most in developing countries, and an increasing share of this growth is captured by larger exports from other emerging and developing countries. Export growth in developing countries is greater, and sometimes very much so for almost all products. However, while the share of OECD countries in world exports falls, these countries continue to dominate export trade for wheat, coarse grains, pork and all dairy products.

- High prices are good for some and bad for others. They are beneficial for many commercial producers in both developed and developing countries. However, many farmers in developing countries are not linked to markets and will draw little or no benefit from currently higher prices. But the poor, and in particular the urban poor in net food importing developing countries, will suffer more. In many low-income countries, food expenditures average over 50% of income and the higher prices contained in this Outlook will push more people into undernourishment.

- For the Least Developed Countries, especially the food-deficit group, the projections thus show greatly increased vulnerability and uncertain food supplies during an era of high commodity prices and high price volatility. This underscores the importance of developing their domestic supply capacity by improving the overall environment in which agriculture operates through enhancing governance and administrative systems and investing in education, training and extension services, research and development and physical infrastructure. While these are longer-term remedies, it is important in the short term that commodity trade functions efficiently to facilitate the allocation of available commodity supplies.

- This Outlook assumes unchanged agricultural and trade policies. The actual evolution of agricultural commodity and food prices, however, hinges importantly on future policy developments. In this context, increased humanitarian aid is needed to reduce the negative impact of high prices on the very poor, and this could be done without any major impact on markets.

- Such effects would result, however, from trade-restricting policies such as export taxes and embargos. These may in the short term provide some relief to domestic consumers but in fact impose a burden on domestic producers and limit their supply response, as well as contribute to global commodity market uncertainty. Similarly, measures to protect domestic producers of agricultural commodities through border measures imposes a burden on domestic consumers; it would also restrict growth opportunities for producers abroad.

- Policy support, as well as oil-price developments, will strongly influence the evolution of future demand from biofuel for agricultural commodity feedstocks. In this context, neither the US Energy Independence and Security Act (EISA) nor proposals for a new EU bioenergy directive are taken into account. Changes in either, or new technological developments would also have a strong impact on projected world prices for agricultural commodities and for the availability for food and feed use. In this report, second generation biofuels are not expected to be produced on a commercial basis over the Outlook period.

- Finally, over the longer term, agricultural supply is facing increased uncertainties and limitations to the amount of new land that can be taken into cultivation. Public and private investments in innovation and increasing agricultural productivity, particularly in developing countries, would greatly improve supply prospects by helping to broaden the production base and lessen the chance of recurring commodity price spikes.

- This year's Outlook has been prepared in an environment characterised by increased instability in financial markets, higher food price inflation, signs of weakening global economic growth and food-security concerns. Although projections for agricultural commodity markets have always been subject to a number of uncertainties, these have taken on more importance in this year's edition.

ISBN 978-92-64-04590-3
OECD-FAO AGRICULTURAL OUTLOOK 2008-2017
© OECD/FAO 2008

Chapter 1

Overview

This version of the *OECD-FAO Agricultural Outlook* is set against a background where world reference prices for most agricultural commodities covered in this report are at or above previous record levels, at least in nominal terms. While some of the reasons for these high prices are transitory, there is strong reason to believe that there are now also permanent factors underpinning prices that will work to keep them at higher average levels than in the past (Figure 1.1).

Figure 1.1. **World commodity prices at higher average levels**

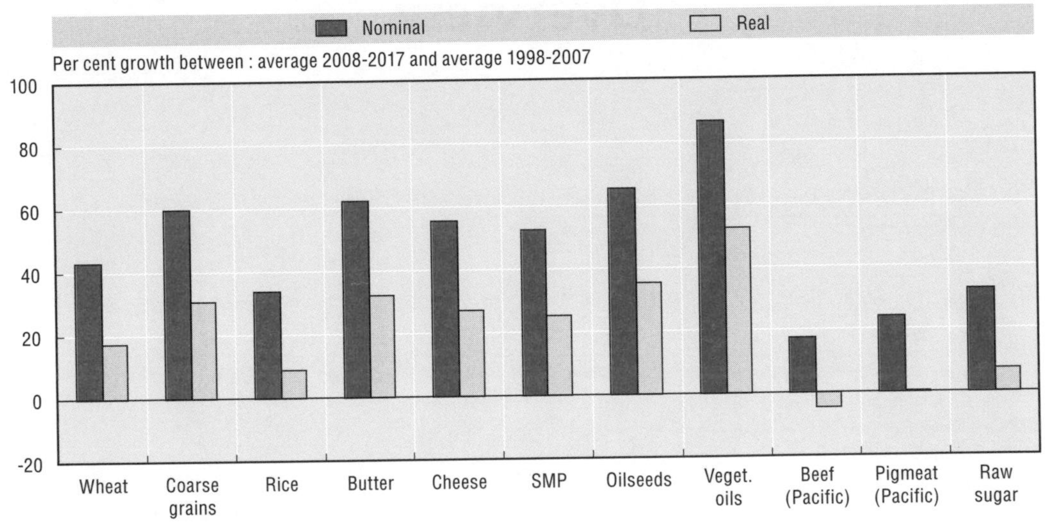

StatLink http://dx.doi.org/10.1787/383556825413

Source: OECD and FAO Secretariats

The *Outlook* paints a picture of a further gradual shift in the epicentre of agricultural production, consumption and trade from OECD to developing countries. This happens against a backdrop of record high prices of almost all agricultural products at the beginning of the *Outlook*. The *Outlook* indicates that current price levels can be explained by both transitory and permanent factors. There is strong reason to suspect that the more permanent factors will result in a structural upward shift in real agricultural commodity prices. But from these sometimes substantially higher average levels, when compared to the past decade, real prices will again begin to decline, though at a more gradual rate than in the past.

The *Outlook* is set in a context of assumed sustained economic growth around the globe, high crude oil prices, contained inflation, constant real exchange rates and unchanged policies. Markets are assumed not to be influenced by "abnormal" weather conditions, and any possible impacts of climate change and water shortages are not considered. Deviations from these assumed conditions would lead to potentially much different market outcomes.

The principal underlying assumptions

Lower but sustained economic and population growth underpins demand

Economic activity at the beginning of the *Outlook* is slowing most notably in the US, the world's leading economy. The slowdown in the US and some other OECD economies is occurring despite continuing robust economic conditions in many other parts of the world. Within this context, growth prospects for OECD countries in the short and longer term are just above 2% (annual average). Robust activity levels in the main emerging economies are projected to remain a major driver of global economic expansion in the near term. In the medium and longer term a modest deceleration is projected. China and India will remain growth leaders among developing countries, with substantial market expansion and GDP growth anticipated for both countries as they become further integrated into the global economy and world trade.

Population dynamics are important determinants of the future global economic environment, directly affecting demand for agricultural commodities. Population growth over the next decade will decline relative to the last 10 years to an average of 1.1% annually to reach approximately 7.4 billion in 2017. The fastest population growth is expected in Africa (annual average above 2%), whereas in Europe, population is expected to essentially stabilise over the coming decade (Table 1.1).

Table 1.1. **Some decline in population growth**
Average annual growth over 10 year period, percentage

	Population growth	
	1998-2007	2008-2017
World	1.23	1.12
Africa	2.37	2.21
Latin America and Caribbean	1.28	1.14
North America	1.01	0.88
Europe	0.30	0.10
Asia and Pacific	1.27	1.11
Oceania developed	1.18	0.92

StatLink ᵃᵍᵖ http://dx.doi.org/10.1787/385000556483

Note: Average annual growth is the least-squares growth rate.
Source: UN World Population Prospects (2006 Revision).

No major hike in inflation despite continued high oil prices

Despite recent hikes in food prices, sustained global growth and world trade expansion, general price levels in many countries have remained remarkably stable. This situation has reinforced expectations that inflation in OECD countries will remain low over the longer term. Measured by the Private Consumer Expenditure (PCDE) deflator, inflation will remain low in the coming decade. For OECD countries as a whole, inflation is assumed to be just above 2% per year. High consumer price inflation continues to plague some emerging and developing countries such as the Russian Federation and India with levels above 5% per annum. Inflation in Russia is, nevertheless, expected to fall to less than half the prevailing rate during 2005-07. A significant decline is also assumed for Argentina, with inflation at below 5% per year.

The world oil price assumption underlying this year's *Agricultural Outlook* is based on that published in the *OECD Economic Outlook* n° 82 (December 2007). It assumes prices to slowly increase over the outlook period from USD 90 per barrel in 2008 to USD 104 per barrel by 2017. This does not exclude the possibility of substantial variations around these levels througout the period or within any given year. However, future oil prices are a major uncertainty in the *Outlook*. Some analysts emphasise that high oil prices will slow demand, ultimately reducing the price of oil. Others argue that consumption, production and processing capacities are relatively inelastic in the short term, sustaining continued high, or even further increasing, prices. This year's *Agricultural Outlook* is based on the high-price scenario. Pressure on oil prices has been maintained thus far as geopolitical tensions combine with processing capacity constraints to keep global supply from the major oil producers below effective demand.

Conditions remain favourable for further growth in biofuel production

For the first time, this *Outlook* specifically includes projections for supply, demand, trade and prices of ethanol and biodiesel derived from agricultural feedstock. The main forces driving further growth in biofuel production are high crude oil prices and continued public support, in particular in OECD countries. However, the latest bioenergy policy changes in the EU and the US are not taken into consideration. Neither do the projections and the assessed impacts on commodity markets take account of the possibility of changes in production technologies. Such changes would modify the economics of biofuel production and affect the market and trade outcomes.

The US dollar is expected to strengthen against most currencies

Under an assumption of constant real exchange rates, inflation differentials *vis-à-vis* the United States are the primary determinant of projections for exchange rates over the *Outlook* period. This implies a strengthening of the US dollar against most currencies, even if currently there are signs of a further weakening of the dollar in the short term. Over the course of the *Outlook* period, the euro exchange rate is projected to remain stable. However, very low levels of inflation in Japan relative to the United States mean that the Yen is expected to appreciate further. The currencies of high growth/high inflation countries such as Brazil, India, Turkey and South Africa will depreciate most over the medium term.

The Outlook reflects policies in place in early 2008

Agricultural and trade policies play an important role in both domestic and international markets for agricultural commodities and food products. While agricultural policies are becoming increasingly decoupled from production decisions, non-agricultural policies, such as those for instance with respect to energy, or the environment, are having a growing impact on the agri-food sector. Policies influence the composition and levels of both production and consumption, thereby creating (or sometimes correcting) market distortions and influencing prices. There is a tendency towards increased price responsiveness on the supply side with ongoing policy reform in some OECD countries. Also, relatively elastic supply and demand in a growing number of developing countries, coupled with an increasing share of these countries in world trade, is improving adjustments in agricultural markets. As in the past, this *Outlook* assumes constant policies over the period to 2017. This implies, notably, that any changes in the new US farm legislation to replace the current FSRI Act, or in the EU's Common Agricultural Policy as a result of the scheduled "health check" or changes in trade policies reflecting a conclusion of the negotiation under the Doha Round, are not considered in this report. In addition, neither the US Energy Independence and Security Act (EISA) nor proposals for a new EU bioenergy directive have been taken into account. However, recently increased export taxes in Argentina are taken into consideration.

Main trends in commodity markets

Grain markets set to remain tight

Despite record wheat and coarse grain crops in 2007/08 and a sustained moderate rise in production thereafter, grain markets are expected to remain tight in the period to 2017. The prolific demand for maize arising from the rapidly expanding ethanol sector in the United States has profoundly affected the coarse-grain market. By 2017, approximately 40% of the country's maize crop could be destined for energy production. Growth in grain-based ethanol industries, in particular in North America and Europe, as well as rising feed requirements for flourishing livestock sectors, look set to further pressure the already critically low global grain stocks-to-use ratio over the course of the *Outlook*.

Owing to currently low stocks and high prices there will be an incentive to plant more land for grain production. In addition to a foreseen sustained recovery in production in drought-stricken Australia, the area under cereals is projected to rise for a number of reasons. There will in particular be some reallocation of land from other crops in the main OECD producers such as Canada, the US or the EU. In addition, land is taken out of set-aside in the EU for 2008. Finally, new land will be taken into cultivation, particularly in South and Latin America, Sub-Saharan Africa and the Commonwealth of Independent States (CIS). However, overall there will be constraints in expanding new arable areas in many countries and competition for land and resources among grain and oilseed crops is set to intensify with those crops offering the highest returns gaining the most ground. As a result, beyond the initial years of the *Outlook*, much of the growth in world grain output is expected to stem from productivity gains, but yield growth is not expected to match the rate attained in the previous decade.

Grain trade to reach new heights

Wheat exports have remained subdued in recent years, reflecting adverse weather in several important countries, especially in Australia and successively poor harvests in the EU. But global wheat trade is projected to expand at an average annual rate of less than 1% over the *Outlook* period. Australia is foreseen to resume the mantle of being the second-largest wheat exporter after the United States. As for coarse grains, the recuperation of traditional export sources will be supplemented by an export expansion in Ukraine.

Developing countries, such as those situated in South and East Asia, as well as Nigeria and Egypt, will continue to fuel global wheat demand. Saudi Arabia is also projected to become a major importer in view of the recent change in its policy to gradually phase out production subsidies. Although the *Outlook* projects expanding exports from OECD countries, most of the growth in import demand will be satisfied through larger shipments from emerging and developing countries, particularly Ukraine and Argentina. Rising per capita incomes and developing food markets are behind increased global demand that has outpaced domestic production capacity. But more generally, growth in per capita food consumption of wheat is expected to remain modest or even to decline, notably in China, as diets slowly shift towards more value-added processed foods given the strong rise in incomes. The growth in international demand for coarse grains will be predominantly driven by increased feed demand from thriving livestock industries in developing economies. Imports by these countries as a group are projected to grow to 94 million tonnes, representing nearly 75% of the world total, which compares to less than 70% over the base period.

Productivity gains underpin rice supply

Global rice production could expand on the order of 10% by the end of the *Outlook*, fuelled by larger crops in South and South-East Asian countries. The overall trend of rising output masks an expected fall in area, which gathers momentum from 2011-12 onwards, reflecting lower plantings in Asian countries due to rivalry with other crops and non-agricultural sectors for land, which leads to an intensification of competition for water and labour resources. Developed countries are also foreseen to plant less by 2017-18, as a reflection mainly of ongoing policies in Japan and the EU. Owing to the dissemination of improved varieties and better production practices, yield growth over the next decade will assume greater prominence in supporting the sector, and this is expected to surpass the growth witnessed over the previous 10-year period.

Rice remains a basic food commodity, and its importance has extended beyond Asia. However, rapid income growth and diversification of diets is expected to depress per capita rice consumption, especially in Asia. In contrast, rice is expected to gain importance in African diets, where per capita consumption rises from 22 kg to more than 24 kg over the 10-year period. As a share of world production, rice trade is expected to fall slightly, indicating a lessening reliance on the global market that is consistent with a return to more stringent rice self-sufficiency policies in several countries. Much of the expansion in world imports is fuelled by demand in Africa and in Asia, with Thailand forecast to account for around one-third of all rice exports. The tendency for declining global rice stocks could be reversed over the course of the *Outlook*, as recent concerns over supply availability and price volatility foster a rebuilding of reserves.

Strong demand drives the oilseed complex

Increasing world livestock production will continue to be the driving force behind the consumption of oilseed-derived protein meal, with most of the growth taking place in non-OECD countries. Comparing 2017 with the 2005-07 base period, oilseed meal consumption in the developing region will rise by almost 50%, with China accounting for roughly half the growth alone, to satisfy its burgeoning livestock sector. While the EU should continue to hold its position as the largest importer of oilseed meals, its import dependency is likely to fall as a growing proportion of the region's protein meal consumption comes from domestically produced and crushed oilseeds, in particular rapeseed meal.

Notwithstanding the foregoing world oilseeds crush is projected to be mainly driven by vegetable oil demand. Largely sustained by income growth, vegetable oils, both from oilseed crops and from palm, will remain the fastest growing commodity in terms of consumption covered in this *Outlook*. Most of the demand growth is for food use, but bioenergy mandates will play an increasing role. Over the *Outlook* period, again comparing 2017 with the 2005-07 base period, the derived demand for vegetable oil in biodiesel production could increase by 14.3 million tonnes, about one third of the total increase in global vegetable oil consumption. The use of vegetable oils for bioenergy purposes is expected to grow strongly, and may alter trade patterns and the consumption mix in diets in some countries depending on policies in place. This may be particularly the case in the EU, where bioenergy use of vegetable oils has been mostly oriented to the use of rapeseed oil and could reach over 8% of worldwide and 41% of domestic vegetable oil consumption by 2017. In addition, biodiesel industries are expected to develop in several other countries, notably in Canada and Australia. Emerging biodiesel production will increase the consumption of domestically produced palm oil in Indonesia and Malaysia and soyabean oil in Brazil at the expense of exports of vegetable oil or oilseeds originating from those countries.

OECD-FAO AGRICULTURAL OUTLOOK 2008-2017 – ISBN 978-92-64-04590-3 – © OECD/FAO 2008

In addition to continued fast growth in feed use, biofuels look set to become a more significant long-term driver of the global oilseed complex, both directly through demand for vegetable oils in the bio-diesel production process and indirectly as increased cereal demand for ethanol production affects the relative prices of oilseeds and thereby the competition for arable land between these crops, especially in the United States. Furthermore, given the relative scarcity of maize, the share of oilmeals in total feed use may well be increasing over the *Outlook* period, even as a source for energy.

Buoyed by higher relative prices, land reallocation from competing crops, diverted pasture lands and new arable land could pave the way for global oilseed output to expand by 28% by 2017 when compared to the base period. Much of the foreseen expansion will be concentrated in Brazil, the EU and Argentina. Bolstered by a differential export-tax system, Argentina looks set to consolidate its position as a regional hub for oilseed crushing, despite a slowdown in the expansion of domestic crushing capacity. The country is expected to reaffirm its status as the world's major centre for shipments of soybean meal and oil, in a context of growing global import demand. China continues to import seeds and crush them domestically to capture the value added from processing oilseeds into protein meals and vegetable oil. Reflecting diminishing consumption growth, China's crushing industry is expected to develop at an average rate of 3.5% per annum compared to 8.5% in the previous decade. By 2017, China will have become the world's second-largest importer of oilseed meals and vegetable oils, after the EU, and it will have further reinforced its position as the leading importer of oilseeds. Brazil's share of global oilseed exports is expected to grow from 30% in 2008 to almost 40% in 2017, when the country easily surpasses the United States as the world's foremost oilseeds exporter.

Steadfast consumption growth and policy reform could lead to some tightening in sugar markets

Brazil is and will remain the world's leading sugar and ethanol producer and exporter, and the major centre of international price discovery for sugar. With the composition of Brazil's private-vehicle fleet increasingly being dominated by flex-fuel vehicles over the *Outlook* period, the derived demand for sugar cane from ethanol is expected to surge over the projection period, especially in the context of high projected crude oil prices. As a result, the projected share of the sugarcane crop going to ethanol increases from 51% on average in 2005-07 to 66% in 2017-18. Nevertheless, this development is not expected to unduly constrain the amount of cane available for sugar production and sugar exports, since sugarcane production in Brazil is foreseen to rise by over 75% from the base period to 2017. However, in the wake of steadfast domestic and international demand, there will be a propensity for sugar prices to strengthen over the projection period.

On the ethanol front, a number of other sugar producing countries are currently embarking on, or reinvigorating existing, renewable energy programmes, such as the EU, Japan, Malaysia, Indonesia, India, South Africa, Colombia, and the Philippines, particularly for use in the transport-fuel sector. Most of these fledgling fuel ethanol programmes, however, are expected to use molasses or starch sources rather than raw sugarcane juice as the preferred feedstock. As molasses is produced as a by-product of the sugar refining process, molasses-based bio-ethanol production should not greatly impair sugar production in these countries and may even stimulate further growth in cane and sugar output. Furthermore, in some regions, such as the EU, specific sugar crops (industrial beets) are being separately designated and developed for non-food uses such as bio-ethanol production.

Following reform of its sugar regime, the EU is expected to reduce production in the context of rising imports and World Trade Organisation (WTO) bound controls on subsidized exports and may eventually emerge as the world's leading sugar importer. Total sugar imports by the EU are expected to increase sharply by 2017-18, driven mainly by preferential exports from least-developed countries (LDCs) under the Everything But Arms (EBA) initiative and from the Africa-Caribbean-Pacific (ACP) group. However, the level of EU preferential imports from the latter group remains an important uncertainty. Mexican sugar exports to the higher priced United States market should increase with duties and restrictions eliminated under NAFTA on 1 January 2008. When considering shipments from third countries in addition to those from Mexico, United States purchases may exceed the import volume trigger for suspending the marketing allotments program of the 2002 FSRI Act, in all years of the projection period. As a result, public stock purchases (CCC) are expected to be required in each year out to 2017-18 to defend the US sugar loan rate price support system with domestic prices driven down to minimum loan-rate levels.

Developing countries account for virtually all the increase in world sugar production and consumption over the *Outlook*, due to faster population growth and rising incomes. India and China account for the lion's share in the increase in global consumption. Demand for sugar in China has been growing rapidly in the current decade from relatively low per capita consumption levels. With tightening government controls on artificial sweeteners, sugar consumption in China is projected to increase by 1.5% per year, implying rising imports that exceed the tariff quota of 1.95 Mt over the outlook period.

Despite increasing feed costs, world meat production continues to grow

Against a backdrop of high feed costs, low profit margins and competition for land resources, the global outlook for meat is characterised by substantial increases in production and consumption in developing countries and a more stable path of development in the mature OECD markets; though overall growth is expected to take place at slower pace than witnessed in the past decade.

Over the *Outlook* period, world meat production is expected to grow on average by 2% per year, but this trend disguises marked differences in growth rates of the different economic regions. Meat production among OECD members is expected to rise annually by around half a per cent, while growth in non-OECD countries could reach around 2.5% annually. Continuing investment, capacity building, better infrastructure and the dissemination of improved production technologies, are the main factors spurring such growth in meat and meat products, particularly in the more dynamic developing economies such as China, Brazil and – for pork and poultry predominantly – also in Argentina. As a result, some of them have been able to increase substantially their presence in supplying international meat markets. Brazil is a prime example of this feat. Given abundant land resources, capital and technology in combination with policy reforms, Brazil is expected to assume a 30% share of total world meat exports by the end of the projections. However, there are lingering concerns about the sustainability of this expansion. With trade recovering from the effects of animal-disease outbreaks, a small number of major exporters including the United States, Canada, Argentina and Australia alongside Brazil will remain dominant in world markets. However, in contrast, the export share of the EU is expected to further deteriorate over the *Outlook*.

Fuelled by greater purchasing power and urbanisation, diets in developing countries are increasingly shifting away from staple foods of vegetal origin towards proteins of animal origin. Meat consumption in developing countries is expected to account for more than 80% of global growth. Much of this expansion will take place in Asia and the Pacific region, and will reflect in particular the rise in consumption of cheaper sources of animal protein, mainly poultry and pork. Consumption of pork in particular is expected to rise in China where pork is traditionally the most important meat and where 2007 consumption was reduced due to an outbreak of Porcine Reproductive and Respiratory Syndrome (PRRS). Import dependency in meat products is likewise expected to grow in many dynamic developing countries as burgeoning demand surpasses the domestic capacity for meat production throughout the duration of the *Outlook*. Among the developed countries, the Russian Federation is set to remain the world's largest net meat importer by 2017, followed closely by Japan.

Tightness in dairy market to ease

A pressing issue for the projections concerns how the global dairy industry will react to the unprecedented price spikes across dairy products that were observed in 2007. There is broad consensus that the industry has undergone structural change, where international markets have shifted from a supply-driven paradigm supported by distorting policies which used these markets as a dumping ground for excess supplies, to a more demand-driven paradigm, responsive to market signals and consumer wants. The growing relative importance of demand factors is further explained by urbanisation and higher incomes which have shifted diets in some developing economies towards a more diversified basket of dairy products, encouraged by growth in dairy marketing and retailing channels.

The *Outlook* foresees that high international prices of dairy products will transmit strong signals for supply response from both traditional and emerging exporters. More importantly, where trade linkages allow higher prices to be transmitted to producers in developing countries, they may create incentives for investment, expansion and restructuring. This will help to reshape their industries, which will be increasingly geared towards higher value-added processing of dairy products. Rising supply potential will enable future production growth and improved domestic marketing linkages, placing these countries in a stronger competitive position in regional and global markets.

Milk production gains over the *Outlook* period will be overwhelmingly driven by output growth in non-OECD countries. Dairy expansion in India, the largest producing country in the world, will be especially marked, where surging demand growth will stimulate a strong increase in milk and butter production. Driven by substantial yield gains, strong growth in milk production is also expected in China. This contrasts with moderate growth in the OECD area, where milk production increases mainly due to gains from Oceania and the United States and is chiefly constrained by domestic production controls in many other countries. These supply developments constitute one of the more prominent trends in the *Outlook* for dairy markets.

Supply response, however, could be checked by higher production costs induced by both higher feed and energy prices. These affect production, processing and distribution of milk products, and will encourage the competitiveness of pasture-based systems. They also will affect trade, as higher transportation costs put local production at greater advantage. The evolution of world dairy markets will also be influenced by extensive policy interventions and by internal food-security concerns, but also increasingly by environmental constraints linked to high livestock populations, water availability and competition for pasture land. Increasingly, a higher production response in many countries will come from higher yields as opposed to increased cattle numbers. A key for the dairy outlook is the potential for dairy markets to adjust in the presence of increased price volatility and low global stock levels of dairy products.

OECD countries continue to dominate world dairy exports

World exports of dairy products are expected to grow for all products, with only a few developing countries able to affect the shares of traditional OECD exporters of Australia, New Zealand and the EU. In the latter, export shares could decline substantially, in light of a tight domestic market. Among the new exporters, Argentina is emerging as a dominant player in markets for whole-milk powder (WMP) and cheese, supported by its rising milk production capacity. Similarly, Ukraine is expected to increase its presence on the export markets mainly for cheese.

Import markets will remain rather fragmented compared to those for exports. The six largest importers of dairy products are expected to cover less than 50% of the world market. In China, despite a strong increase in milk-production, demand will continue to outpace supply and imports are expected to grow over the *Outlook*, in particular for milk powders, where China will become one of the leading importers. Russia is foreseen to remain as the world's most prominent importer of butter and cheese, with imports rising by more than 60% over the *Outlook* period compared with the 2005-07 base. Driven by milk-reconstitution needs, global imports of milk powders will grow by over 3% annually over the medium term, mostly in Asia and the Middle East.

Biofuel production and use on an upswing

Production and use of both ethanol and biodiesel have increased significantly in recent years. Production of fuel ethanol tripled between 2000 and 2007, with the US and Brazil accounting for the majority of this growth. However, a large number of other countries either commenced renewable energy programmes or increased fuel ethanol production in this period as well. Biodiesel output witnessed an even more pronounced expansion over the same period, having grown from less than one billion litres to almost 11 billion litres. Initially the EU accounted for more than 90% of global biodiesel production, but with increased biodiesel output in many other countries, in particular the US, its share has declined to less than 60% in 2007.

Near-record prices for maize, wheat and vegetable oils at the start of the *Outlook* have reduced the economic viability of biofuel production in many countries, despite strong public support and increasing fossil fuel prices. Public support in the form of tax concessions and tax credits, blending obligations and regulations, and import tariffs are widely applied to help offset higher production costs of biofuels compared to fossil fuels. The one exception is bio-ethanol production from sugarcane in Brazil. In this case, lower world sugar prices associated with a large global surplus have improved the economic viability and profitability of ethanol production in Brazil, which remains competitive with gasoline at a crude oil price of around USD 55 per barrel. Most commodity prices are expected to fall from current highs over the *Outlook* period with larger crop production. Coupled with expected high crude oil and biofuel prices over the next few years, the economic situation of biofuel producers should improve compared to the situation in 2007 but remain less favourable than in 2005 and 2006.

Ethanol production to grow as prices stabilise at higher levels

Global ethanol production is projected to increase rapidly and to reach some 125 billion litres in 2017, twice the quantity produced in 2007. World ethanol prices are expected to exceed USD 55 per hectolitre in 2009 as crude oil prices rise, but should fall back to levels around USD 52-53 per hectolitre over the remainder of the projection period as production capacity expands in a number of countries. Following increased mandates international trade in ethanol is expected to grow rapidly to reach 6 billion litres in 2010 and almost 10 billion litres by 2017, despite continuing trade protection. Most of this trade will originate in Brazil, and will be destined for markets in the EU and the US.

Global biodiesel production and use to be driven mainly by public policy

Global biodiesel production is set to grow at slightly higher rates then for bioethanol – which maintains the largest share – to reach some 24 billion litres by 2017. This growth in output occurs despite the fact that world biodiesel prices are expected to remain well above production costs of fossil diesel, and to stay within the range of USD 104-106 per hectolitre, for most of the projection period. As in the case of ethanol, increased blending mandates should stimulate demand and boost international trade in the initial years of the *Outlook*. World trade is, however, projected to remain largely unchanged in following years due to technical constraints in the use of palm-oil based biodiesel in the colder climates and as production in the main consuming countries increases. Most of the trade should originate in Malaysia and Indonesia with the EU as the main destination.[1]

Main developments in trade in agricultural commodities

Rapid expansion of world trade overall, dominated by developing countries

When measured by imports, world trade is expected to grow for all commodities covered by the *Outlook*. The weakest growth is projected for wheat, with total world imports by 2017 exceeding the average for 2005/07 by nearly 15%. The highest growth rates of between 40 and 50% over this period are projected predominantly for vegetable oils and for certain livestock products (Figure 1.2).

Figure 1.2. **Overall strong growth in world trade**

Imports in 2017 compared to the 2005-2007 average

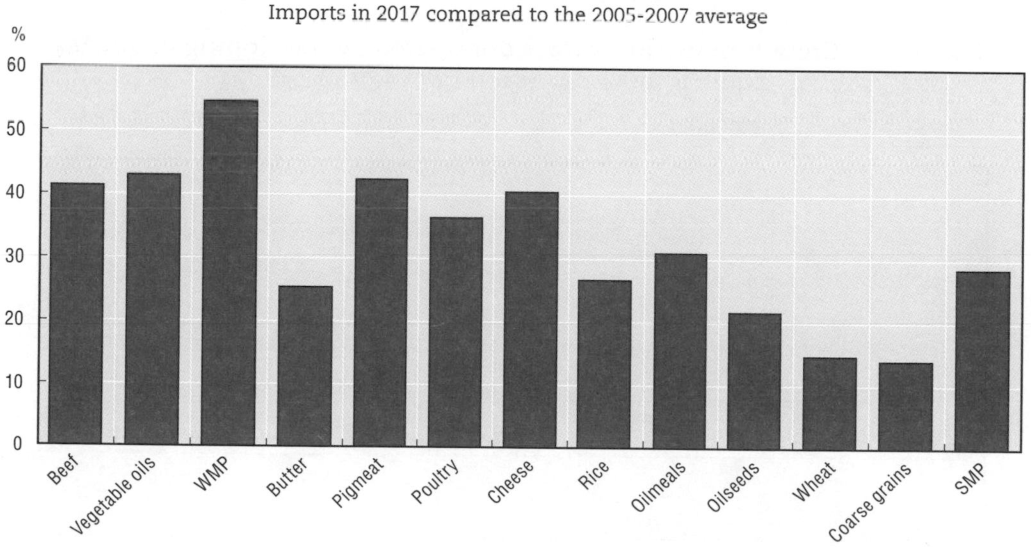

StatLink http://dx.doi.org/10.1787/383568281505

Source: OECD and FAO Secretariats.

When the focus is on crop imports, the projections show that for all crop products in the *Outlook*, except vegetable oils, developing countries dominate the picture of trade expansion. For wheat, sugar, oilseeds and oilmeals, most of the growth takes place in Asian developing countries. For oilseeds, import growth in Asia exceeds even total trade expansion and is offset to some extend by a decline in imports by OECD countries. For rice and coarse grains, most of the growth in imports takes place in African developing countries, and much of that in the LDCs.

Turning to imports of livestock products, the picture is much different. For the relatively expensive products such as beef, pork and cheese, import growth is dominated by OECD countries. For poultry and milk powders, most of the growth in global imports is explained by larger imports in Asian developing countries. While these countries also represent over 40% of import growth for butter, the largest contribution to the trade expansion for this product is due to larger imports in the CIS countries.

Emerging exporters challenge the dominance of OECD countries

Developing countries not only dominate import growth for most of the commodities in the *Outlook*, they also show with few exceptions the strongest growth rates for exports. For all products in the *Outlook* but rice, sugar and vegetable oils the growth in exports from developing country origin exceeds those from OECD countries. The leading growth position for the OECD for these products has to be seen in the context of trade growing from a small base, and in 2017, the OECD share in world exports is only 6% for vegetable oils and 14 and 10% for sugar and rice, respectively. Export growth in developing countries is greater – and sometimes much greater – for all other products, leading to declining shares of OECD countries in world exports for these products. Nevertheless, these countries continue to dominate the world export picture with shares of world trade ranging from 58 to 70% for wheat, coarse grains, pork and all dairy products. It is only for beef and poultry where the export share from developing countries of about 60% exceeds those of the OECD (Figure 1.3).

Figure 1.3. **Growth in world exports dominated by developing countries**

Exports in 2017 compared to the 2005-2007 average

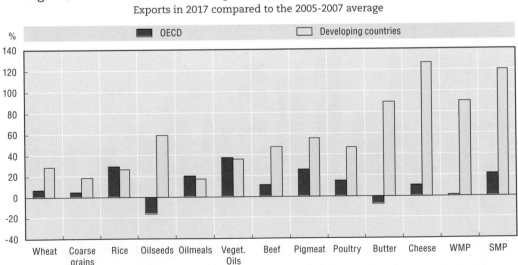

StatLink ᴀᴤᴧ http://dx.doi.org/10.1787/383607761103

Source: OECD and FAO Secretariats.

The outlook for world prices

World prices to retreat from current highs but firmness expected to prevail over the medium term

In the context of generally lower global stocks in recent years, biofuels impose an additional dimension to global demand for grains, oilseed products and sugar. Coupled with sustained global income growth which is particularly underpinning demand for food and feed in certain developing and emerging countries, with limitations to land and productivity based increases in supply and with higher oil prices which raises production costs, this situation is expected to underpin international quotations. All three of these factors are expected to lift price levels for arable crops that are, on average, substantially higher than in past projections. Higher average crop prices and associated feed costs, in turn, lead to higher livestock product prices over the *Outlook* period as well. When compared to the average for 1998 to 2007, prices projected for the period 2008 to 2017 will – in nominal terms – on average be around 20% higher for beef and pork, some 30% for raw and white sugar, 40 to 60% for wheat, maize and skim milk powder, more than 60% higher for butter and oilseeds and over 80% higher for vegetable oils (Figures 1.4 and 1.5).

Figure 1.4 Outlook for world crop prices to 2017
Index of nominal prices, 1996 = 1

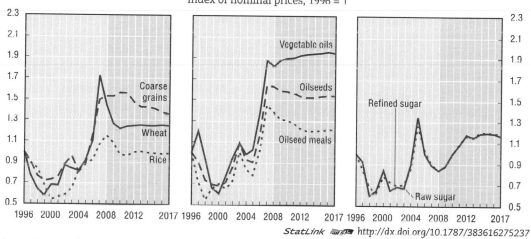

Source: OECD and FAO secretariats.

StatLink http://dx.doi.org/10.1787/383616275237

Figure 1.5. Outlook for world livestock product prices to 2017
Index of nominal prices, 1996 = 1

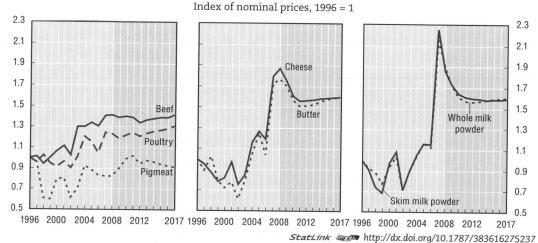

Source: OECD and FAO Secretariats.

StatLink http://dx.doi.org/10.1787/383616275237

When expressed in real terms, the decade-over-decade increase is obviously smaller, but remains very substantial for crops and dairy products.

Despite this rise in their average level, prices of most agricultural commodities fall and are expected to remain below current or recent peak levels by the end of the *Outlook*. In addition, there would not appear to be any structural changes in the functioning of markets that would suggest reduced price variability. On the contrary, a number of factors are at play that may well render market prices more variable than in the past. Such factors include continued low stock to use ratios, a possibility of more variable weather conditions, less responsive consumer demand to farm level price changes as the commodity share in the food bill falls, increased industrial demand for agricultural commodities, which also tends to be less price-sensitive than food and feed demand, and massive amounts of non-commercial investment funds that may enter or leave agricultural futures markets with either net long or net short positions as profit opportunities dictate.

Low stock-to-use ratios support cereal prices and prices in the oilseed complex

In spite of the expectation of a strong recovery in grain production in 2008, prevailing low stock levels suggest continued market tightness, especially when demand prospects for food, feed and fuels show no sign of abating. Cereal markets are expected to remain closely balanced over the *Outlook* as stock to use ratios are expected to remain low in the years to come and despite growth in cereal production. This implies high grain prices throughout most of the *Outlook*. However, continued productivity increases in line with their long-term trend and some increase in areas planted are expected to see prices below their 2007 peak levels. For wheat this is the case throughout the *Outlook* period, while for coarse grains prices are likely to remain high for some years to come before falling below present record levels. Despite this decline, grain prices will average above their mean levels of the previous decade, even in real terms. From that higher level, however, real prices continue their long-term downward trend.

International rice prices are anticipated to remain firm in the short term, as countries replenish rice inventories. While weaker prices are projected from 2010, they are unlikely to fall much in consideration of higher production costs. With lower buffer stock levels projected on thin world markets, world prices are likely to manifest much higher volatility than in the past, as the market becomes more vulnerable to supply and demand shocks.

Rising demand for vegetable oils, for both food and the growing biodiesel sector, is expected to weigh heavily over the medium term, leaving stock to use ratios in the oilseed complex under pressure. The combination of strong demand and low inventories will be extremely supportive to prices in the next few years, but from then on prices will gradually fall back as supply and demand adjust. As is the case for cereals, prices for oilseed and oilseed products, once corrected for inflation, are expected to decrease in real terms but to stay considerably above their long-term trend.

Sugar prices strengthen with increasing premium for white sugar

As the world market is brought into closer balance and excess sugar stocks drawn down, world indicator prices for raw and white sugar are projected to rise strongly in nominal terms, but will still trend downwards in real terms over the projection period. The margin between raw and white sugar prices should widen over the *Outlook* given expectations of increasing supply of raw sugar and rising costs of refining. With reforms having reined in the use of exports subsidies in the EU, reducing its role as a major white-sugar exporter, the white-sugar premium in future years should reflect more the cost of further sugar refining.

Meat prices projected to stay above current averages, but dairy prices expected to gradually retreat from 2007 record levels

Given rising feed costs and strong meat demand in the major emerging economies, meat prices are expected to rise above historic levels in the medium term. Non-ruminant production is notably affected by high cereal and oilseeds prices as low-priced distiller's dry grains (DDGs) cannot easily be integrated into their feed rations. These higher input costs are expected to result in increased meat prices over the next decade.

World dairy prices are expected to weaken somewhat over the next two years as supply responds sufficiently to strong price incentives. While prices are anticipated to decline from currently high levels, the expectation is that they will remain firm over the entire outlook and stay higher compared to the previous decade. As with the majority of other agricultural commodity prices, when expressed in real terms the well-established longer term falling trend was reversed radically in recent years. However, dairy products are expected to resume a modest declining trend in future years, albeit from a much higher level than in the past.

Some major issues and uncertainties

This year's *Outlook* has been prepared in an environment characterised by increased instability in financial markets, higher food price inflation, signs of weakening global economic growth and food-security concerns. The commodity markets have shown dramatic rises in prices across a range of commodities on a weekly basis, attracting the attention of the daily press and stimulating discussion on the food-feed-fuel debate. Although projections for agricultural commodity markets have always been subject to a number of uncertainties, these have taken on more importance in this year's edition. As in the past, weather conditions, animal-disease outbreaks, the macroeconomic environment and domestic policies are all factors that will continue to affect agricultural market outcomes. The question for the forthcoming period is how these key factors and uncertainties will change over time and to what extent they will change the market outlook. Some of these uncertainties are discussed in detail in a separate section in this report.

On the supply side, weather-related production shocks have always been the single most important factor for agricultural production and recent bad weather spells in several important producing regions have been responsible for much of the supply shortages on commodity crop markets. Is the recent spell of bad weather merely an episodic event, or does it foreshadow more systematic changes linked to global warming and more variable weather patterns around the world? In the presence of high prices and the related increased food security concerns, what is the scope for further productivity gains, technological advances and breakthroughs in production and harvesting or for bringing new areas into cultivation? In developing countries, what is the potential for the expected plateau of higher average prices to be transmitted to domestic markets, reinvigorating agricultural industries and improving their competitive position in local and international markets? What will be the timing of the availability of second generation biofuel production technologies? Coupled with unforeseen changes in crude oil prices, how will this affect the production of biofuels and agricultural commodity markets?

The uncertainties on the demand side seem to be lesser as steady year-on-year income driven consumption growth remains a basic feature of many commodity markets. Nevertheless, macroeconomic conditions are playing a crucial role for future market developments and a slowdown in economic growth as compared to that assumed in the *Outlook* would moderate demand, international trade and agricultural commodity prices. In addition, exchange rate developments could have an important influence on the markets as a change in domestic currencies *vis-à-vis* the US dollar would affect comparative advantages and domestic market responses given price changes on international markets. A particular uncertainty on the demand side of agricultural markets is the growing presence and investments of non-commercial interests, such as financial funds, in futures trading on commodity markets. To what extent is the growing demand for financial derivatives affecting demand, risk management strategies and spot market prices for crops? And how will this further evolve in the future.

Policy interventions can also create uncertainty in commodity markets. Changes in biofuel policies, either to raise or to lower domestic targets or to review current policy incentives downwards, could be of major importance for agricultural markets given that biofuel production is one of the important factors lending strength to these markets over the medium term. In more general terms, there will be changes to domestic policies in key producing and trading countries such as new farm legislation in the United States, any changes that may results from the "health check" of the EU CAP or an eventual outcome to the current round of the Doha multilateral trade negotiations. Such and other changes have not been anticipated in this *Outlook* and would affect market outcomes. Finally, high international commodity prices have recently lead governments in several countries to introduce measures to restrict exports. While such policies may in the short term provide some relief to domestic consumers, at the expense of some further belt tightening by their neighbours, they impose a burden on domestic producers, dampen the supply response in these countries, and aggravate the global commodity market situation.

The policy issues

The key feature of this year's *Outlook* is the record-high level of many agricultural commodity prices. These are partly due to short-term factors such as drought in major cereal-producing areas and speculative activity. Once the influence of these transitory factors is removed or changes, prices will fall from current highs. However, there are factors at play that will keep prices well above average levels over the past decade. These include the steady growth in demand linked to population and income growth as well as changing diets in emerging economies, in particular China and India. But there are also factors that are uncertain into the future: energy prices, the diversion of land and crops for bioenergy, and climate change.

High prices are always good for some and bad for others. They are good for producers of farm produce, including in many cases for the people they employ, even though high prices of cereals, for example, mean higher costs for producers of cereal-based animal products. High prices are not only beneficial for some farmers in OECD countries, but may also be good news for commercial producers in developing countries. Insofar as those higher prices more than offset higher energy and other input costs in these countries, higher farm incomes can have important multiplier effects and lead to higher income levels in rural areas. For farm households producing mainly for their own consumption or for local markets that are insulated from price fluctuations on national and international markets, the impacts will be mitigated. But for the poorer segments of the population, and in particular for those in the net food importing developing countries, the impacts will be strongly negative as an even higher share of their limited income will be required for food consumption.

What are appropriate policy responses?

According to an old adage, the best remedy for high prices is high prices. High prices stimulate supply and dampen demand on agricultural markets, the balance will change and prices will come down. But the *Outlook* also shows that prices are likely to continue to average around substantially higher levels than in the past, possibly with larger variations around that higher average.

The *Outlook* for lower prices in the foreseeable future with the possibility of a turnaround being more rapid than is currently foreseen calls for caution in taking any precipitous policy action. However, the fact that certain groups in the population and certain countries suffer from current high prices and may continue to be worse off in a context of sustained higher price levels in the future provides a policy challenge.

In the short term, humanitarian aid for the populations in countries most severely affected is urgently required. Before recent price increases, although there had been improvements, hundreds of millions of people were going hungry because they could not afford food. With higher prices, the numbers of people suffering from extreme hunger has increased even further and the first UN Millennium Development Goal has become an even greater challenge. As suggested recently by the World Bank, aid in the form of cash or vouchers is more appropriate in many cases than commodity shipments, provided supplies can be procured. Such aid may also be more effective than short term measures, such as export taxes or embargoes, that restrain exports in order to ensure domestic market supplies.

In the medium term, there is a real need to foster growth and development in poor countries and to assist in developing their agricultural supply base. In some of the poorest countries, investment in agriculture, including in agricultural research, extension and education, which has been lagging in recent years, is often the best way to cut poverty and stimulate economic activity. Expected high farm prices may provide an incentive for this. In other situations, investment in agriculture may be helpful, but there is also a need to diversify the structure of the economy. In general, investments in improving the overall environment in which agriculture operates may be most appropriate. These include improving governance and administrative systems, macroeconomic policy, infrastructure, technology, education, health, and defining and enforcing property rights.

Agricultural trade policies require further reform. Trade restricting policies – whether they restrict exports or imports – have undesirable and often unintended impacts, especially in the medium and long term. On the import side, "protecting" domestic producers of agricultural commodities by providing high price support and border protection – including the increasing resort to non-tariff barriers – restricts growth opportunities for producers abroad and imposes a burden on domestic consumers. Export taxes and embargoes may in the short term provide some relief to domestic consumers – including to the wealthier ones who may not need these measures – but they impose an even larger burden on domestic producers and limit their supply response, as well as contribute to global commodity market uncertainty.

It is also necessary to examine more closely the causes and impacts of the recent price increases. On the supply side, the link between production and yield shortfalls, climate change and water availability warrants further analysis, both in terms of trends, variability and risk. Investments in R&D, technology transfer and extension services, particularly in less developed economies, could do much to increase productivity and output and there may be a role for governments to foster this, especially where there are wider public benefits. In addition, the future development of genetically modified organisms (GMOs) also offers potential that could be further exploited, both to improve productivity and to enhance the attributes of crops destined for either food or non-food uses.

The largely policy driven nature of the rapid increase in the supply and demand for biofuels is one of the reasons for current and future higher prices. OECD/IEA analysis to date[2] suggests that the energy security, environmental, and economic benefits of biofuels production based on agricultural commodity feed stocks are at best modest, and sometimes even negative, and are unlikely to be delivered by current policies alone. Alternative approaches may be considered that offer potentially greater benefits with less of the unintended market impact, such as policies that encourage reduced energy demand and greenhouse-gas (GHG) emissions, provide for freer trade in biofuels, and accelerate introduction of "second-generation" production technologies that do not rely upon current commodity feed stocks.

Notes

1. For a detailed analysis of the market impacts of biofuel policies, see OECD/IEA Economic Assessment of Biofuel Support Policies (forthcoming).

2. For further details, see OECD/IEA Economic Assessment of Biofuel Support Policies (forthcoming).

ISBN 978-92-64-04590-3
OECD-FAO AGRICULTURAL OUTLOOK 2008-2017
© OECD/FAO 2008

Chapter 2

Are High Prices here to Stay?

Introduction

World prices of maize, wheat and oilseed crops all nearly doubled in nominal terms between the 2005 and 2007 marketing years (Figure 2.1). Those prices continued rising into early 2008, competing with oil-price hikes in capturing media and policy attention. These developments have led to a fuller awareness and a justifiably heightened concern about food security and hunger, especially for developing countries where food availability at affordable prices is precarious. The analysis in this chapter does not attempt a comprehensive explanation of all of the factors responsible for the recent run up in prices. Rather the focus of the discussion is predominantly on the contribution – qualitative or quantitative – of various factors in determining price developments over the medium term.

Figure 2.1. **Food commodity prices, 1971-2007 with projections to 2017**

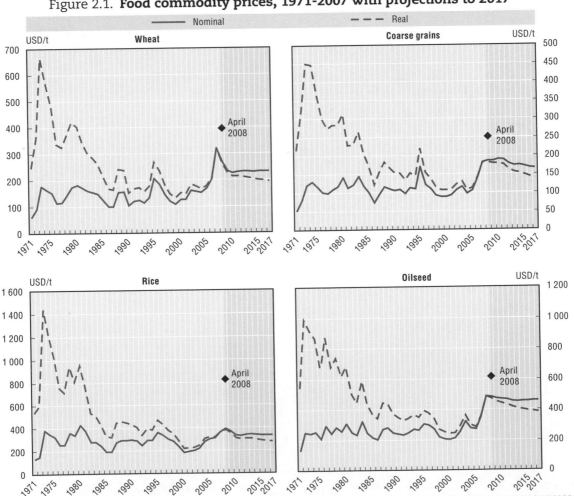

StatLink http://dx.doi.org/10.1787/383632210563

Note: Real prices deflated by USA GDP deflator; 2007 = 1 (April 2008: montlhy price quotation).

Source: OECD and FAO Secretariats.

OECD-FAO AGRICULTURAL OUTLOOK 2008-2017 – ISBN 978-92-64-04590-3 – © OECD/FAO 2008

Meat and poultry prices have also seen increases during this period but only very modest ones. There have been substantial increases in prices of dairy products in 2007 although the pressure on the international dairy market has already abated somewhat. As the international debate has focused recently on the implications of increases in crop markets, the primary focus of this chapter is on prices for cereals and oilseeds.

Agricultural commodity price increases have been a significant, but not the only, factor driving up the cost of food. High oil prices and the resulting higher costs of food processing, transportation and distribution have driven food costs higher still. Food price inflation is generally running well ahead of general price inflation but especially so in many developing countries (Box 2.1). Higher food costs are of course more painful for

---

Box 2.1. **Measuring the impact of rising commodity prices on food prices**

Agricultural commodity price increases are making headlines and there is much debate and concern about what these extraordinary price increases mean for food prices, particularly in developing countries. Policy makers have become extremely concerned by recent price developments because of the implications for consumers' ability to meet their most basic of needs, food. This is a critical issue for developing countries where large portions of the population have income levels that are low or at subsistence levels. But increasing prices reduces the purchasing power of incomes also in relatively high-income countries, where it will be the low-income groups that are particularly affected. In general, households with low incomes are more heavily penalized when the price of necessities rise because these absorb a larger share of their income.

The increase in food prices from a government perspective is however not generally measured by the change in one or two commodities or in one or two cities, but by a fixed basket of foods consumed in urban areas of the entire country; this measure is known as the food price index. Changes in the food price index are important because of their contribution to overall inflation rates, that is, the change in the Consumer Price Index (CPI).[a] The impact of food prices on this indicator varies across countries according to the share of income which consumers allocate to food and the rate of increase of food prices.

How important are commodity price increases for food prices?

The direct links between current commodity prices and retail food prices are often difficult to make without an analysis of the food production and distribution structure as well as the relative costs of inputs. For importing countries, the link between international commodity prices in local currency depends on a number of factors, including exchange rates, transportation costs and border policies, as well as the structure of the food distribution system. The local price of wheat for a consumer in such countries is not simply the international price in USD at say US Gulf Ports, but the Gulf Port price of wheat times the exchange rate plus the cost of transportation and insurance to the point of delivery in addition to any import duties imposed by the country. So in this case, recent domestic price increases not only reflect the higher price of wheat but also increased freight (transportation and insurance) costs, which have risen by 250% since early 2006, and are now at record high levels.[b] Nevertheless, price increases in domestic currency terms may be less than the increase in the dollar price of wheat in countries where the US dollar has depreciated significantly vis-à-vis their currency.

Box 2.1. **Measuring the impact of rising commodity prices on food prices** (cont.)

Trade policy measures such as import tariffs also add to the price of imported commodities. These costs can be easily modified by governments so as to limit price increases, for instance, if governments adopt import tariffs which decrease automatically if the price of the imported commodity rises beyond a certain level, as in the case of rice for Bangladesh, or even be suspended if the world price rises beyond a threshold level, such as in Indonesia. These mechanisms function to moderate price increases once goods reach the border. In the face of rising domestic prices of key commodities, exporting countries may put in place export taxes or bans. India and Vietnam recently banned rice exports when prices reached what were deemed to be unacceptable levels in domestic markets.

Once commodities reach the domestic market, the issue of price transmission through the supply chain to retail markets predominates. The link between commodity prices and retail food prices is a hotly debated issue, and depends on many factors that vary by country. In general, farm gate prices of agricultural commodities in many developed countries account on average for 25 to 35% of the final retail price. While this is not negligible, the share is often much less and varies across fresh and processed foods. The higher the degree of processing, the lower will be the share of the raw commodity in the final price at retail. This means that food prices reflect not only commodity price changes but also those of other inputs, in particular wages, energy, transport and storage. It also means that depending on the circumstances, retail food prices can change by more or by less than what would be determined by the change in commodity prices if these factors do not change to the same degree.

In developing countries the share of processed goods in the food basket is generally small, thus the increases in commodity prices are likely to be more directly transmitted through to retail prices. This fact, coupled with a larger share of income devoted to food expenditures, implies that the rise in agricultural commodity prices has a significant impact on developing country consumers. Both of these elements will determine the extent of the contribution of food price changes to the overall CPI or inflation.

How important is the food component in the CPI?

The weight of the food component in the CPI varies significantly across countries, reflecting the structure of household expenditures. The food price component ranges from less than 10% in the United States to over 30% in Turkey and Poland, but for the majority of OECD countries food expenditure shares range between 13% and 20%. In developing countries the share of food expenditure in the budget is much higher; for instance, it is 28% in China, 33% in India, and absorbs more than half of total household expenditures in countries such as Kenya at 51%, Haiti at 52%, Malawi at 58% and Bangladesh at 62%.

These observations confirm Engel's Law, which displays an inverse relationship between food expenditure shares and income (Figure 2.2). The implication is that for countries where food expenditure accounts for an important share of income, high food prices will have a negative impact on the purchasing power of incomes. In these countries, rising food prices mean an erosion of the capacity to meet basic needs, and this is likely to become a potential source of political tensions and even violence. Low-income households are those that will be most affected by an increases in food prices. As the share of income they spend on food is relatively high, they have little remaining income left to reallocate expenditure from other goods to meet food needs. They may simply be forced to consume less food and other basic necessities as a result of higher food prices.

Box 2.1. **Measuring the impact of rising commodity prices on food prices** (*cont.*)

Figure 2.2. **Food expenditure shares and per capita income**

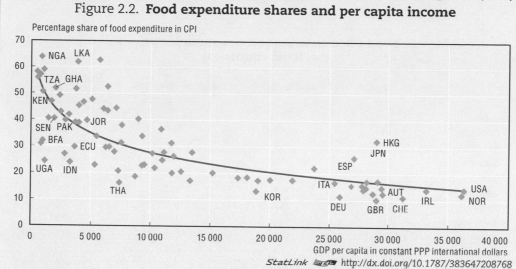

Source: FAO Secretariat (HLC/08/INF/1: Soaring food prices: Facts, perspectives, impacts and actions required. April 2008).

How fast have consumer food prices been rising?

For most countries consumer food price inflation has recently exceeded overall inflation rates (see Table 2.1 for selected countries), and food price inflation in developing countries has exceeded that in OECD countries. For most developing countries this is likely due to the rise in agricultural commodity prices. Since a larger share of foods consumed in developing countries is unprocessed, the commodity portion of food has a larger weight in retail prices. Furthermore, food price inflation in developing countries has exceeded that in developed OECD countries.

Since the food price component is an aggregate measure, it can hide price variations for specific products. It is difficult to summarize the products that have increased most rapidly over the past year, as this depends largely on country situations. Using data for February 2008 compared to February 2007, milk product prices have generally risen sharply, as shown by those for butter with price increases of 50% in Poland, 40% in France, 36% in Spain, 32% in the Czech Republic, about 36% in Jordan and some 12% in Malaysia. Eggs prices have also risen sharply, by 34% in the US, 30% in the UK and the Czech Republic and 10% in Spain. Vegetable oil prices rose 18% in India and 47% in Botswana in the past year. Meat prices rose sharply in some countries such as China, where the increase was 45% but this was largely due to disease issues in their pork sector. The increase in prices for cereals and bakery products was much more moderate; prices rose by 5.7% in the US, 6.9% in the UK and 3% in France and Korea, and about 6% in both China and India.

What is the effect of food price increases on overall inflation?

It is clear from Table 2.1 that consumer food prices are contributing to the overall rate of inflation in most countries. For developed countries, where food price inflation is moderate and the share of food in the total consumer basket is small, the contribution of food price inflation to overall inflation is correspondingly moderate. In most countries it contributed less than 1 percentage point to the overall CPI increase over the year from February 2007 to February 2008. But as would be expected, the impact of food price inflation on overall inflation in developing countries is much larger. As shown in Table 2.1 it contributes 6.5 percentage points of the total inflation of 8.7% in China, 7.6 points of the total inflation of 10.6% in Pakistan, 9.2 points of the total of 10.3% in Bangladesh, 12.4 points out of total inflation of 15.4% in Kenya, and 1.9 points out of total inflation of 4.6% in India.

Box 2.1. **Measuring the impact of rising commodity prices on food prices** (cont.)

Table 2.1. **Food price contribution to consumer price inflation (selected countries)**

	Total CPI % change[1]	Food price inflation[1]	Expenditure share of food	Food contribution to total change in CPI[3]
Developing		- % -		
Guatemala	8.04	11.6	38.9	4.5
Sri Lanka[2]	19.37	25.6	62	15.9
Botswana	7.7	18.3	21.8	4.0
India[2]	4.6	5.8	33.4	1.9
Indonesia	6.8	11.4	26.7	3.0
Pakistan[2]	10.6	18.2	41.5	7.6
South Africa	8.6	13.6	21	2.9
Jordan	5.4	9.1	39.7	3.6
Peru	4	6.4	29.6	1.9
Senegal	5.8	10.9	40.3	4.4
Egypt	9.5	13.5	41.5	5.6
Haiti	9.9	11.8	50.3	5.9
Kenya	15.4	24.6	50.5	12.4
Bangladesh	10.3	14.2	64.5	9.2
China	8.7	23.3	27.8	6.5
Developed				
USA	4.0	5.1	9.8	0.5
France	2.8	5.0	16.3	0.8
Germany	2.8	7.4	10.4	0.8
UK	2.5	5.6	11.8	0.7
Japan	1.0	1.4	19.0	0.3
Greece	4.4	6.6	17.8	1.2
Spain	4.4	7.1	21.9	1.6
Switzerland	2.4	2.2	11.0	0.2
Poland	4.3	7.1	30.4	2.2
Sweden	3.1	5.9	13.4	0.8

StatLink ᴍᴸ║ http://dx.doi.org/10.1787/385014651524

1. Percentage change February 2007 to February 2008.
2. Includes beverages and tobacco.
3. Contribution is column 2 x 3/100.
Source: OECD Secretariat. For OECD member countries, April 2008. FAO Secretariat for non-OECD countries.

The main conclusion is that for developing countries food price inflation makes an important contribution to overall inflation. For the urban poor the situation is particularly distressing since low incomes, often not much above USD 2 a day, combine with rising food costs and no access to land resources to produce at least part of their food supplies. The *Outlook*, with its projected sustained higher level of prices, implies an important decline in the purchasing power and welfare of millions of people across the globe.

a) In most OECD countries core inflation, which excludes food and energy prices because of their high variability, is the guiding indicator for policymaking in monetary and fiscal policies.
b) The International Grains Commission freight cost index rose from 4 125 at the start of 2006, to 10 347 in March 2008.

consumers in poorer segments of the population, in particular those in food-importing developing countries, where the food bill constitutes a dominant share of total consumer expenditures.

The causes of the price spike are complex and are attributable to a combination of mutually reinforcing factors at play in international agricultural markets. The list includes: droughts in key grain-producing regions; sharply increased biofuel demand for food commodities; rising oil prices and a continuing devaluation of the US dollar, the currency in which indicator prices for the commodities of interest are typically quoted.[1] Critically, these supply and demand developments occurred after there had already been a run-down in stocks, which under more normal circumstances could have dampened price movements. Finally, the turmoil in commodity markets has occurred against the backdrop of a severe world financial crisis that is widely believed to have sparked a substantial increase in speculative interest in agricultural futures markets (Box 2.2).

Box 2.2. **Prices in cash and derivative markets**[a]

Derivative markets prices in the US, such as options and futures for wheat, soybeans and maize, are widely quoted as indicative prices and are the focus of much commercial activity. Long-time participants have been surprised at recent increases and daily changes – some daily changes in prices in 2008 have been greater than levels of prices a few years ago. New market participants are seen to bring vast amounts of money and some observers question if they contribute to both the direction and variability of prices in these markets.

A key concern now is the participation of new agents that are perceived to be motivated by risk-diversification to the exclusion of serious assessment of price levels. Institutional investors are known to be hedging other risk in their portfolios typically by taking long positions (a commitment to buy) on near-by contracts, as opposed to short positions (commitments to sell). Data relating to the activities of non-commercial traders in the US derivatives markets provides some information about institutional investors' trading patterns and scale.[b] Total open interest in maize, for example, has increased from 0.66 million contracts in February 2005 to 1.45 million February 2008 during which period non-commercial traders' share in opening interest in long positions increased from 17% to 43%. For wheat, contacts increased from 0.22 million to 0.45 million over this period and the non-commercial traders' share of opening long interest rose from 28% to 42%. The pattern for soybeans is similar whereas sugar contract volumes increased over this period but non-commercial traders' share in open long sugar positions remained at about a third. Monthly trading volumes have increased during this period by 85% for maize, 125% for wheat and 56% for soybeans, and by threefold for sugar. Supplemental data from this source confirm that institutional investors tend to take one-sided (long or buying) positions, and that these entities, along with other non-traditional participants such as banks, account for a growing share of the market.

Analysis of the role of institutional investors should not be reduced to the level of caricature. But a sound strategy for one firm may not be so wisely pursued by all. The aggregate effect of all their activities may be upward pressure on derivative market prices in the short term. The jury is still out on the longer term impacts on price levels. But increased price volatility seems a plausible result given the volume of these non-commercial investments and given the fact that they may move in and out off commodity trading as alternative profit opportunities dictate.

Box 2.2. **Prices in cash and derivative markets**[a] *(cont.)*

Ideally, derivative markets help pool information at low costs to help discover prices and provide a venue for trading risk. The surge of new moneys invested into commodity markets by non-traditional sources is seen by some observers to test the institutional designs of derivative markets and of the link between them and cash markets.

a) The material of this box is based on a contribution by Frank Rose, formerly Senior Vice-President, CBOT, now Assistant Professor, Lewis University.
b) Commitments of Traders Report, Commodity Futures Trading Commission.

The projections contained in this *Outlook* are based on implicit assumptions concerning which of the contributory factors are temporary and which are permanent. Further analysis examines how variations in these assumptions affect the robustness of the view that higher prices, though not as high as today's levels, are here to stay.

Recent food commodity price hikes in an historical context

The commodity price spikes witnessed in the last couple of years, and particularly most recently, are exceptional when viewed from the perspective of the last decade or so but not so much so when seen in a longer historical context. Figure 2.1 shows the evolution of annual average world prices of wheat, coarse grains, rice and oilseeds from 1970 to 2007, with projections from 2008 to 2017. Monthly average prices for April 2008 are also included to indicate most recent developments.[2]

For each commodity there are two lines, one tracing dollar-denominated nominal prices and one tracing that same series adjusted for inflation (labelled "real" prices). Nominal price trends are convenient indicators of short-run price developments but to be economically meaningful, longer-run price trends need to be looked at in inflation adjusted terms. The first thing to notice from these four graphs is that a high degree of price volatility is characteristic of world food commodity markets, even when one looks at annual averages. Prices are typically sensitive to short run shocks to either supply and demand because of, *e.g.*, delays between production decisions and output and the resulting slow adjustment of quantities demanded to price changes. Volatility on international markets is further enhanced by policy interventions that shift price risk away from producers or even outside of the country entirely.

The second thing to notice from the data plotted in Figure 2.1 is that the recent price spike is neither the only, nor even the most important, one to occur in the last 30-plus years. In inflation adjusted terms, today's prices fall well short of peaks achieved in the early 1970s, and neither current maize nor wheat prices are averaging much above levels achieved as recently as the mid-1990s.

Of course, having weathered previous food commodity price storms does not negate the need for or the urgency of policy action to deal with this one. However, deciding which policy actions are most appropriate requires an understanding of the various forces driving recent price moves and knowing which of those various forces may be assumed to be temporary and which are likely to be permanent features of future commodity markets.

Crop and vegetable oil price changes: What happened and what happens next?

What happened...

Wheat and coarse grains

Between the 2005 and 2007 marketing years, world planted area of wheat and coarse grains (maize, barley, sorghum, oats,) was basically flat, although regional changes were at times quite large (Table 2.2). Within the OECD region, a sharp decrease in EU area planted to these grains was offset by an increase in plantings in the US. The lower area planted to wheat and coarse grains in the EU defies the increasing world prices, even if less pronounced in euro, but may be consistent with domestic market incentives caused by policy changes. An analysis of the relative impacts of policy reform and other factors on recent changes in EU wheat and coarse grains areas goes beyond the scope of this report.

Table 2.2. **Supply of wheat and coarse grains**

	2005 level	2007 level	Change 2005 to 2007		2017 level	Change 2005 to 2017	
			Absolute	Per cent		Absolute	Per cent
Prices, USD/t (Nominal)							
Wheat[a]	168	319	150	89	231	62	37
Maize[b]	106	181	75	71	165	59	56
Area harvested, m ha							
World	525	531	6	1	539	14	3
OECD	177	177	0	0	177	−1	0
Australia and Canada	36	35	−1	−2	37	1	3
European Union	62	57	−6	−9	58	−4	−7
United States	55	61	5	10	58	3	5
Non-member economies	348	354	6	2	362	14	4
Brazil	16	16	0	−2	17	0	1
China	52	52	0	1	48	−4	−7
India	52	56	4	8	60	8	15
Indonesia	4	3	0	−2	4	0	1
South Africa	4	4	−1	−13	4	0	−10
Yield, t/ha							
World	3.1	3.1	0.1	2	3.5	0.5	15
OECD	4.5	4.5	0.1	1	5.3	0.8	17
Australia and Canada	2.5	2.0	−0.5	−21	2.6	0.1	3
European Union	4.4	4.5	0.1	2	5.4	1.0	22
United States	6.5	6.7	0.3	4	7.7	1.3	20
Non-member economies	2.4	2.4	0.1	3	2.7	0.3	14
Brazil	2.7	3.5	0.8	31	3.8	1.1	42
China	4.7	4.9	0.2	4	5.7	1.0	21
India	1.9	1.9	0.0	0	2.0	0.1	4
Indonesia	3.6	3.6	0.1	1	3.8	0.3	8
South Africa	3.3	2.6	−0.7	−22	3.2	−0.1	−2
Production, mt							
World	1 615	1 661	46	3	1 906	291	18
OECD	792	801	9	1	928	135	17
Australia and Canada	90	70	−20	−22	95	5	6
European Union	277	256	−21	−8	313	36	13
United States	356	407	51	14	446	90	25
Non-member economies	823	860	37	5	978	155	19
Brazil	43	56	12	29	62	19	44
China	245	257	11	5	276	31	13
India	102	110	8	8	122	20	19
Indonesia	13	12	0	−1	14	1	9
South Africa	14	10	−5	−32	12	−2	−12

StatLink 📊 http://dx.doi.org/10.1787/385058145577

a) No. 2 hard red winter wheat, ordinary protein, USA f.o.b. Gulf Ports (June/May).
b) No. 2 yellow corn, USA, f.o.b, Gulf ports.
Source: OECD and FAO Secretariats.

The impact of weather shocks in this period is clear: yields of two major exporting countries, Australia and Canada, fell by about a fifth in aggregate. In the case of Canada, the shock may to some extent be a reduction from atypically good yields in 2004 and 2005, but in Australia the poor crop represents one of several poor yield outcomes in recent years (Figure 2.3). The trend yield in Australia was assumed in this figure, rather than estimated. If estimated over this interval, the trend yield in Australia would be negative due to the persistent drought. To reduce the inconsistency as compared to longer historical patterns and the *Outlook* assumptions, a trend growth rate of 0% over this interval is assumed for these calculations. The graph shows that yields overall were at or below trend in many countries. In contrast, there was a recovery from poor yields experienced in 2005 in some places, such as in Brazil.

Figure 2.3. **Deviations from trend of wheat and coarse grain yields**

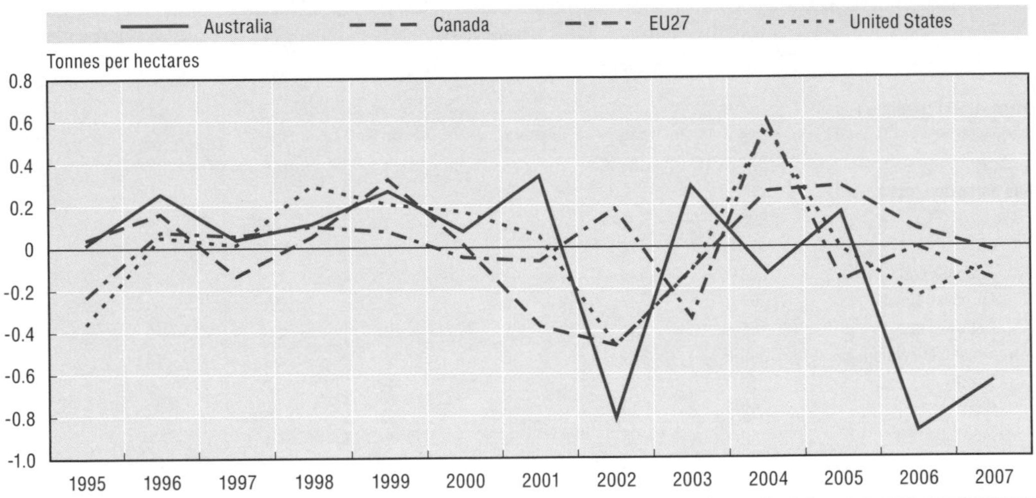

StatLink ⟨⟨⟨ http://dx.doi.org/10.1787/383680730253

Note: Yield trends are estimated over these years to be 0.7% for the EU (27), 1.0% for Canada, and 2.6% for the US, and assumed to be 0% for Australia.

Source: OECD and FAO Secretariats.

On the demand side, use of food grains to be processed into biofuels stands out as an important component of demand growth between marketing years 2005 and 2007 (Table 2.3). Wheat and coarse grain use overall increased by about 80 Mt, or 5%. Within this aggregate, biofuel use doubled, rising by 47 Mt, thus accounting for over half the increase in world grain use. The US biofuel use of grains alone explains the vast majority of this change, up by 41 Mt even after adjusting for distillers grains co-produced with ethanol and added to feed use. But these data also show that an attribution of all the grain price increases to ethanol would be incorrect.

Despite a doubling of some grain prices and broad increases overall, global food and feed use per capita were sustained, implying that the generally strong economic performance of the last two years has been manifested in outward shifts of demand that – in combination with relatively inelastic demand in the short term – has offset the impact of higher prices on quantities demanded. In non-OECD countries, food use of grains was 3% higher in 2007 than in 2005, and feed use was 2% higher indicating that the expansion in livestock consumption and production in these countries, discussed in previous editions of the *OECD-FAO Outlook*, has continued. Excluding biofuels, the total of other uses of wheat and coarse grains – non-food and non-feed uses such as for industrial processes – was flat between 2005 and 2007.

OECD-FAO AGRICULTURAL OUTLOOK 2008-2017 – ISBN 978-92-64-04590-3 – © OECD/FAO 2008

Table 2.3. **Demand for wheat and coarse grains**[a]

	2005 level	2007 level	Change 2005 to 2007 absolute	Change 2005 to 2007 percent	2017 level	Change 2005 to 2017 absolute	Change 2005 to 2017 percent
Prices, USD/t (Nominal)							
Wheat[b]	168	319	150	89	231	62	37
Maize[c]	106	181	75	71	165	59	56
Food, mt							
World	642	662	21	3	725	83	13
OECD	166	175	9	6	178	12	8
Australia and Canada	7	7	1	9	8	1	17
European Union	86	85	−1	−1	87	1	1
United States	31	34	3	10	34	3	10
Non-Member Economies	476	487	11	2	547	70	15
Brazil	16	16	0	−2	19	2	15
China	105	104	−1	−1	100	−5	−5
India	89	92	3	4	102	13	15
Indonesia	10	11	0	4	12	2	15
South Africa	7	8	0	1	8	0	4
Feed use (Include ethanol co-products for USA), mt							
World	749	761	12	2	840	91	12
OECD	430	431	1	0	454	23	5
Australia and Canada	31	31	0	0	31	0	0
European Union	167	165	−2	−1	169	2	1
United States	176	179	3	2	198	22	12
Non-Member Economies	318	329	11	3	386	68	21
Brazil	31	32	0	1	38	7	22
China	107	110	4	3	130	23	21
India	8	9	1	11	14	5	67
Indonesia	4	5	0	6	6	1	20
South Africa	4	4	0	−10	4	0	−8
Other uses, mt							
World	232	270	47	20	365	133	57
OECD	121	163	43	35	238	118	97
Australia and Canada	5	8	2	44	15	9	175
European Union	17	19	2	12	39	23	136
United States	78	115	37	48	162	84	107
Non-Member Economies	111	116	5	4	127	16	14
Brazil	5	5	0	1	7	2	41
China	35	38	3	9	46	12	34
India	8	9	0	4	9	0	4
Indonesia	3	3	0	0	3	0	0
South Africa	1	1	0	−36	1	0	−16
of which, biofuel (ex. feed co-product)							
World	46	93	47	103	172	126	275
European Union	1	6	4	323	24	22	1 720
United States	41	81	41	100	131	91	222
Total use, mt							
World	1,622	1,702	80	5	1,930	307	19
OECD	717	770	53	7	870	153	21
Non-Member Economies	906	932	27	3	1,059	154	17
World ending stocks, mt	427	359	−68	−16	399	−28	−7

StatLink http://dx.doi.org/10.1787/385125431745

a) Historical data on the use of cereals for biofuels are estimates and subject to revision.
b) No. 2 hard red winter wheat, ordinary protein, USA f.o.b. Gulf Ports (June/May).
c) No. 2 yellow corn, USA, f.o.b., Gulf Ports.
Source: OECD and FAO Secretariats.

Oilseeds

The vegetable oil markets have experienced a broadly similar pattern of demand growth between the 2005 and 2007 marketing years, but without much of a shock to supply (Table 2.4).The area planted to oilseeds has decreased globally, whereas oilseed yields grew faster than was the case for grains. The reduction in oilseed plantings is explained by reallocation of area in the US, and decreases in Brazil and China. The poor oilseed yields of Australia and Canada do not offset better performance elsewhere. World vegetable oil production, which includes palm oil as well as oils crushed from oilseeds, grew 7% over this two year period.

Table 2.4. **Supply of oilseed and vegetable oil**

	2005 level	2007 level	Change 2005 to 2007		2017 level	Change 2005 to 2017	
			Absolute	Per cent		Absolute	Per cent
Prices, USD/t (Nominal)							
Oilseeds[a]	269	486	217	81	457	188	70
Vegetable oil[b]	556	1 015	459	82	1 055	499	90
Area harvested (oilseeds[c]), m ha							
World	145	142	−3	−2	164	19	13
OECD	48	46	−2	−4	50	3	5
Australia and Canada	7	8	1	10	10	2	27
European Union	9	10	1	13	11	2	28
United States	31	27	−4	−12	28	−2	−7
Non-member economies	97	96	−1	−1	113	16	16
Brazil	23	21	−3	−11	28	5	20
China	18	16	−2	−9	18	0	0
India	16	17	0	2	18	2	12
Indonesia	1	1	0	−19	0	0	−26
South Africa	1	1	0	−11	1	0	44
Yield (oilseeds), tons/ha							
World	2.0	2.1	0.0	1	2.3	0.3	15
OECD	2.6	2.4	−0.2	−8	2.8	0.2	6
Australia and Canada	1.9	1.5	−0.4	−20	1.8	−0.1	−6
European Union	2.6	2.4	−0.2	−7	3.1	0.6	22
United States	2.8	2.7	−0.1	−5	3.0	0.2	6
Non-member economies	1.8	1.9	0.2	9	2.2	0.4	22
Brazil	2.2	2.8	0.6	26	2.9	0.7	31
China	1.8	1.7	0.0	−3	1.9	0.2	11
India	1.0	1.0	0.0	1	1.1	0.1	15
Indonesia	1.3	1.3	0.0	1	1.5	0.2	15
South Africa	1.3	1.3	−0.1	−5	1.4	0.1	4
Production, vegetable oil, mt							
World	99	106	7	7	143	45	45
OECD	26	27	1	4	33	7	25
Australia and Canada	2	2	0	−3	3	1	72
European Union	11	12	1	8	14	3	27
United States	10	10	0	3	12	2	19
Non-member economies	73	79	6	8	111	38	52
Brazil	6	6	0	−1	7	2	28
China	11	11	0	3	17	6	51
India	4	4	0	1	5	1	29
Indonesia	16	19	3	18	28	12	74
South Africa	0	0	0	−13	0	0	46

StatLink ⟨⟩ http://dx.doi.org/10.1787/385160411654

a) Weighted average oilseed price, European port.
b) Weighted average price of oilseed oils and palm oil, European port.
c) Defined as rapeseed (canola), soyabeans and sunflower.
Source: OECD and FAO Secretariats.

World vegetable oil use increased faster between marketing years 2005 and 2007 than production (Table 2.5). Of the demand increase, biofuel use of oils accounted for over half. Excluding biofuel use, other uses rose by over 4% during these two years, or at roughly the rate of population growth. In the face of strong prices, this increase indicates a shift in demand for traditional uses that offsets the price effect, compounding the strong growth in use as biofuel feedstock.

Table 2.5. **Demand for vegetable oil**[a]

	2005 level	2007 level	Change 2005 to 2007		2017 level	Change 2005 to 2017	
			Absolute	Per cent		Absolute	Per cent
Prices, USD/t (Nominal)							
Oilseeds[a]	269	486	217	81	457	188	70
Vegetable oil[b]	556	1 015	459	82	1 055	499	90
Use, vegetable oil, mt							
World	96	105	8.8	9.2	143	47.5	49.5
OECD	34	37	3.1	9.2	50	16.3	48.2
Australia and Canada	1	1	0.0	0.8	2	1.0	85.8
European Union	17	19	1.9	11.4	29	12.3	72.5
United States	10	11	1.3	13.1	12	2.5	25.2
Non-member economies	62	68	5.7	9.2	93	31.1	50.2
Brazil	3	3	0.0	−0.3	6	2.6	78.3
China	17	20	2.3	13.3	25	7.7	43.9
India	9	9	0.2	2.2	11	2.4	27.6
Indonesia	4	5	0.9	22.6	8	3.9	100.4
South Africa	1	1	0.1	11.7	1	0.3	32.8
of which, biofuel							
World	4	9	4.9	113.9	21	16.9	388.0
European Union	3	6	2.3	68.8	12	9.0	266.8
United States	1	2	1.2	162.3	2	0.9	121.8
World ending stocks, mt	9	8	−1.1	−11.9	9	0.2	2.6

StatLink ⟨⟨⟨ http://dx.doi.org/10.1787/385178837100

a) Historical data on the use of cereals for biofuels are estimates and subject to revision.
b) Wheighted average oilseed price, European port.
c) Wheighted average price of oilseed oils and palm oil, European port.
Source: OECD and FAO Secretariats.

What happens next...

Permanent and temporary factors in future prices and price volatility

Given how global supply and demand changed between 2005 and 2007, it may appear as if nothing much dramatic has happened that could possibly trigger the big price increases actually observed. Yet, there has effectively been a gap between growth rates of demand and supply wide enough to cause prices to rise significantly on markets where neither supply nor demand (can) respond elastically and swiftly to price changes – at least not in the short term. In the market for cereals (wheat and coarse grains), production has grown by 46 Mt (3%), between 2005 and 2007, while total use increased by nearly double that amount, i.e. 80 Mt (5%), over the same period. In the market for vegetable oil, the gap between production and use growth was also about two percentage points. Had stocks been easily available they might have helped to bridge these gaps. But that was not the case, as shown below.

Outlook data permit an assessment of the permanent and temporary nature of the various contributing factors to recent price increases. Those of a short-term nature do not affect future prices as in the *Outlook* they are not assumed to recur. But the permanent factors are expected to influence the level and trends of future prices.

Recent *negative yield shocks* in key agricultural commodity-producing regions have contributed to the price increase. This particular phenomenon can be viewed as *temporary* in the *Outlook*, barring underlying climate change or water constraints that lead to permanent reductions in yield.

Macroeconomic conditions have favoured higher world prices. Good economic growth increased purchasing power in most countries during the recent past, leading to strong demand growth for most agricultural commodities. Moreover, a weak USD typically leads to higher USD-denominated prices of traded goods, as they will not be as expensive when priced in other currencies – although prices of most commodities in most currencies are more expensive than two years ago. This factor is assumed to be *permanent* in the *Outlook*. These are not new factors, however, and, certainly GDP growth in developing countries has been a feature of commodity markets for many years. These factors should be considered to *slow the decline in real prices* in the future, not to lift average prices to permanently higher levels.

The *oil price*, and energy prices more generally, are important contributing factors to the recent increase in agricultural commodity prices. While the effects of higher oil prices on biofuel demand may be the focus of discussion, traditional effects of energy prices, namely on costs of commodity production and on costs of transportation, processing, distribution and marketing intermediate and final products, are also important. In any case, the *Outlook* assumptions reflect the widely held belief that the oil price increases are *permanent* and that further gradual increases are likely. Higher oil prices result in a structural increase in agricultural production costs and contribute to lifting future prices to higher average levels.

Available data suggest that somewhat more than half of the increase in the quantity of demand for grains and vegetable oils between 2005 and 2007 was due to *biofuels*. Based on *Outlook* assumptions of further modest increases in the price of oil, continuation of policies that support for biofuel production and use and no dramatic technology change, feedstock demand for biofuel production appears to represent a *permanent* factor. While biofuel use of grains and vegetable oils is anticipated to represent a falling share of the overall increase in demand for these food commodities, it is nevertheless a new source of demand which is seen as one of the factors *lifting prices to higher average* levels in the future.

Stocks of wheat, coarse grains and vegetable oil have fallen to low levels relative to use (Figure 2.4), reducing the buffer against shocks in supply and demand. This has been one reason for the recent run-up in prices. During the 10-year outlook period stocks are projected to remain low, implying that tight markets are a *permanent* factor in the *Outlook*. This should not lead to permanently higher prices but certainly provides the background for more price *volatility* in the future.

There has recently also been a surge of new moneys invested into *futures commodity markets* from non-traditional sources. The long-term aggregate effect of these activities on the level of derivative market prices and related prices in cash markets is still very uncertain. Adjustment in market procedures and participants' behaviour argue that any effect on price *levels* will prove *temporary* relative to the 10-year *Outlook*. As these funds are very large, however, and can and will move rapidly in and out of commodity markets as profit opportunities dictate, this development may well be a new and *permanent* element in future price *volatility* (Box 2.2).

2. ARE HIGH PRICES HERE TO STAY?

Figure 2.4. **Stocks-to-use ratios of maize and wheat**

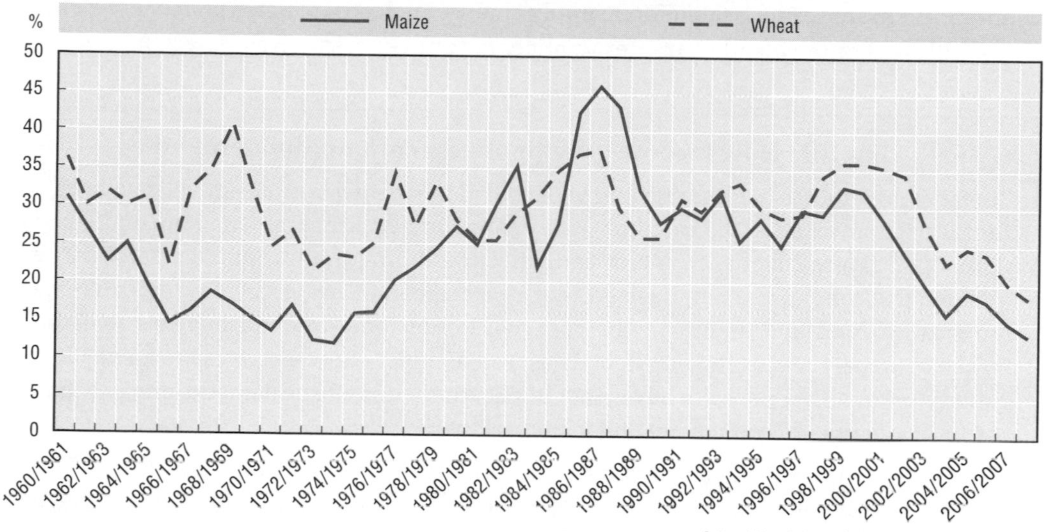

Source: US Department of Agriculture PSD View database, April 2007.

StatLink ᴍᴄ﹩ http://dx.doi.org/10.1787/383723077040

A more general point concerning price volatility relates to the "thinness" of markets, or the share of imports and exports relative to the volume of global consumption and production (Table 2.6). For coarse grains, the share of imports in consumption and exports in production is on the order of 10-12%. For rice the share is even lower whereas for wheat, these ratios are higher, but still less than 20%. In contrast, the share of vegetable oil production that is exported and the share of consumption that is imported are about 44%.

Table 2.6. **World coarse grain, wheat and vegetable oil market indicator ratios**

	Ratio	2005	2007	2017	Growth rate (2005-2007)	Growth rate (2005-2017)
Coarse grain	Export/Production	11.1%	11.7%	10.4%	4.6%	-6.3%
	Import/Consumption	10.4%	11.2%	10.5%	8.6%	1.1%
Wheat	Export/Production	17.8%	17.4%	18.3%	-2.4%	3.0%
	Import/Consumption	17.5%	17.9%	18.3%	2.1%	4.9%
Vegetable oil	Export/Production	44.8%	44.1%	44.0%	-1.4%	-1.7%
	Import/Consumption	44.0%	43.7%	44.1%	0.6%	0.2%

StatLink ᴍᴄ﹩ http://dx.doi.org/10.1787/385236851201

Source: OECD and FAO Secretariats.

Thin markets reflect barriers to trade – of a natural (*e.g.* transport costs) or policy (*e.g.* import tariffs) nature – that prevent agents from seeing world price signals. Thus prices must change more to accommodate an external shock to traded quantities, all else being equal, when markets are thinner. The assumptions on which the *Outlook* is based, however, do not include a change in natural or policy determined trade barriers. Thus, while such market characteristics are a *permanent* feature in the *Outlook*, there is no assumed change in the degree of market thinness and the impact on price *volatility* over time.

The *nature and composition of demand*, on the other hand, are factors that may increase the future variability in world prices. As discussed, industrial demand for grains and oilseeds – such as for the production of biofuels – constitutes a growing share of total use. This demand is generally considered less responsive to prices than traditional food and

OECD-FAO AGRICULTURAL OUTLOOK 2008-2017 – ISBN 978-92-64-04590-3 – © OECD/FAO 2008

49

feed demand. In addition, food demand elasticities may be further reduced by rising incomes and more sophisticated food supply chains. Such changes are *permanent* elements in the *Outlook* that may lead to greater *volatility* in future world prices (Box 2.3).

Box 2.3. **How income growth affects commodity demand**

Income growth has been strong and widespread in recent years, despite a slowdown of the US economy and some cases of poor economic performance. The consequence is higher per capita income in many countries, including many non-OECD countries. Previous *Outlook* reports emphasized that rising incomes are associated with greater demand for food and a shift in the composition of food demand towards livestock products, namely meats and dairy goods as well as fruits and vegetables, and away from staple crops. But they may also have other implications: less elastic demand, and new links from energy prices to commodity and food markets.

Income growth tends to be simultaneous with urbanization. Many countries with the greatest growth rate are also experiencing migration from rural areas to cities. As people move away from rural centres of food production and as they rely more on the infrastructure of countries and cities to deliver foods to their area, the marketing chain between commodity production and food consumption adapts. These changes may lead to longer transportation, refrigeration, and other activities whose costs vary with energy prices, as well as wages and other costs that may themselves be affected indirectly by energy prices. In short, food prices increasingly depend on oil and energy prices independently of commodity prices as income rises.

The share of commodity price in food price may also decrease as the marketing chain lengthens. In the US, the commodity cost component of the total food bill has fallen from about one-third in the 1960s to about one-fifth since the mid-1990s.[a] As the share of commodity costs in the food bill falls, the expected proportional change in food prices for a given percentage change in commodity costs decrease: a doubling of commodity prices will have a greater effect on final food consumers if commodity costs initially already accounted for almost all of the food costs, whereas a similar doubling of commodity prices would have a smaller proportional effect for food consumers if the commodity costs were only a small fraction of the total food bill. Thus, as income increases and market chains extend, the responsiveness of demand to farm-level prices may decrease.

Economics of demand indicate that consumers tend to care less about prices of goods that represent a small share of their budget. As incomes expand and the share of budgets spent on a necessity like food fall, consumers are expected to be somewhat less sensitive to price changes, and a shock to supply of a given size will require a greater price signal to compel consumers to adjust their purchases. Higher incomes that tend to reduce demand elasticity may lead to greater variability in world prices.

This has certain implications. Greater income and purchasing power leading to less sensitivity to prices means that fewer people are pushed into starvation by rising prices. But people who have not enjoyed anything like the average income growth rate will face more variability in prices, including higher peaks, without the additional purchasing power, and these groups will be worse off than before. Thus, higher food prices strain budgets of the poor, even if food is still purchased.

a) US Economic Research Service (*www.ers.usda.gov/data/FarmToConsumer/marketingbill.htm*).

Wheat and coarse grains

The inventory of short-term and permanent factors and how these may affect future prices helps to disentangle what may happen next in cereals and oilseed markets. Looking ahead to marketing year 2017, the end of the *Outlook* period, wheat and maize prices are expected to remain higher than in 2005, but not as high as in 2007. Area is not expected to be a main source of new production, although some increase is expected. There is likely to be a geographic reorientation of sorts, as the US focuses on grains and the EU on oilseeds and the total area planted to wheat and coarse grains in the EU decreases. On a world scale wheat and coarse grain area is expected to increase some, but certainly not dramatically despite the higher level of prices as compared to 2005. Yields are expected to grow along historical trend patterns, but this assumption obscures two important caveats discussed below: weather-related yield shocks will certainly occur, and the effect of higher prices on yields is unclear.

Demand for these grains to be used as feedstocks in biofuel production is not expected to continue to expand at the rate of the last two years.[3] However, cereal use for biofuel production is projected nearly to double from 2007 to 2017, though its share of the overall increase in quantities of wheat and coarse grains used is expected to fall from about 60% to just over 40%. The US is likely to continue to be the centre of grain-based ethanol production, assuming no new technologies displace current practices, but use in the EU is likely to expand, too. The larger part of the growth in use is explained by rising food and feed demand particularly in non-OECD countries, where both categories rise by 15% on average or more whereas OECD food and feed uses increase at a lower rate. The assumed continuation of strong economic growth of recent years underlies these shifts in grain demand.

Oilseeds

The baseline previews a strong vegetable oil price even as by 2017 oilseed prices (and oilseed meal prices) are expected to retreat from recent levels. The higher prices of 2007 bring about a supply response that results in more land allocated to this sector and good yield growth. Area planted to oilseeds is expected to increase over the period, with some growth in the OECD area, apart from the US, and strong growth should be seen in non-OECD countries. A large share of this growth is expected to take place in Brazil and Argentina, but oilseed area will expand in Ukraine and Russia, too. During the projection period, yield grows on average at the historical trend rate. Palm-oil production is expected to grow quickly, increasing by two-fifths between 2007 and 2017.

Biofuel use of vegetable oils accounts for more than a third of the growth in vegetable oil use from 2005 to 2017. This is very strong growth in percentage terms, as world biofuel use increases more than five-fold from the very small base in 2005. But the growth in other uses amounts to an increase of about 33% over this period as well. These consumption increases worldwide take place at a nearly constant real world price, and while growth rates vary widely, they are indicative of strengthening demand. Income growth drives much of this expansion of demand, with non-OECD countries increasing their consumption of vegetable oils by half in 2017 relative to 2005.

Uncertainties

The foregoing paragraphs provided a discussion of the baseline results for cereals and oilseeds prices over the *Outlook* period. Based on the projected developments in supply and demand for these commodities, prices are expected to remain strong, albeit not as high as what they currently are. But these outcomes reflect the assumptions underlying the projections, and whether or not these assumptions become reality is uncertain. Some of these uncertainties are first discussed qualitatively in the following paragraphs. The next section shows what the quantitative impact of some of these factors may be.

Commodity market *volatility* will continue, and the direction of changes is uncertain. The fact that prices currently are at historic peak levels does not mean that swings in the other direction should be excluded. In the short term, low stocks-to-use ratios may lead to greater price movements for a given shock, either up or down. Higher income in most of the world may lead not only to greater demand and a change in the composition of demand, but also to lower responsiveness of demand to price changes. Thin markets with few stocks and increasingly inelastic components of total demand experience greater price volatility.

There will be shocks to *yields* and to *macroeconomic conditions, including oil prices*, that increase or decrease world prices. Crop harvests fail. Recent history abounds with predictions of constant strong economic growth of a country into the future that have been wide off the mark and a reduction in income leads to lower demand. Widespread expectations of climate change lead to predictions of declining yields, and diminishing water supplies lead to predictions of abandoned areas. Systemic and massive shocks are often assumed to be negative. But there are also "risks" in the opposite direction. Good weather can lead to exceptional yields, additional investments and technological breakthroughs may improve yields more than expected, and economic growth can beat predictions.

Policy response to the price situation is also an unknown. In response to concerns about domestic prices, will more countries use *trade policies or domestic market interventions* in order to reduce the increases in their domestic prices? If countries insulate their domestic market from world prices through beggar-thy-neighbour policies, then world prices will rise even further before the remaining countries that are paying or receiving these prices adjust quantities of demand and supply so that markets balance. There is also some uncertainty regarding future *agricultural policies*. For instance, there is the potential for another world trade agreement and there are scheduled policy decisions, such as the US farm bill that is pending at the time of writing or the "health check" of the CAP to be undertaken by the EU. *Environmental policy* continues to be a source of uncertainty. Producers in many key exporting countries meet standards that are intended to encourage sustainable practices. Environmental policies introduced to address potential climate change, *e.g.*, carbon taxes or credits, could lead to rapid changes in the profitability of farmland use and practices.

Biofuel policies are also a source of uncertainty. By the time of this publication, the representation of key biofuel policies in some countries is already out of date in this *Outlook*. An array of new US mandates and the potential consequences of an EU Directive promoting larger quantities of biofuel use are not included. These or other policies to promote biofuel production and use, whether through mandate or subsidy, will lead to greater purchases of feedstocks for biofuel production. Alternatively, of course, if policies to support biofuel use and production are deferred, waived, or overwritten with lesser efforts, then feedstock purchases will decline, reducing average prices in the future below the projections in this report.

Feedstock purchases may differ radically from current and projected patterns if *new biofuel production technologies* become viable, through whatever combination of commercial profit and subsidy. New processes that generate biofuels from feedstocks that do not directly compete with existing commercial crops, or are even co-products of such crops, could lead to a departure from the *Outlook*, possibly a fairly radical one. But such a possibility is explored elsewhere by the OECD, as it raises complicated questions that defy cursory analysis.

A key question is the *long-run capacity of supply*. One argument reiterates messages of climate change and water overuse, suggests that yields are peaking, and sees little scope for further supplies. Another argument emphasizes the potential of human innovation to continue or even quicken yield trends, particularly when motivated by a high price, and the unrealized potential of countries that are still in stages of development that are associated with low productivity. The *Outlook* is not the place to look for answers to these arguments. Neither is it a place to look for unconditional support for either case. Here, historical trends in technology growth are assumed to continue into the medium-term future.

More generally, *high prices are their own worst enemy*. Price increases lead to supply and demand responses, which lead to lower prices. A high price spurs producers to find new means of raising output, and encourages consumers to choose alternatives or to use goods more effectively. It may take time to introduce extreme changes, such as new processes of making a good, using a good for intermediate processing, introducing substitute goods or adjusting lifestyles. The scale and delay of such responses to high prices are uncertain, but that agents will respond in ways that work against sustained price increases is certain.

How important are the *Outlook* assumptions in determining future prices?

After having argued qualitatively the impacts of a number of factors with uncertain outcomes on the level and variability of prices, the discussion below tries to quantify some of these effects. The recent spikes in food commodity prices surprised most economic forecasters, reminding us of the inherent vulnerability of projections to unanticipated developments. The baseline assumptions of normal weather and stable economic performance are necessary, but the future will not follow that smooth path. Negative and positive yield shocks are a permanent feature of agricultural commodity markets. So, too, are macroeconomic shocks that reduce or raise income, alter exchange rates, and induce or limit inflation. Similarly there is growing discussion over whether governments will continue to subsidise the conversion of food commodities to biofuel production with the same enthusiasm as during recent years.

To give some idea of the sensitivity of the baseline to alternative assumptions regarding these factors, the economic model underlying those projections was used to perform sensitivity analysis. Two kinds of simulations were performed. In one, five versions of the baseline were simply reproduced, progressively replacing original assumptions about key determining variables with plausible alternative values. In the second, a stochastic simulation was undertaken wherein the assumptions of normal weather and a stable macroeconomic environment are replaced by a range of plausible yield values and macroeconomic variables.

Scenario results

The five key assumptions that were examined are: 1) biofuel use of grains and oilseeds, 2) petroleum prices, 3) income growth in major developing economies: China, India, Brazil, Indonesia and South Africa (labelled EE5 countries in Figure 2.5), 4) the exchange rate of the USD relative to the currencies of all other countries, and 5) crop yields. Figure 2.5 shows results for the first set of simulation experiments. To simplify the presentation, all the shocks chosen for these experiments were implemented such that they move prices below those projected in the baseline. Obviously, the opposite would have been possible as well. To further aid exposition, the focus here is just on the price outcomes for the terminal year of the baseline projection period, 2017.

In interpreting these findings it should be noted that, taken one by one, these alternative assumptions might seem equally realistic as those made for the baseline. Of course, the likelihood that they would all come together in the way that is assumed here is low. But, indeed, recent years have seen just such a coincidence of developments in all these factors, all pushing prices in the same, upward, direction. While those developments cannot explain the entire run-up in food commodity prices that has occurred since 2005, they surely help to explain much of it.

It is noteworthy that even seemingly modest changes in assumptions can lead to significant differences in projected prices. For coarse grains and vegetable oil, the price outlook would be most affected if biofuels production were to remain constant at 2007 levels. Changes in demand for these commodities as feedstocks for biofuel production are a source of uncertainty, no matter whether the cause is an oil price change, a change in biofuel support policies or a new technological development that lead processors to buy different feedstocks. Holding biofuels production constant at its 2007 level takes around 12% off the 2017 projected prices for coarse grains and around 15% off the projected price of vegetable oil.

Figure 2.5. **Sensitivity of projected world prices to changes in five key assumptions, percentage difference from baseline values, 2017**

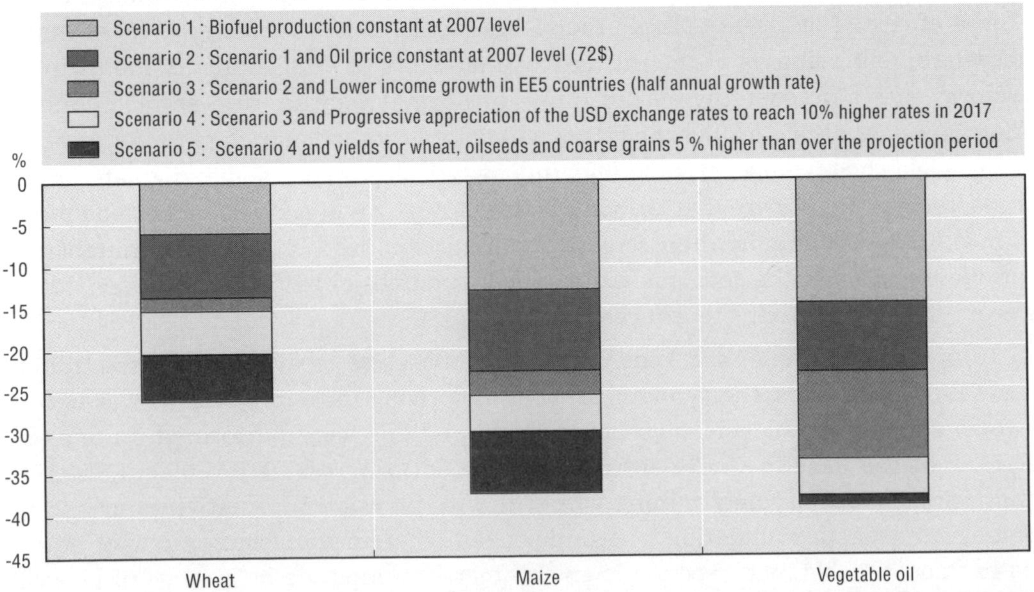

Scenario 1 : Biofuel production constant at 2007 level
Scenario 2 : Scenario 1 and Oil price constant at 2007 level (72$)
Scenario 3 : Scenario 2 and Lower income growth in EE5 countries (half annual growth rate)
Scenario 4 : Scenario 3 and Progressive appreciation of the USD exchange rates to reach 10% higher rates in 2017
Scenario 5 : Scenario 4 and yields for wheat, oilseeds and coarse grains 5 % higher than over the projection period

StatLink http://dx.doi.org/10.1787/383750187035

Source: OECD and FAO Secretariats.

OECD-FAO AGRICULTURAL OUTLOOK 2008-2017 – ISBN 978-92-64-04590-3 – © OECD/FAO 2008

The second scenario shows that wheat, coarse grains and vegetable oil price projections are all shown to be highly sensitive to petroleum-price assumptions. This sheds light on the important role that the recent sharp escalation in crude oil prices is playing in driving up food commodity costs. This single external factor not only is a crucially important feature of the macroeconomic context but also directly affects the energy costs of agricultural production, transportation, and food processing. Many countries tend to have better economic growth if the oil price is low, but others benefit from a high oil price. Under the constant oil price assumption, the prices of maize and vegetable oil are about 10% lower and the wheat price falls 7% in 2017 when compared with the baseline projection.

GDP growth in developing countries is a source of recent increases in demand that many observers take to be a permanent feature of the medium-term future. Trend-line extrapolations of 8-10% GDP growth in a country that are extended into the indefinite future beg the question: when will this growth stop? The sensitivity of prices to increases in GDP is tested with respect to the hypothetical case where the rate of growth in GDP is reduced to half the rate assumed in the *Outlook*. This scenario gives wheat and coarse grains prices that are only modestly (1 to 2%) below the baseline. For vegetable oils, reflecting presumably a much higher income elasticity of the demand and a greater influence of EE5 countries in world trade, the simulated price difference is over 10%.

These results may be less surprising than they seem on first sight. First, while EE5 countries are rapid growth markets for wheat and coarse grains, they are still relatively small players in world trade. This is not the case for vegetable oils, where China and India are very large importers and where lower GDP growth has a substantial world price effect. Second, this scenario does not take account of any second-round effects that lower income growth in EE5 countries may have on economic growth elsewhere. So there may be some downward bias to the outcomes presented here.

A fourth scenario was defined to simulate the results of a stronger US dollar. Thus, USD exchange rates were progressively appreciated to reach rates in 2017 some 10% higher than was assumed for the baseline. A stronger US dollar raises prices in domestic currency terms in exporting countries, providing greater incentives to increase supplies. At the same time, a stronger US dollar reduces the import demand in importing countries. The combination of greater export supply and weaker import demand puts additional downward pressure on world prices. By 2017, wheat, coarse grain and vegetable oil prices are all some 5% below the corresponding baseline projection.

The scenario under which cereals and oilseeds yields are assumed to be 5% higher leads to projected wheat and maize prices for 2017 that are 6 and 8% lower respectively than the corresponding baseline value, but make little difference for projected vegetable oil prices. Yield trends are a source of great uncertainty. Some observers see constraints to agricultural productivity owing to vanishing water resources and even greater potential constraints to agricultural production as a consequence of global warming. Global warming is argued to lead directly to greater incidence of negative yield shocks and sustained negative pressure on production in heat stressed climatic zones. But yields may actually increase in regions with moderate climates so the net effect on world production is uncertain. Furthermore, it could lead to the introduction of policies such as carbon trading that may also tend to reduce agricultural output by raising land and energy costs.

Other observers note that sustained high prices lead to surges in investment and foresee that recent events will spur greater technology growth. The more optimistic view even looks to another Green Revolution that raises yields in some of the poorest regions of the world, much as the previous one raised yields in parts of South and Southeast Asia and Latin America. Such optimists reply to concerns about greater weather variability by noting the consequent incentive to develop technologies and to turn to commodities that are less susceptible.

Stochastic results

Stochastic analysis, in which ranges of key input variables are used instead of fixed values, provides a more balanced and comprehensive look at the underlying uncertainty of the projections.[4] The choices of alternative values for them were based on historically observed patterns in the data. The result is that for each year of the baseline a statistical distribution of price projections is produced for every commodity, rather than one single price projection.

The essence of the findings from this exercise is captured by looking only at the simulated distribution of price outcomes obtained for 2008 and 2017. Figure 2.6 summarizes results for those two projection years in terms of the median, and the values of the 10th and 90th percentiles of the distributions of the price projections for wheat, coarse grains and vegetable oil prices.

The median values of these distributions are nearly identical to the deterministic values projected for the baseline. The 10th percentile is an indicator of the lower end of the range; the 90th percentile indicates the upper end. These should not be read as representing low and high extremes, but rather as indicating plausible alternative futures based on past variation in key variables driving commodity prices.

Figure 2.6. **Stochastic crop prices in 2008 and 2017 in nominal terms**

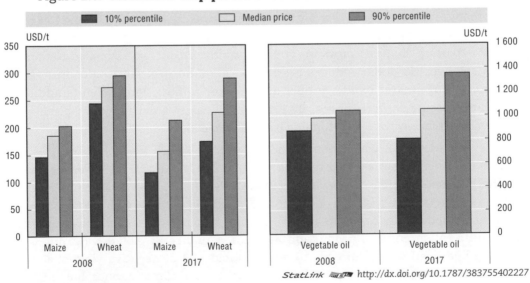

StatLink http://dx.doi.org/10.1787/383755402227

Source: OECD and FAO Secretariats.

For the projected maize price in 2008, the 10th percentile is USD 146 per tonne and the 90th percentile is USD 204. The corresponding values for wheat price are USD 244 per tonne and USD 296. In both cases, the 10th and 90th percentile are farther apart in the 2017

OECD-FAO AGRICULTURAL OUTLOOK 2008-2017 – ISBN 978-92-64-04590-3 – © OECD/FAO 2008

results than in 2008, reflecting the compounding effects of uncertainty in early years, particularly as regards underlying trends. In both cases, the distribution shifts downward. The 10th percentile falls to USD 117 per tonne for maize and USD 174 per tonne for wheat, whereas the 90th percentile changes little.

The lower level of the distribution in 2017 reflects the underlying assumptions of the *Outlook*. The potential for deviations from those assumptions to result in either much lower or constant grain prices relative to current values based on the historical variations represented here reflects the degree of uncertainty that is known and readily modelled. The distribution of vegetable oil prices in 2017 indicates that in that case, too, assumptions of these projections and historical variations that are most readily measured imply the potential for prices to be either one-fifth lower or two-fifths higher than the price projected for 2008 in the *Outlook*.

The bottom line

In this chapter, a number of temporary and permanent factors have been identified which help to understand how future commodity prices are expected to evolve. On the basis of the analysis, the response of this report to the question "Will prices remain as high as they are today?" is "Very unlikely". While prices can be expected to fall from current highs, and to resume a gradual decline, they are expected to do so from a higher level than what is seen historically.

To summarise, the main factors that have contributed to the current spike and will help to determine developments in the future can be summed up as follows:

● Demand has grown faster than supply because of, among other reasons, growth in biofuels production.

● Supply would normally have grown more, but unfavourable weather conditions in some important producing countries reduced production and export supplies to world markets. Future supply response will be dampened by high oil prices.

● The sensitivity of demand to price changes appears to be falling for various reasons. Thus, a shock to supply of a given size will require a greater price change to bring about the demand adjustment required to balance the market.

● At the same time, global stocks have declined to record-low levels over the last decade, such that any variations in quantities produced and demanded cannot be buffered and hence have a proportionally much greater effect on market prices.

● The sharp increase of financial fund activity in futures commodity markets may have further contributed to the short term price hike, but the extent to which this has been the case is uncertain.

● Border measures that have been taken by many countries in an effort to increase domestic market supplies have reduced supplies on world markets, further magnifying the price increases.

These developments have combined to lift prices to very high levels. But an element of uncertainty about future developments appears to have had a strong impact as well, particularly recently, as both governments and investors are acting in ways that sometimes contribute to further price increases and future price volatility. Without these additional influences, prices would most likely not have been as high as what they are in reality.

With respect to future price trends over the *Outlook*, scenario results have shown the relative impact on prices of different assumptions with respect to macroeconomic developments, exchange rates, oil prices, biofuel production and yield trends. When taken together, these changed assumptions could lead to cereal and vegetable oil prices that are some 25 to 40% lower than baseline values in 2017.

While these scenarios were implemented in a manner to reduce prices to demonstrate their relative contribution, they may also occur in a different configuration that would lead to prices being stronger than projected in the baseline. However, the stochastic analysis that was carried out for this *Outlook* assessment suggests that at least for cereals, the downside risk for prices in the future seems to be increasing.

Notes

1. Dollar-denominated prices have risen substantially, but the generally weakening dollar over this period means that the price increases elsewhere have often been less pronounced than headline prices might lead one to believe. With the exception of few countries, domestic and import crop price increases have been substantial but somewhat less dramatic than in USD terms. Moreover, many countries, in both the OECD and non-OECD region intervene in agricultural markets with policies such as tariffs, leading to even lower transmission of changes in the prices of traded goods to domestic markets.

2. Price projections for 2008 in the *Outlook* baseline clearly do not, and could not possibly, match the recent extreme price hike. The baseline, generated to provide an impression of possible medium to longer-term market developments, necessarily has to abstract from some of the short-term factors inherent in commodity markets. These can result in monthly price variations that are much larger than those that can be observed from annual averages which are used in the *Outlook*.

3. Note that the EISA in the United States and proposals for new mandates in the EU have not been taken into account in this analysis.

4. Stochastic simulation techniques and output have been elaborated in previous Outlook reports. The annual projected values of yields and macroeconomic variables (including the petroleum price) are not assumed to be single numbers in the projection period, as for the baseline. Rather, random perturbations in yield levels, trends, and in macroeconomic variables are drawn from historically determined distributions, respecting to the greatest extent possible correlation among errors and relationships among macroeconomic variables. Several hundred such randomly determined values are fed into the model which is solved for each set. The output represents a wide range of yield values and macroeconomic settings that may be relevant during the Outlook period. As an example, for the oil price in 2008, the 10th percentile is USD 73 per tonne and the 90th percentile is USD 140. Details on how the partial stochastic analysis has been performed are given in the Methodology section of the full Outlook report.

OECD-FAO AGRICULTURAL OUTLOOK 2008-2017 – ISBN 978-92-64-04590-3 – © OECD/FAO 2008

ISBN 978-92-64-04590-3
OECD-FAO AGRICULTURAL OUTLOOK 2008-2017
© OECD/FAO 2008

Chapter 3

Macroeconomic and Policy Assumptions

The main underlying assumptions

Robust economic growth in emerging economies and optimism for OECD countries after several setbacks

Economic activity is now slowing with the distinct possibly of the US, the world's leading economy, sinking into recession in 2008. The slowdown in the US and some other OECD economies is occurring despite continuing robust economic conditions in many other parts of the world. One cause of this moderation is the global credit crunch that has buffeted financial markets and shares worldwide recently. However, this shock has occurred in a period of robust economic performance and this has to some extent softened its impact. Another underlying cause is the cooling of housing markets, which will act to reduce consumers' wealth and slow down growth in the future. Adding to the downside risks, is the fact that the financial turmoil that began over the 2007 summer has not yet come to an end, with the eventual fallout on the real economy still hard to gauge. At the same time, increases in the prices of oil, food and other commodities have led to a pick-up in headline inflation rates in many countries, reducing purchasing power and consumer demand, the stalwart of growth in many OECD economies.

The strength of the housing market in the majority of OECD countries had already slowed before the emergence of the recent turmoil on financial markets, with housing investment and house price inflation decelerating in most countries. The question is whether the adjustments taking place in the housing market will impact adversely on consumption demand and lead to an overall decline in growth or be contained to this market and result in the removal of one ingredient which was previously seen as a key factor in underpinning consumer demand.

Within this context, growth prospects for OECD countries in the short and longer term are just above 2% (annual average). Despite the persistence of financial and housing market turmoil, adjustments in monetary policy by the Federal Reserve in the United States are expected to be sufficient to keep the US out of recession. At the time of writing this *Outlook*, the decline in real house prices in the United States has not yet been translated into weaker private consumption. In Japan, the export sector is expected to continue to support economic activity, but its efficacy should decline as the benefits of past improvements in competitiveness fade and recent exchange rate appreciation partially reverses the earlier gains.

With the exception of Mexico, none of the OECD countries are expected to achieve stronger growth than in the previous years (Figure 3.1). Mexico solidifies its position as a growth leader within the OECD with GDP growth rates around 4%. Strong economic activity remains a feature of Korea and Turkey with, respectively, 4% and 5.4% growth per annum. However, the performance of these economies remains dependent on what happens to the larger economies of the OECD area and elsewhere.

Robust activity in the main emerging economies is projected to remain a major driver of global economic expansion in the near term. In the medium and longer term a modest

OECD-FAO AGRICULTURAL OUTLOOK 2008-2017 – ISBN 978-92-64-04590-3 – © OECD/FAO 2008

Figure 3.1. **Lower GDP growth in selected countries**
Annual growth in real GDP, percentage change from previous period

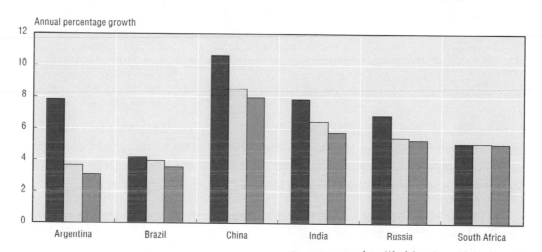

StatLink ⟐⟐⟐ http://dx.doi.org/10.1787/381348211474

Note: Average annual growth is the least-squares growth rate (see glossary).
Source: OECD Economic Outlook No. 82 (December 2007), World Bank Global Economic Prospects 2008 (November 2007).

deceleration is projected. China and India will remain growth leaders among developing countries, with substantial market expansion and GDP growth anticipated for each country as they become further integrated into the global economy and world trade.

In China, GDP growth is expected to slow somewhat from extremely high levels in the long term, but is still to remain substantial. Growth in India should remain strong despite a recent currency appreciation (Figure 3.3). In Brazil, exports and strong domestic demand will continue to support economic activity, with a robust growth, supported by an expected depreciation of the Real in coming years.

Population is expected to slow in the coming decade

Population prospects and dynamics are important determinants of the future global economic environment, affecting both the supply and demand for agricultural commodities. Population growth over the next decade will decline relative to the last 10 years to an average of 1.1% annually to reach approximately 7.4 billion in 2017. The largest population growth is expected in Africa (annual average above 2%), whereas in Europe, population is expected to essentially stabilise over the coming decade (Table 3.1).

In the European Union, population is projected to grow at less than half the rate of the previous decade at 0.2% per annum for EU15 and 0.1% per annum for EU27. The same scenario is projected for Korea for the next decade. Within the OECD area, Turkey, Mexico, Australia and the United States maintain their leadership positions in terms of population growth. On the other hand, some decline is expected in Japan with –0.18% growth per annum to 2017.

Table 3.1. **Slow down in population growth**
Average annual growth over 10 year period, percentage

	Population	
	1998-2007	2008-2017
World	1.23	1.12
Africa	2.37	2.21
Latin America and Caribbean	1.28	1.14
North America	1.01	0.88
Europe	0.30	0.10
Asia and Pacific	1.27	1.11
Oceania Developed	1.18	0.92

StatLink ᴍᴏᴍ http://dx.doi.org/10.1787/384856142260

Note: Average annual growth is the least-squares growth rate (see glossary).
Source: UN World Population Prospects (2006 Revision).

Population growth in China is assumed to follow the current slow trend for the next decade, at close to 0.66% per annum (adding approximately 9 million additional people each year). High population growth is predicted in India and Brazil with growth of 1.31% and 1.16% per annum, respectively.

Despite recent hikes in food prices, inflation throughout the OECD should remain at levels close to 2% per annum

Despite recent hikes in food prices, global growth and world trade expansion, general price levels in many countries have remained remarkably stable. This has reinforced expectations that inflation in OECD countries will remain low in the long-term. Measured by the Private Consumer Expenditure (Deflator (PCED), low inflation will continue in the coming decade. For OECD countries as a whole, inflation is assumed to be just above 2% per annum.

High consumer price inflation continues to plague Turkey, Russia and India with levels above 5% per annum. Inflation in Russia is, nevertheless, expected to fall to less than half the prevailing rate during 2005-07. A significant decline is also assumed for Argentina, with inflation at below 5% per annum.

In the United States the Federal Reserve has attempted to counteract the financial turmoil through monetary policy adjustments, notably reducing interest rates and facilitating loans to banks. But behind the cheaper credit lies the risk of emerging inflation in the period ahead through fuelling excessive demand for goods and services.

The recent emergence of high food price inflation in China is not reflected in the *Outlook* assumptions. Increased purchasing power and supply disruptions are key elements to explain this recent climb in food prices.

Figure 3.2. **Despite an increase in some countries, inflation expected to remain under control**

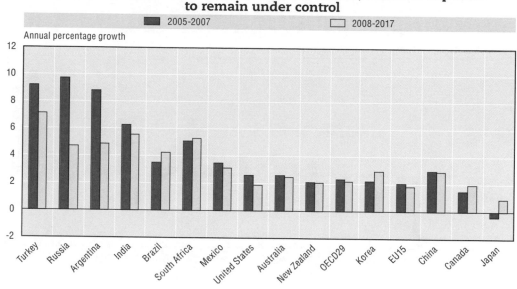

StatLink http://dx.doi.org/10.1787/381476682356

Note: Average annual growth is the least-squares growth rate (see glossary).

Source: OECD Economic Outlook No. 82 (December 2007), World Bank Global Economic Prospects 2008 (November 2007).

World oil price is expected to remain at high levels

The world oil price assumption underlying this year's *Agricultural Outlook* is based on that published in the *OECD Economic Outlook* No. 82 (December 2007). It assumes prices will slowly increase over the *Outlook* period from USD 90 per barrel in 2008 to USD 104 per barrel by 2017. However, future oil prices are a major uncertainty in the *Outlook*. Some analysts emphasise that high oil prices will slow down demand, ultimately reducing the price of oil. Others argue that consumption, production and processing capacities are inelastic, sustaining continued high, or even further increasing, prices. This year's *Agricultural Outlook* is based on the high price scenario. Price pressure thus far has been maintained as geopolitical tensions combine with processing capacity constraints to keep global supply from the major oil producers below effective demand.

Inflation will drive down the value of certain dynamic economy currencies over the longer term

Under an assumption of constant real exchange rates, inflation differentials *vis-à-vis* the United States are the primary determinant of projections for exchange rates over the *Outlook* period. This implies a strengthening of the US dollar against most currencies. Assumptions on exchange rates are critical to the baseline projections as they can strongly influence relative competitiveness and hence agricultural trade across regions. The US dollar is the currency in which the majority of agricultural trade is denominated.

Over the course of the *Outlook* period, the euro exchange rate is projected to remain stable. However, very low levels of inflation in Japan relative to the United States mean that the yen is expected to appreciate further.

The currencies of high growth/high inflation countries such as Brazil, India, Turkey and South Africa will depreciate most over the medium term, improving their prospects for agricultural exports, while putting a break on imports with the change in their terms of trade.

Figure 3.3. **US dollar strengthening against most other currencies**

In local currency *versus* US dollar

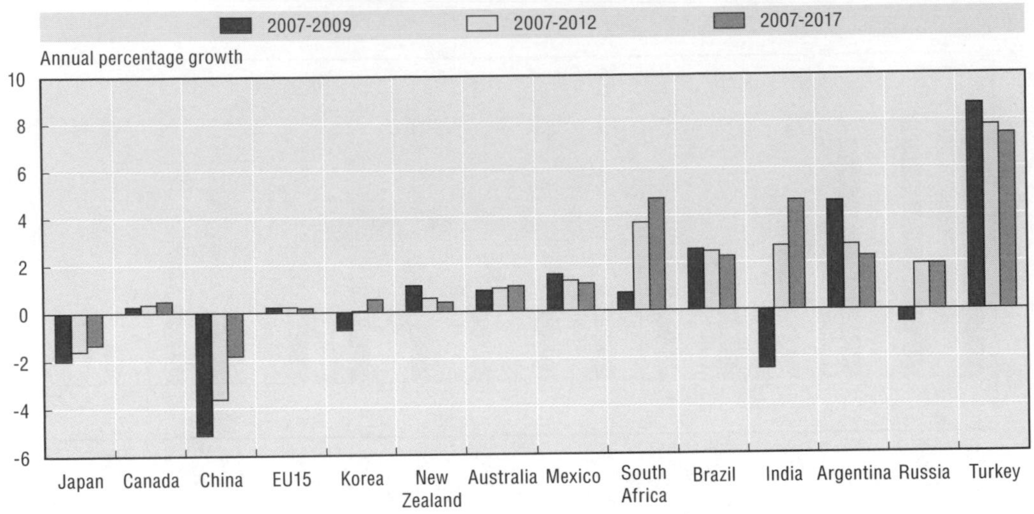

StatLink ⬛📊 http://dx.doi.org/10.1787/381502738604

Note: Average annual growth is the least-squares growth rate (see glossary).

Domestic support and trade policies affect agricultural markets

Agricultural and trade policies play an important role in both domestic and international markets for agricultural commodities and food products. Agricultural policies are becoming increasingly targeted and directed towards achieving specific objectives and beneficiaries within broader objectives in relation to national, regional or global concerns. At the same time, non-agricultural policies, such as energy, environment and rural development policies, are having a growing impact on the agri-food sector. Policies influence the composition and levels of both production and consumption, thereby creating (or sometimes correcting) market distortions and influencing prices. There is a tendency towards increased price responsiveness on the supply side with ongoing policy reform in some OECD countries. Also, relatively elastic supply and demand in a growing number of developing countries, coupled with an increasing share of these countries in world trade, has assisted adjustments in agricultural markets.

No conjecture is included in the *Outlook* projections for the future outcome of negotiations underway in the WTO for the Doha Development Agenda and, consequently, it is assumed that trade policies as agreed in the Uruguay Round Agreement on Agriculture (URAA) will hold for the entire period to 2017. Trade flows are increasingly influenced by policies that have been negotiated as part of regional trade agreements such as the North American Free Trade Agreement (NAFTA), the Everything But Arms (EBA) initiative of the European Union and the Mercosur Agreement between Argentina, Brazil, Paraguay and Uruguay. The policy assumptions of the *Outlook* take into account the provisions of these agreements, in addition to existing bilateral preferential trade provisions covering specific agricultural commodities. Regional or bilateral trade agreements have not always been explicitly taken into account in the underlying modelling system but allowance for such agreements has been made where they are expected to have an impact on growth in trade. This is the case for both the Central American Free Trade Agreement (CAFTA) and the Free Trade Agreement with Australia (AUS FTA), which is expected to have a substantial impact on Pacific region beef trade.

OECD-FAO AGRICULTURAL OUTLOOK 2008-2017 – ISBN 978-92-64-04590-3 – © OECD/FAO 2008

This *Outlook* makes no anticipation of changes to agricultural policies which may be part of forthcoming farm legislation in the United States. Although current legislation is due for expiry in 2007, the programmes and provisions of the *Farm Security and Rural Investment Act* (FSRI) of 2002 are assumed to continue for the entire *Outlook* period and moreover, no changes are anticipated in crop loan rates which are extended at constant levels through to 2017. The requirements of the Renewable Fuels Standard in the United States (the *Energy Policy Act* of 2003, modified in 2005) have been taken into account, as discussed elsewhere in this report under the assumptions related to biofuel production. In December 2007, the US *Energy Independence and Security Act* (EISA) was signed into law. This new energy legislation is not taken into account in this *Outlook*. Neither are the proposals for the new biofuels directive in the European Union. The main policy elements of the EU Common Agricultural Policy Reform of 2003, as described in previous editions of the *Outlook*, are assumed to remain unchanged. The EU set-aside rate is assumed to be 0% in 2008 but to be set at 10% again in the years thereafter. For other countries, established support measures and policy programmes (such as PROCAMPO in Mexico) are implemented as legislated. Where well-defined termination dates exist, they are factored into the projections; otherwise payments, provisions and other policy measures are assumed to continue through 2017.

For sugar, projections take into account the EU sugar reform implemented as of 1 July 2006. These included the progressive reduction of import duties, followed by unrestricted sugar exports to the EU from LDC countries under the EBA initiative from 2009 and other ACP countries under Economic Partnership Agreements from 2015. Other policy changes included the elimination from 2008, of all remaining trade restrictions and duties on North American sugar trade in conformity with the NAFTA.

ISBN 978-92-64-04590-3
OECD-FAO AGRICULTURAL OUTLOOK 2008-2017
© OECD/FAO 2008

Chapter 4

Biofuels

World market trends and prospects

Key market drivers

High energy prices and growing concerns on global warming have, among other factors, increased public interest in renewable energies in general. Within these, biofuels – liquid transport fuels produced from biomass – receive particular attention; production technologies based on starchy, sugary or oily agricultural commodities (such as cereals, sugar cane and oilseeds, respectively) are relatively simple, and the resulting fuels – ethanol and biodiesel – can be used in conventional combustion engines with no or comparatively little modifications.[1] While the *OECD/FAO Agricultural Outlook 2007-2016* for the first time explicitly considered feedstock use for biofuel production as an important factor in agricultural markets, this *Outlook* report includes full projections for supply, demand, trade and prices of ethanol and biodiesel.

Production and use of both ethanol and biodiesel have increased significantly in recent years. Production of fuel ethanol tripled between 2000 and 2007 to reach 52 billion (bn) litres (F.O. Licht's, 2008), and while the US and, to a lesser degree, Brazil, accounted for the majority of this growth, a large number of other countries have begun or increased fuel ethanol production as well. Biodiesel output saw an even more pronounced expansion over the same period, having grown from less than 1 bn litres to almost 11 bn litres. Until 2004, the EU accounted for more than 90% of global biodiesel production, but with increased

Figure 4.1. **Production costs of major biofuel chains**

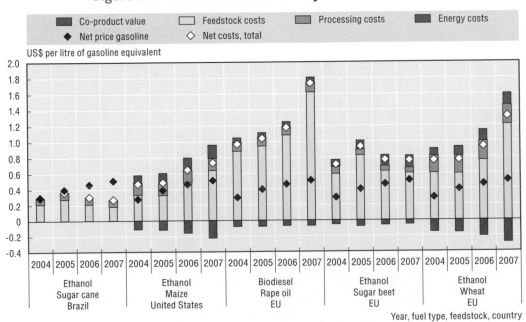

StatLink ᵐᵖ http://dx.doi.org/10.1787/381506048475

OECD-FAO AGRICULTURAL OUTLOOK 2008-2017 – ISBN 978-92-64-04590-3 – © OECD/FAO 2008

biodiesel output in many other countries, in particular the US, this share has declined to less than 60% in 2007 (F.O. Licht's, 2008; EBB, 2008; EIA, 2008; Agra-Informa, 2008).

With crude oil prices having doubled between 2004 and 2007, the value of biofuels as substitutes for, or blending components in, petrol-based gasoline and diesel has increased significantly. This, however, was not sufficient to improve the economic viability of most biofuel production processes: as world prices for a number of feedstocks including maize, wheat and vegetable oils have increased by 86%, 110% and 91% during the same period, costs of ethanol and biodiesel production in OECD countries have increased significantly. Indeed, in many cases the gap between biofuel production costs and the energy value of the final fuel has further widened (Figure 4.1). In consequence, biofuel production and use in most countries remains dependent on public support,[2] and despite this support, profit margins have declined considerably and in many cases have become negative. With continued rises in crude oil and biofuel prices over the next few years, however, the economic situation of biofuel producers is expected to improve.

Main market developments – ethanol

Global ethanol production to increase rapidly as ethanol and feedstock prices stabilise at higher levels

Global ethanol production is projected to increase rapidly and to reach some 127 bn litres, twice the quantity produced in 2007 (Figure 4.2). World ethanol prices exceed USD 55 per hectolitre in 2009 as crude oil prices rise, but will fall back to levels around USD 52 per hectolitre as production capacities expand. Following the increased mandates and other forms of support to biofuel demand, international trade in ethanol will grow rapidly to reach 6 bn litres in 2010 and above 10 bn litres by 2017. Most of this trade will originate in Brazil, and be imported by the EU and the United States.

Figure 4.2. **World ethanol projections**

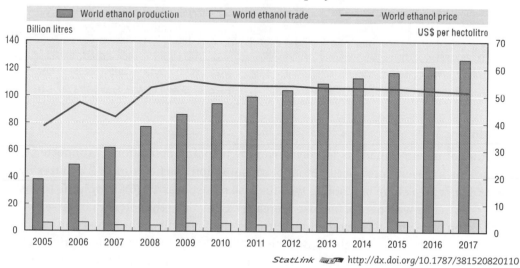

StatLink http://dx.doi.org/10.1787/381520820110

European Union

EU ethanol use in low-level blends is largely determined by mandates in several Member States, while the amount of ethanol used in high-level blends (E85) in flex-fuel vehicles remains limited despite tax advantages. The share of ethanol in gasoline types of transport fuel grows substantially, but production costs particularly of grain-based ethanol are projected to remain high relative to fossil gasoline due to cereal prices' staying well above historical levels. With 4.9%, this share remains below the 5.75% target in energy terms[3] set out in the 2003 biofuel directive,[4] unless additional policy measures come into force or technological developments significantly improve economic viability. Total ethanol use reaches 15 bn litres by 2017 – almost tripling from its 2007 level (Figure 4.3). Ethanol production in the EU remains dominated by wheat as the main feedstock, followed by coarse grains and sugar beet. Domestic ethanol supply increases by more than 10% per annum on average, but remains significantly below domestic use. Cereal use for ethanol production increases to almost 24 million (m) tonnes by 2017, more than 4 times the 2007 quantity; 81% of these cereals are projected to be wheat. Sugar beet use increases significantly in 2008 and further until 2011, but remains largely unchanged thereafter. Despite an important import tariff, net imports of ethanol increase to around 3 bn litres by 2009 and 2010 following the strong increase in blending obligations which can only partially be met by EU production. As production capacities increase, EU net imports of ethanol should fall to between 2 and 3 bn litres per annum.

Figure 4.3. **EU ethanol market projections**

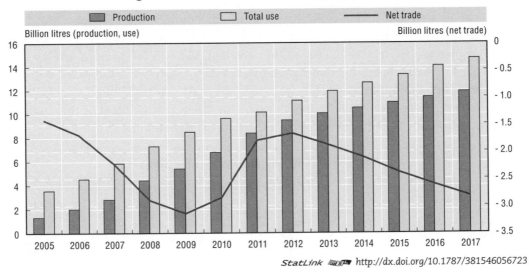

StatLink http://dx.doi.org/10.1787/381546056723

Canada

Ethanol use in Canada is largely driven by blending obligations,[5] supported by tax exemptions in several provinces.[6] Ethanol consumption reaches almost 3 bn litres by 2012 (Figure 4.4), with a share in gasoline type fuel use of just over 4% (6% in volume terms), but grows only in line with overall fuel use thereafter. Canadian ethanol production growth will largely keep pace with domestic ethanol use for the first half of the projection period, but slows down as producers' margins decline after 2010 due to lower ethanol prices. Most of the ethanol is produced from maize – partly domestically grown and partly imported from the US – while a smaller quantity comes from wheat. With production growth slowing from 2010, net imports are projected to float between 0.25 and 0.4 bn litres per annum for the second half of the projection period despite a tariff for non-NAFTA imports.

OECD-FAO AGRICULTURAL OUTLOOK 2008-2017 – ISBN 978-92-64-04590-3 – © OECD/FAO 2008

Figure 4.4. **Canadian ethanol market projections**

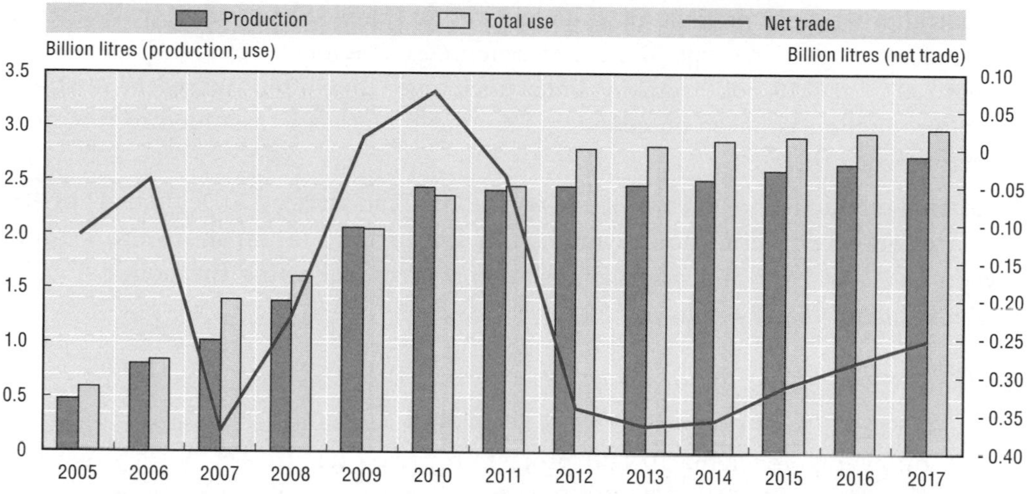

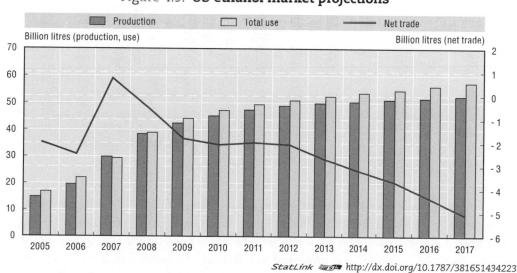

StatLink 🔗 http://dx.doi.org/10.1787/381637431042

United States

US ethanol use, supported mainly by tax credits to fuel blenders, doubles between 2007 and 2017 (Figure 4.5). Growth should slow down, however, as ethanol-gasoline price ratios stabilise. By 2017, the ethanol share in gasoline type fuels, which was 3.4% in 2007, should reach 6% in energy terms, or close to 9% in volume terms. While the majority of ethanol will be used in low-level blends with gasoline, some 7% will be consumed as high-level blends (E85) in flex-fuel vehicles, which are assumed to represent some 3% of the vehicle fleet by 2017. Despite producer margins improving somewhat after having been negative in 2007 due to high corn- and low ethanol prices, production growth is slowing down significantly after 2009, to reach some 52 bn litres by 2017. In consequence, net imports are expected to grow and to reach some 9% of the ethanol used in the US by 2017. Still, with 41% of global production, the US remains the largest ethanol producer.[7]

Figure 4.5. **US ethanol market projections**

StatLink 🔗 http://dx.doi.org/10.1787/381651434223

Other OECD

Australian ethanol production and consumption grows from very low levels. The ethanol share in gasoline type fuel use is assumed to increase from near zero to 3.3% between 2007 and 2010, but to remain almost unchanged thereafter. Most of the Australian ethanol production is based on coarse grains, but molasses is assumed to remain an important feedstock, too.

Ethanol production in Turkey is set to reach 81 million litres by 2017, about 47 m litres below projected consumption. Ethanol net imports by Japan more than double between 2007 and 2017 and reach almost 1.5 bn litres, following the political will to stimulate ethanol use as a transport fuel.

Brazil

Ethanol production in Brazil remains a rapidly expanding sector, growing by more than 6% on average over the 10 year projection period (Figure 4.6). With sugar cane remaining the cheapest of the main feedstocks for ethanol, Brazil will continue to be very competitive on expanding international markets. Growth in domestic use is driven mainly by the growing fleet of flex-fuel vehicles (expected to account for more than half the vehicle fleet (67% of the spark-ingestion cars) in Brazil by 2017), and total ethanol use is projected 32 billion litres by 2017 as the ethanol price at the pump remains significantly and increasingly lower than that of gasoline. Despite this growth in domestic use, Brazil expands its ethanol exports and remains the world's largest ethanol supplier, with net trade reaching 8.8 bn litres by 2017. By that year, 85% of global ethanol exports are projected to originate in Brazil.

Figure 4.6. **Brazil ethanol market projections**

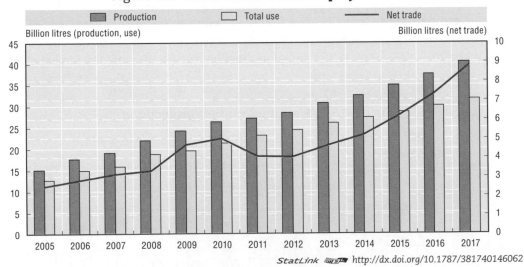

StatLink ᗡᓵᔭᔕ http://dx.doi.org/10.1787/381740146062

China

Until recently, China had ambitious expansion plans for its ethanol sector. Following the high food prices, however, the focus on ethanol production particularly from grains was reduced somewhat. In consequence, while ethanol consumption is set to about double by 2017, domestic production is projected to fall short of ethanol use. This means that the country switches from being a net exporter to becoming a net importer of ethanol by

OECD-FAO AGRICULTURAL OUTLOOK 2008-2017 – ISBN 978-92-64-04590-3 – © OECD/FAO 2008

around 2016, even though traded quantities are projected to remain small. While much of the growth will be based on corn, other feedstocks such as sweet sorghum, other low-quality cereals and sweet potatoes are also important sources, or are subject to ongoing research in the context of ethanol production.

Colombia

Besides Brazil, Colombia is the only other South American country which has established a fuel ethanol sector in recent years. Based on sugar cane, ethanol production for fuel use began in 2005 and reached about 420 m litres in 2007, growing to 800 m litres in 2017. Since 2006, domestic consumption has been governed by blending requirements of 10% in cities with populations exceeding 500 000. Lower blending ratios can be authorised in smaller cities. Based on these regulations, domestic use is projected to stay relatively flat, leaving an increasing exportable surplus. The US-Colombian Trade Promotion Agreement will eliminate US import duties on ethanol and biodiesel from Colombia which will stimulate exports to the US market.

Africa

There is substantial interest in developing ethanol production in Africa, and investments are being made in many African countries. Developing a biofuels/bioenergy sector is considered an important opportunity for development, as a generator of higher rural incomes, and as a substitute for high cost imported energy. Potential feedstocks include maize and cassava, but these have been ruled out in some countries as these crops are considered food security crops. The most important feedstocks are both sugarcane and molasses, although most, if not all, of current production is from molasses. The economics of exporting for some least developed countries such as Mozambique and Tanzania may be influenced considerably by the EBA initiative which would allow these countries to export ethanol duty free into the EU, taking advantage of a high tariff preference incentive. However, a fuller assessment of this is necessary, as tariff free access to the sugar market also may affect sugar *versus* ethanol production and exports from these countries. Total ethanol production in African countries included in this projection totals over 800 m litres by 2017, more than twice current production levels. While there appears to be much room for yet higher growth, a careful assessment of the implications of increased biofuel production for food availability and food prices, and in particular the implications for the poorest, is required.

Thailand

In Thailand, ethanol production is projected to reach 1.8 bn litres, with roots and tubers displacing molasses and cane as the main feedstocks. Ethanol consumption is set to expand by 19% over the projection period to reach 1.5 bn litres in 2017. This growth is underpinned by Government objectives to reduce reliance on imported oil and to meet the rising demand for energy. The energy share from ethanol in gasoline type fuel is assumed to increase from 2% to 12% between 2008 and 2017. Thailand is foreseen to export up to 600 m litres annually during the projection period.

India and others

In light of depressed domestic sugar prices, the Government of India is keen on developing a biofuel industry to provide sugarcane producers with a viable and sustainable alternative source of revenue. Ethanol production is set to increase to 3.6 bn litres, while consumption is projected at 3.2 bn litres, leaving about 383 million litres for net trade. With favourable margins on fuel ethanol production, plant capacity should rise annually by 8.3% between 2008 and 2017. Ethanol production in Vietnam, the Philippines, Malaysia, and Indonesia is projected at 532 m litres, 126 m litres, 84 m litres, and 227 million litres, respectively.

Main market developments – biodiesel

Global biodiesel production and use remains driven mainly by public policy

Stimulated by mandates and tax concessions in several countries, predominantly in the European Union as the largest biodiesel market, global biodiesel production is set to grow at slightly higher rates than ethanol – though at substantially lower levels – and to reach some 24 bn litres by 2017 (Figure 4.7). World biodiesel prices remain well above production costs of fossil diesel, and float within the USD 104-106 per hectolitre for most of the projection period. As in the case of ethanol, increased mandates should drive international trade up in the initial years of the *Outlook*, but little change in total trade is projected for the out years. Most of the trade is projected to originate in Malaysia and Indonesia with the EU as the main destination.

Figure 4.7. **World biodiesel projections**

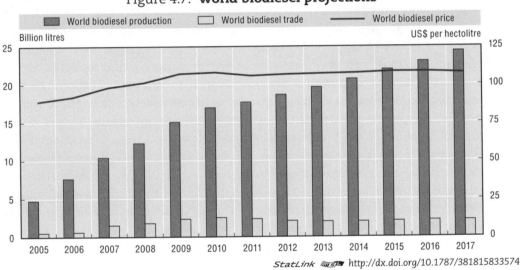

StatLink ꞏ http://dx.doi.org/10.1787/381815833574

European Union

Biodiesel use in the EU remains bound by mandated blending, following increasing obligations in several member States, while others offer substantial tax concessions to biodiesel consumers. While biodiesel production costs remain significantly above net costs of fossil diesel, both these tax reductions and the blending obligations help to stimulate use and, finally, domestic production. The share of biodiesel in diesel type fuels is growing to some 5% (6.2% in volume terms) for a total biodiesel quantity of almost 15 bn litres. While declining slightly in relative terms, the EU is projected to still account for more than 60% of global biodiesel use by 2017. This strong demand will be met by both increased domestic production and growing biodiesel imports. Production margins are projected to improve considerably from the very difficult year 2007, but to remain tight. In consequence, production is set to fall short of domestic use particularly in the early years

OECD-FAO AGRICULTURAL OUTLOOK 2008-2017 – ISBN 978-92-64-04590-3 – © OECD/FAO 2008

of the projection period, and net imports, facing only modest tariffs compared to ethanol, could reach 2 bn litres in 2010 before stabilising at levels between 1.3 and 1.6 bn litres per year thereafter.[8]

Figure 4.8. **EU biodiesel market projections**

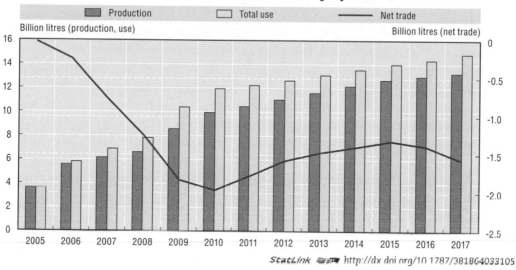

StatLink ⓢ http://dx.doi.org/10.1787/381864033105

Canada

Canada is set to introduce a biodiesel blending mandate of 1.6% (2.0% in volume terms) by 2012. Tax-reductions at provincial levels further support biodiesel use, while concessions at the federal level have been replaced by a direct payment for biodiesel producers. With the price of biodiesel projected to decline relative to that of fossil diesel, biodiesel use in Canada could represent 2.8% (3.5 vol.-%) by 2017. Good producer margins due to high biodiesel prices are projected to stimulate Canadian biodiesel output to slightly outpace domestic use for much of the projection period, with net trade fluctuating between zero and some 80 m litres.[9] These outcomes depend, however, on whether and how support may be changed once the national target of 2% in volume terms is reached.

Figure 4.9. **Canadian biodiesel market projections**

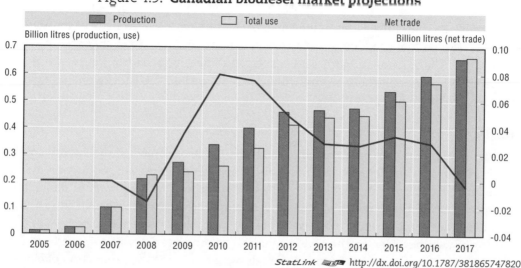

StatLink ⓢ http://dx.doi.org/10.1787/381865747820

United States

US biodiesel use, which tripled in both 2005 and 2006, is projected to remain largely unchanged between 1.3 and 1.7 bn litres throughout the projection period, as biodiesel remains expensive compared to fossil diesel (Figure 4.10), despite a blenders credit of USD 0.26 per litre (USD 1 per gallon). In consequence, the share of biodiesel in all diesel fuels declines to less than 0.5% in energy terms (0.6 vol.-%) by 2017. Producer margins are not expected to reach the high levels observed in 2005 and 2006 and biodiesel production is therefore projected to stagnate and, indeed, to decline. This in turn causes current net exports to disappear by the end of the projection period. Not taking into account the 2007 *Energy Independence and Security Act (EISA)*, biodiesel is expected to continue to play only a minor role as a transport fuel in the US.[10] With the continued payment of the blenders credit, however, the US is assumed to maintain an incentive for re-exports of foreign, in particular South-East Asian, biodiesel to regions with specific support to biodiesel use, such as the European Union.

Figure 4.10. **US biodiesel market projections**

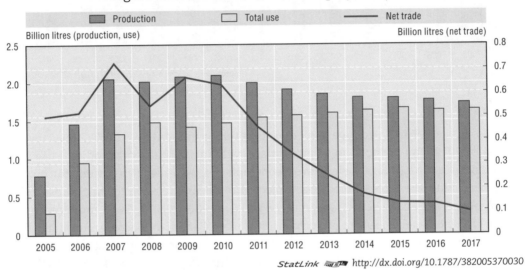

StatLink http://dx.doi.org/10.1787/382005370030

Australia

When compared to ethanol, biodiesel is projected to play a much more important role in Australia. Biodiesel use is set to double to 0.9 bn litres in 2008, equivalent to more than 8% of diesel type fuel use, and to increase thereafter with growing overall fuel use. While some 40% of the Australian biodiesel is expected to be produced from oilseed oils (soya, rapeseed and palm oil), the majority will be based on other feedstocks, including tallow and used cooking oil.

Brazil

Biodiesel production in Brazil, which started in 2006, is projected to expand rapidly in the short term due to increased biodiesel prices and hence improved production margins. In the longer run, however, biodiesel production is set to slow down and to be limited to meet domestic demand, which should grow to some 2.6 bn litres by 2017 (Figure 4.11). By then, the share of biodiesel in total use of diesel type fuels is projected to be 3.6% (4.5 vol.-%) – not anywhere close to the levels seen in gasoline markets in the medium term. Originally, biodiesel programs in Brazil were designed to foster the production of biodiesel

OECD-FAO AGRICULTURAL OUTLOOK 2008-2017 – ISBN 978-92-64-04590-3 – © OECD/FAO 2008

from non-food oil crops such as castor-beans from small farms, but soya oil use for biodiesel is expected to grow considerably as well.

Figure 4.11. **Brazil biodiesel market projections**

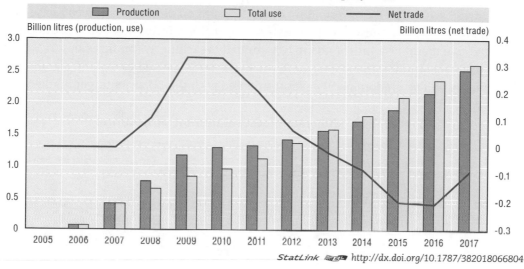

StatLink ⬛⬛ http://dx.doi.org/10.1787/382018066804

Indonesia

The Indonesian government reduced and then eliminated price subsidies on fossil fuels in 2005, allowing the biofuel industry to become economically viable. Biodiesel production started in 2006 on a commercial scale and expanded to an annual production of about 600 m litres by 2007. Fuelled by domestic palm oil production, the industry enjoys a competitive advantage which will propel Indonesia to become the second largest producer in the world. It is anticipated that production will expand rapidly throughout the entire projection period, reaching 3 bn litres by 2017. Based on the consumption targets established by the government, domestic demand is expected to develop right along with production. By 2025, biodiesel should account for 20% of the national transportation diesel oil consumption, or 5% of total national consumption.

Figure 4.12. **Indonesia biodiesel market projections**

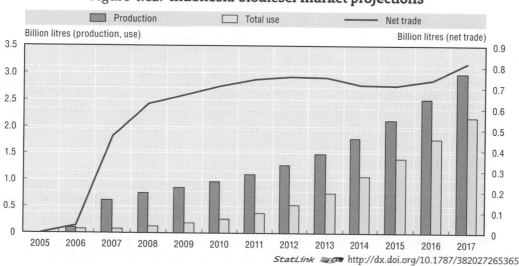

StatLink ⬛⬛ http://dx.doi.org/10.1787/382027265365

Malaysia

Malaysia is the second largest palm oil producer in the world which puts it also in a prime position to play a major role in the world biodiesel market. Biodiesel production started in 2006 on a commercial scale and expanded to an annual production of about 360 m litres by 2007. Steadily expanding domestic palm oil production serves as the basis for a rapid growth of the biofuel industry during the coming decade. Production is projected to expand at a rate of about 10% annually reaching 1.1 bn litres by 2017. In the absence of consumption mandates, domestic use is not expected to expand significantly. The industry will be predominantly export-oriented with the EU as its target market.

Figure 4.13. **Malaysia biodiesel market projections**

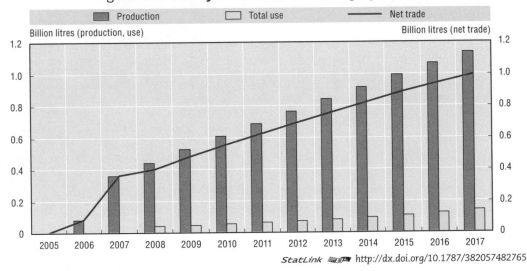

StatLink ▀▒▒ http://dx.doi.org/10.1787/382057482765

Biodiesel from jatropha

Investments in jatropha curcas production have been made with the purpose of stimulating biodiesel production on marginal lands in Africa and India. Behind these investments were high bio-diesel prices and an interest in developing rural economies and in reducing dependence on imported oil, which is costly to transport to interior locations with poor infrastructures. It is difficult, if not impossible, to establish a projection for production, as experience with commercial production of this crop is limited. In this *Outlook*, preliminary estimates for Ethiopia, Tanzania, Mozambique and India have been undertaken which show a total production between 60 000 and 95 000 tonnes per country. For African countries, it is assumed that all bio-diesel production will come from jatropha seed, as limited budgets and high vegetable oil prices are restraints on any biodiesel production from that feedstock. The potential of jatropha – and related biodiesel production is one of the uncertainties in the *Outlook*.

Key issues and uncertainties

While biofuel developments have become a major driver in agricultural markets, a number of uncertainties affect the projections for biofuel use, trade and production. Most importantly, the projections outlined above assume that basic agricultural commodities, including cereals, sugar cane and beet, molasses, roots and tubers such as cassava, and vegetable oils such as rape and palm oil, will continue to represent the vast majority of the

OECD-FAO AGRICULTURAL OUTLOOK 2008-2017 – ISBN 978-92-64-04590-3 – © OECD/FAO 2008

feedstocks for ethanol and biodiesel throughout the decade to come. Technical and economic constraints are assumed to remain prohibitive in the production and marketing of biofuels produced from other feedstocks that do not directly compete with their use for human or animal nutrition.[11] In particular, ethanol produced from celluloses and other plant material (both crop residues such as straw, and dedicated biomass such as willow trees and switchgrass), and biomass-based diesel fuels (so-called Biomass-To-Liquid or BTL) are assumed to remain economically unavailable at any meaningful scale during the projection period. It should be noted, however, that in numerous countries, significant efforts have been made to overcome existing constraints; it is possible now that first commercial production plants for second-generation biofuels might appear online during the decade to come. Indeed, existing or upcoming biofuel legislation in a number of countries, including in particular the US and the EU, is based on the expectation that these products will represent a considerable share of biofuel supply in rather a short time. This would significantly alter the interactions between biofuel production and agricultural markets, in particular where feedstocks for these fuels would come either from crop residues or from land not suitable for food production.[12]

Other uncertainties relate to future developments in fossil energy markets – in particular, the development of crude oil prices is likely to be key in further biofuel growth – as well as in agricultural markets. While biofuel production and corresponding crop use obviously creates an important and growing additional demand on the commodity markets, feedstock prices represent a large share in total biofuel production costs and hence have a significant impact on the economic viability of the sector. Prices for both coarse grains and vegetable oils are, when expressed in US dollars, projected to remain at relatively high levels compared to the past, despite some decline in the short run, and sugar prices should increase after 2008. In consequence, production costs for most biofuels are likely to remain an important constraint over the projection period.

Finally, it should be noted that in most countries, biofuel production remains dependent on public support. Tax concessions and tax credits mainly encourage biofuel use where production costs are above those for fossil fuels, blending obligations stimulate demand for biofuels at the cost of consumers, import tariffs protect domestic biofuel producers from foreign – mainly southern competition. The discussion about potential and actual benefits from supporting biofuel production and use is ongoing, and support schemes are in rapid development.

Box 4.1. **The US Energy Independence and Security Act**

In December 2007, the US *Energy Independence and Security Act* (EISA) was signed into law. This new energy legislation defines, among other elements, a new Renewable Fuel Standard calling for US biofuel use to grow to a minimum of 36 billion (bn) gallons per annum (bngy) or 136 bn litres per annum (bnly) by 2022. Corn-based ethanol is to grow to 15 bngy or 57 bnly until 2015 and to remain constant thereafter. Given that the US is the only major producer of corn ethanol, this consumption requirement can be seen as a production mandate as well. Requirements for first-generation biodiesel are given only for the period 2009-12. Beyond 2012, further growth in biodiesel use is included in a total for biofuels other than corn-based and cellulosic biofuels. Production of biofuels from cellulosic materials is scheduled to start in 2010 at low levels, but with 16 bngy (60.6 bnly) to represent the bulk of biofuel use in 2022. The EISA institutes several safeguards that allow waiving some or all of these requirements in the case of adverse impacts on agricultural markets or for fuel cost reasons.

Box 4.1. **The US Energy Independence and Security Act** *(cont.)*

While these requirements are not taken into account in the baseline for this *Outlook*, and no second-generation biofuels are assumed to become available on a commercial scale within the baseline period, a full implementation of the EISA would imply changes in agricultural market projections relative to those outlined in this report. US corn use for ethanol production would be higher by up to 14.2 million tonnes (mt), whereas the requirements of soya oil would more than double to some 3.7 million tonnes (mt) by 2017. Despite the increase in US biodiesel production, the US would become a major importer of this fuel.[a] The implications of the growth in second-generation biofuels can only be approximated as it depends on a large number of factors. In particular, ethanol from corn stover and straw would have very different market and environmental effects than ethanol from dedicated biomass such as switch-grass or fast growing wood. Also, different biomass crops could have quite different yields of dry matter and hence of ethanol per hectare. It is assumed that ethanol and BTL yields from biomass increase from 31 to 43 hl/ha and from 26.2 to 29.7 hl/ha, respectively, both due to higher biomass yields and improved conversion. It is further expected that crop residues will represent the majority of the feedstock used in the initial years, but that this will be increasingly overtaken by dedicated biomass. Despite the yield improvements, the large production of second-generation biofuels would likely require the re-allocation of substantial amounts of crop area into dedicated biomass production and hence reduce US crop supplies.[b]

In consequence, international prices for most commodities would be higher than projected. The impact of higher biodiesel use would be particularly pronounced, resulting in substantially higher prices for biodiesel as well as for vegetable oils. The reduction in US crop land due to production of fuel-biomass would further increase prices, an effect that is particularly important for coarse grains due to the relative importance of the US in international grains markets.

Figure 4.14. **Potential impact of the US EISA on world commodity prices, 2013-17 average**

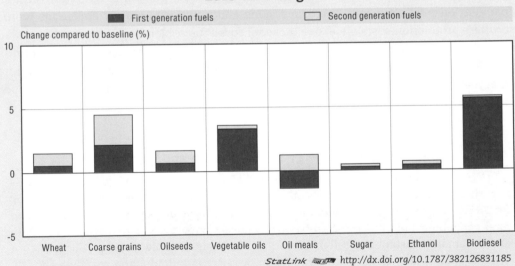

StatLink ᶜᵐˢᵖ *http://dx.doi.org/10.1787/382126831185*

a) In this analysis growth in first-generation biodiesel is assumed to represent half the increase in biofuels other than maize and cellulose-based ones. In consequence, first-generation biodiesel use would increase to 1.675 bngy or 6.3 bnly by 2017, compared to little more than 1.6 bnly projected in the baseline.

b) In principle, the biomass could be produced on land not otherwise used for crop production. In that case, the impact on crop markets would obviously be minimised. It is, however, unlikely that all the biomass could be produced on marginal and other unused area. Here, it is assumed that 50% of the biomass would come from crop land.

OECD-FAO AGRICULTURAL OUTLOOK 2008-2017 – ISBN 978-92-64-04590-3 – © OECD/FAO 2008

Notes

1. Technical constraints and other technical questions related to ethanol and biodiesel are discussed in OECD (2006): *Agricultural Market Impacts of Future Growth in the Production of Biofuels*.

2. This *Outlook* does not consider the EU Directive of Renewable Energy, proposed by the EU Commission in early 2008, nor the US Energy Independence and Security Act. As the latter was signed into law in late 2007, a box at the end of this chapter deals with its potential implications for the baseline.

3. Note that this target, set by the 2003 EU Biofuel Directive, is indicative only. All biofuel use shares are expressed on the basis of energy contained unless otherwise specified.

4. A new directive currently discussed, raising biofuel shares to 10% by 2020, is not taken into account.

5. Assumptions include a 10% blending mandate in Ontario not yet enacted.

6. Tax exemptions on the federal level were eliminated in 2008 and replaced by a direct payment scheme.

7. These projections do not account for the US *Energy Independence and Security Act* as recently passed. For a discussion of potential implications see the special box.

8. Biodiesel from palm oil faces some technical problems in the colder climates of northern Europe where in winter times it may block up fuel filters. Without further treatment its use in these areas is therefore limited.

9. Note that the Canadian biodiesel use might be underestimated here due to its blending into heating oil as well.

10. See the special box on the US Energy Independence and Security Act for a discussion of potential implications.

11. This *Outlook* considers explicitly an expansion of biodiesel on the basis of non-food feedstocks, such as tallow used cooking oil, and jatropha. Quantities remain small, however, when compared to vegetable-oil based biodiesel production.

12. An analysis of these issues is part of an upcoming OECD report.

ISBN 978-92-64-04590-3
OECD-FAO AGRICULTURAL OUTLOOK 2008-2017
© OECD/FAO 2008

Chapter 5

Cereals

World market trends and prospects*

Key market drivers

In spite of the increase in world cereal production in 2007, a tight global cereal supply and demand situation prevailed throughout the whole marketing season. The bulk of the increase in world cereal production came from a record maize harvest in the United States, which boosted world coarse grains output in 2007. Wheat production also increased compared to the previous year but not as much as expected because of unfavourable weather conditions in some parts of the world; especially droughts in eastern parts of Europe and Australia. World rice production increased marginally in 2007, mostly driven by larger harvests in Asia. However, total cereal supplies remained low in comparison to world demand, which showed little sign of abating despite high prices. The increase in world production was not sufficient to compensate for dwindling stock levels, carried over from the previous season. As a result, world cereal reserves are expected to fall even below their already low opening levels at the end of the 2007-08 marketing season. In looking more closely at developments in 2007-08, cereal stocks held by major exporters were significantly depleted during the year, driven down by strong domestic demand and exports. These developments led to a rapid rise in world prices, starting in maize markets and spreading to wheat and rice markets as the season progressed. This price boom was also accompanied by much higher price volatility than in earlier seasons. Increased volatility reflected greater uncertainty in the market due to a tighter supply and demand balance for cereals, but increasingly, also due to developments in other agricultural markets as well as in energy and financial markets.

Among the major cereals, the increase in wheat prices were most pronounced. In 2007, international wheat prices averaged close to 60% above the level in 2006. Low stocks and reduced 2006 production levels were among the many reasons for the initial increase, but other factors soon became more prominent. The increase in world prices was aggravated by a growing number of trade intervention policies as several exporting countries (including Argentina, China, and the Russian Federation) decided to put in place export restriction measures, ranging from quotas and punitive taxes to complete export bans, in order to contain rising domestic prices. Another important factor has been the slide in the US dollar against many currencies, the euro in particular, having made wheat imports from the United States cheaper. This is reflected in the surge of wheat imports from the United States which helped to push US wheat prices higher. In February 2008, for example, the export price of US No. 2 Hard Red Winter averaged USD 450, some 115% higher than a year earlier.

In the coarse grains markets, maize prices increased progressively from the middle of 2006 through February 2007. This was followed by a brief period of declining prices as

---

* All dates are on a marketing year basis (e.g. 2007 represents the 2007/08 marketing year) unless stated otherwise. While in general these are June/May for wheat, September/August for coarse grains and January/December for rice, data for individual countries may use slightly different periods.

markets began to take note of a huge increase in plantings in the United States, the world's largest producer and exporter of maize. Indeed, the United States harvested a record crop in 2007 as plantings increased by over 16% and weather conditions remained favourable throughout the growing season. However, in view of the massive increase in domestic use of maize for production of ethanol in the United States and reduced export availabilities in a number of other exporting countries, maize prices resumed their upward trend. In 2007, international maize prices averaged 34% above 2006 and in February 2008, the US yellow maize (No. 2 Gulf) export price averaged USD 220 per tonne, some 25% above that of February 2007. The recent strength in maize prices was driven by similar factors responsible for the increase in wheat prices, such as export restrictions and the sliding dollar. Maize prices also benefited from soaring petroleum prices in world markets which increased the attractiveness of ethanol production in a context of substantial public support in many countries. This is a factor which is likely to continue to underpin prices in the coming years in the light of biofuel support measures and mandates for its use in the new United States and other countries.

In the EU, feed shortages resulted in a robust import demand and this also provided support to international prices; not only of maize but also sorghum and other major coarse grains. Wheat is a leading grain used for feed in the EU. Following its production shortfall last year and limited export availabilities from the Black Sea, wheat prices in the EU continued to increase, a factor which encouraged imports of alternative feeds, especially maize and sorghum. In fact, the surge in imports by the EU was the single most important factor for the expansion of world trade in coarse grains in 2007 to a record level. Prices of barley, another important cereal, also soared in 2007. Supply problems in Australia and Ukraine, tighter availability of maize and other feed grains, compounded with strong import demand, have contributed to the doubling of prices of both feed and malting barley.

Global paddy rice production increased by less than 1% in 2007; this was well below the rate of population growth. Much of the increase was concentrated in Asia, as adverse weather, often associated with "La Niña" conditions, depressed output in Africa, Latin America and the Caribbean (LAC) and Oceania. World rice trade expanded vigorously in 2007, sustained by a dynamic import demand, which, in the light of relatively short export availabilities and a weak US dollar, also fuelled a 17% increase in world prices to levels unseen since 1996. The rise in prices became particularly pronounced in the last quarter of 2007, when several key suppliers to the world market took measures to limit exports, and, even more so, in the first months of 2008.

Given the prevailing high prices and prospects for strong prices to continue for at least another season, world cereal production is expected to increase in 2008. The bulk of the expansion is likely to come from higher wheat production but larger coarse grains and rice harvests are also expected in 2008. Assuming normal weather, production in many countries, which suffered from unfavourable weather conditions last year, is set to recover significantly this year, particularly in Australia, Canada, the EU, Morocco and Ukraine. Policy changes will also be an important factor in boosting production levels in 2008, such as the suspension of the 10% compulsory set-aside requirement in the EU. In response to high grain prices and as a notable departure from recent practices, many governments in developing countries also started providing more support to cereal production; by increasing procurement prices (e.g. for wheat in Pakistan) and/or boosting input subsidies (e.g. on fertiliser for maize production in the Philippines).

In spite of the expectation of a strong increase in production in 2008, given the low level of stocks, the global supply would still be tight considering the continuing strong demand prospects, especially for feed and fuels. As a result, the global supply and demand is projected to remain closely balanced which implies another season of high prices for most cereals. This strong price prospect is expected to prevail over the projection period. With the growth in production continuing, on the back of further advancements in yields, some increase in areas planted, and with demand for fuels stabilising in later years, a more comfortable supply and demand balance is projected to emerge by 2017. Yield growth, albeit lower than in the past decade, is expected to account for most of the growth in production as area expansion is limited largely to regions within the CIS countries and South America. These developments will result in lower prices than those observed in 2007, but the general trend will still exceed the low price levels which characterised the situation for most of the previous decade. Even in real terms, cereal prices tend to be above those of the previous years.

Figure 5.1. Nominal wheat, coarse grain and rice prices to remain relatively strong, increase in real prices compared to the last decade

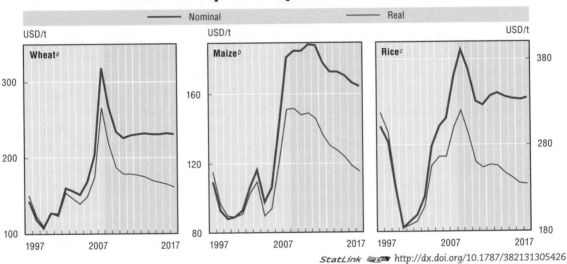

StatLink 📊 http://dx.doi.org/10.1787/382131305426

Note: Real prices are deflated using the US GDP Deflator (2000 = 1).
a) No. 2 hard red winter, ordinary protein, wheat, US, f.o.b. Gulf Ports.
b) No. 2 yellow corn, US, f.o.b., Gulf Ports.
c) White rice, 100% second grade, f.o.b. Bangkok.
Source: OECD and FAO Secretariats.

Main market developments: Wheat and coarse grains

Food, feed and fuel use drive up demand for wheat; fuel and feed rule coarse grains

Global demand for wheat in the next decade is expected to expand by around 1% annually. This represents a slightly faster growth than observed in the past and is mostly due to the projected increase in the use of wheat for production of biofuels among the OECD countries, particularly in Canada and in the EU27 (Figure 5.2). However, total wheat use for ethanol production remains small compared to expanding food and feed use. Indeed, food consumption in developing countries and animal feed use in the OECD area continue to increase as well. Half of world wheat feed use is currently located in the EU and this share is likely to remain stable over the Outlook period. Food consumption accounts for most of the growth in total wheat utilisation in developing countries, particularly in Asia

OECD-FAO AGRICULTURAL OUTLOOK 2008-2017 – ISBN 978-92-64-04590-3 – © OECD/FAO 2008

Figure 5.2. **Growing cereal demand inside and outside the OECD**

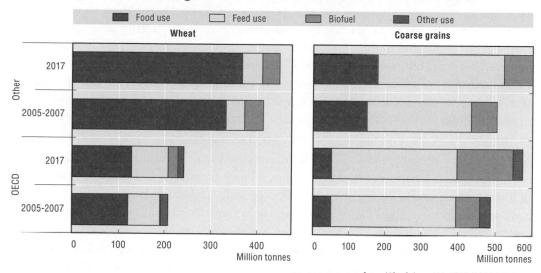

Source: OECD and FAO Secretariats.

StatLink ⬛⬛ http://dx.doi.org/10.1787/382135207605

and Africa. However, global wheat food consumption is projected to increase at a slightly slower pace than in the past decade. This mainly reflects slower population growth and changes in diets. Per capita food consumption of wheat in China and to a lesser extent in India are projected to decline as diets in those countries slowly shift towards more value added food driven by increased incomes.

Total utilisation of coarse grains is projected to increase by just over 1% annually over the projection period, nearly half as fast as during the past decade, but a strong rate of growth nonetheless. This increase is partially driven by the projected rise in feed use to satisfy growth in meat production. However, industrial use is projected to increase even faster, mostly because of a continuing strong demand for maize as a raw material for the production of ethanol in the United States. In the OECD, total use of maize for production of biofuels is projected to expand by nearly 90 m tonnes between 2007 and 2017. Most of this increase takes place in the United States. In contrast, outside OECD countries, feed utilisation and food consumption will contribute to most of the increase in total demand. In recent years, China emerged as one of the largest users of maize for production of ethanol outside the United States. However, this trend is likely to slow down based on recent policy decisions to halt utilisation of food crops for industrial use.

Increasing wheat and coarse grain production

World wheat production is projected to increase at a faster pace than in the previous decade; although by less than 1% per annum. Driven by high prices, the suspension of the compulsory 10% set-aside in the EU, and the expected recovery from two seasons of severe droughts in Australia, total area planted to wheat as well as average wheat yields are expected to rise sharply, boosting world wheat output in 2008. Following this initial strong growth, world wheat production is projected to keep pace with demand and reach roughly 690 m tonnes by 2017, up from 608 m tonnes in the 2005-07 base period. The EU, China, India and the United States are expected to remain the four largest wheat producers, with a combined share in total production of about 56%, slightly less than their current share. As in the previous decade, yield growth is projected to be the main factor for the increase in world production in nearly all major producing countries. Total wheat area is also projected to increase, although the rate of growth will be slower than in the past, as competition with other crops (maize and oilseeds in particular) could lower wheat plantings in China, Brazil and the United States. Another country (albeit a small wheat producer) where production is projected to decline significantly over the projection period is Saudi Arabia, following a government decision to gradually phase out its production subsidy due to water constraints. In contrast, wheat area is projected to increase in Argentina, India and several countries in the CIS region.

After a sharp rebound in world production of coarse grains in 2007, total production of coarse grains is projected to continue its expansion but at a slower pace throughout the projection period. Strong demand and higher relative returns set the scene for continuing high production levels during the projection period. Production is projected to increase most notably in the United States (maize and sorghum), China (barley and maize), Nigeria (maize, millet, and sorghum), Turkey (barley), the EU and Ukraine (barley and maize). With more than 1.2 bn tonnes in 2017, world coarse grains production is projected to grow more rapidly than wheat at an average rate of 1.3% per annum The United States, China and the EU will remain the three largest coarse grain producers, supplying about 60% of global production. While yield growth is projected to be less pronounced than in the previous decade, most of the increase in production would still be driven by the rise in yields. The area planted will also expand, albeit at a slower pace than in the past decade and only in some countries, *e.g.* the United States, Ukraine and a few other producers in Africa and Latin America. The wheat/coarse grain harvested area ratio is expected to remain nearly constant but among coarse grains, the anticipated higher return from maize compared to sorghum, barley and other cereals will give rise to a larger maize area.

Figure 5.3. **Variety share of coarse grains shifts towards maize**

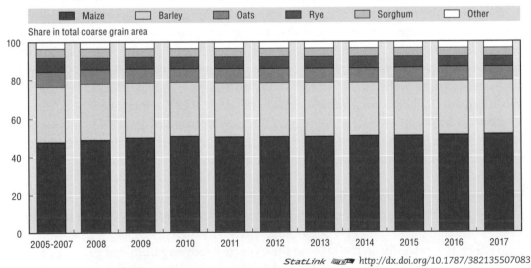

StatLink ⬛🖳 http://dx.doi.org/10.1787/382135507083

Source: OECD and FAO Secretariats.

Stocks recover but stay at historically low levels given high prices

Following sharp declines in world wheat stocks for two consecutive seasons, some rebuilding of world inventories is expected in 2008, given the anticipated increase in global production. Over the projection period, inventories held by the world's largest wheat

OECD-FAO AGRICULTURAL OUTLOOK 2008-2017 – ISBN 978-92-64-04590-3 – © OECD/FAO 2008

exporting countries and mainly in the private sector, which are the main buffer against any major production shortfall, are projected to recover from their current critically low level driven mostly by expected replenishments in Canada and the United States. Wheat inventories in India are also projected to remain steady while some increases are projected for China. However, wheat stocks are unlikely to return to the high levels of the previous decade and the world stocks-to-use ratio is projected to remain close to the current low level of around 25% which signals a continuation of generally tight market conditions. In view of this *Outlook* and given the prospects for much higher production costs than in the past (mostly driven by the high crude oil prices assumed for the projection period), wheat prices in a historical perspective are likely to remain higher on average to 2017, but below the recent peaks.

Figure 5.4. **Stock levels stay low in historical perspective**

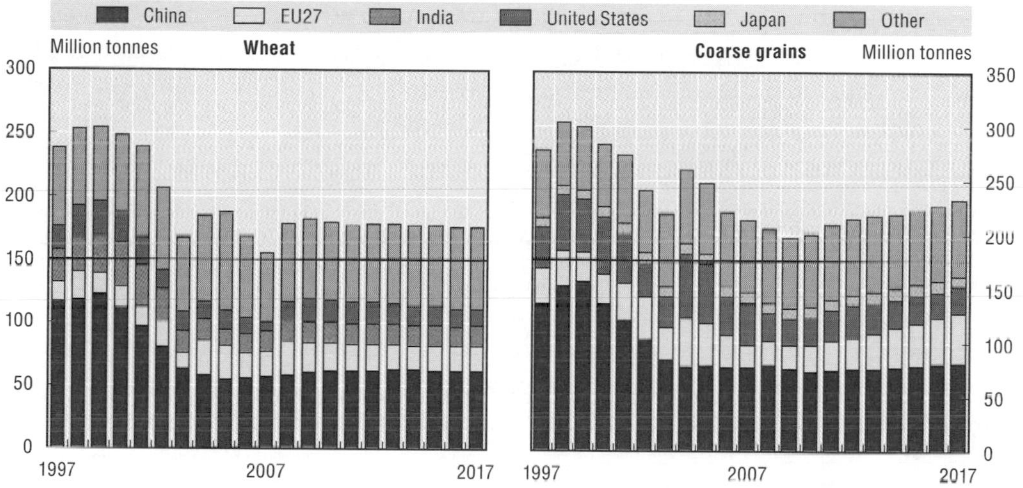

StatLink ≣≣⊞ http://dx.doi.org/10.1787/382152475623

Source: OECD and FAO Secretariats.

In spite of a small recovery in world carryover stocks of coarse grains, world inventories remain significantly below the levels observed over the past decade. This is because most of the growth in world production in 2008 is expected to be absorbed by a rapid increase in utilisation leaving little margin for replenishing stocks. As a result, the world stocks-to-use ratio, which in 2007 fell to a low of 19%, will not recover significantly in 2008, pointing to the continuation of a tight supply and demand balance for at least another season. The low ratio is likely to continue throughout the projection period, mainly because of tight supply and demand prospects in the United States, the world's largest producer, exporter and consumer of coarse grains. In contrast to wheat, this *Outlook* expects coarse grains prices to remain at current high levels for several more seasons, before they start declining. The price of United States yellow maize (No. 2, yellow corn f.o.b.) is projected to reach USD 161 per tonne by 2017 down from about USD 180 per tonne in 2007. But again, in a historical context, prices are likely to remain above those of the previous decade, even in real terms.

While wheat and coarse grain prices in real terms are expected to stay above those prevailing over the previous decade, from this higher level, the long term declining trend is projected to continue (Figure 5.1). The main factors which seem to be influencing the markets and contributing to this price pattern stem mostly from the growing demand for grains as raw materials for the production of biofuels and for feed use in developing countries. A continuation of high crude oil prices will not only reinforce the demand for alternative energy but will increase the cost of cereal production (through higher prices for fuel, fertiliser, chemicals pesticides, insecticides, etc.), accentuating the rise in prices.

Moderate growth in wheat trade but stronger increase for coarse grains

World wheat trade contracted in the 2007 marketing season, mostly reflecting reduced imports from several countries because of their own larger harvests in 2007. Trade is expected to rebound in 2008 and then to expand at a modest rate of below 1% annually, to reach about 126 m tonnes by 2017. The United States will remain the largest wheat exporter despite a modest decrease in sales after 2008. Assuming normal weather conditions and hence a recovery in production, Australia will return to the world market as the world's second largest wheat exporter after 2008 and is projected to remain a leading exporter during the projection period. Shipments from other major exporters such as Argentina and Canada are expected to remain steady or to increase. In addition, the Russian Federation and Ukraine are projected to expand exports considerably. On the other hand, a slight drop is projected in wheat exports by the EU.

A notable result of the projection is that wheat imports in the EU, in addition to declining exports, are remaining relatively high compared to historic levels. Strong demand for feed and biofuels wheat is behind this development. Other importers include Egypt, Nigeria, Japan, and Brazil, although imports in the latter two countries, and particularly in Brazil, will be on the decline. Saudi Arabia is also projected to show growing imports in view of the recent change in its policy to gradually phase out production subsidies. Aggregate imports by countries not belonging to the OECD are projected to reach 100 m tonnes by 2017, accounting for 80% of the world total, a bit higher compared to the current ratio (78%).

Figure 5.5. **Wheat trade increases moderately**

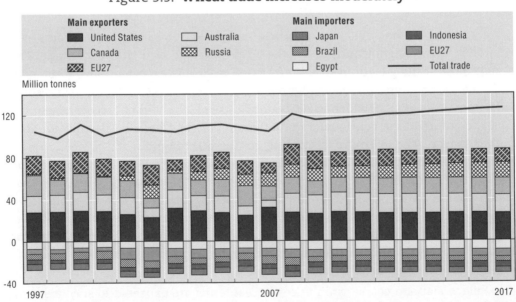

StatLink ᴍᴍ http://dx.doi.org/10.1787/382160047604

Source: OECD and FAO Secretariats.

After having reached a record volume in 2007, mostly due to large imports of maize and sorghum by the EU, world trade in coarse grains is projected to return to a more normal level in 2008 and then to follow an upward trend at a rate of 1.6% per annum – slightly faster than during the previous decade. Exports from the United States are forecast to decline sharply in 2008 and follow a gradual decline until 2011 and an increase thereafter. By 2017, the United States will still be the largest exporter, but its world share is expected to drop from about 51% over the past decade down to 43% in 2011 and back to 48% in 2017.

However, exports from a number of other countries are projected to increase sharply over the projection period, particularly from Australia (barley), Argentina (maize) and Ukraine (maize and barley). Exports from Canada (barley) are likely to remain generally steady around current levels. China, which has been a substantial exporter over the past decade, is projected to export less and become a net importer by 2017. Exports from the EU are also projected to decline below the average of the previous decade, although above the level in 2007 when the region emerged as a major net importer because of shortages in domestic markets.

Regarding imports, Japan will remain the world's leading importer in spite of some declines in its maize purchases. However, purchases by several other countries, especially some of the developing countries, are projected to increase, driven mostly by strong feed demand. Outside the OECD, imports are projected to grow to some 75 m tonnes, representing nearly 60% of the world total. This compares to less than 50% over the past decade. Countries where imports are projected to increase most notably include: Canada, Egypt, Iran and Saudi Arabia.

Figure 5.6. **Sharp increase in coarse grain exports**

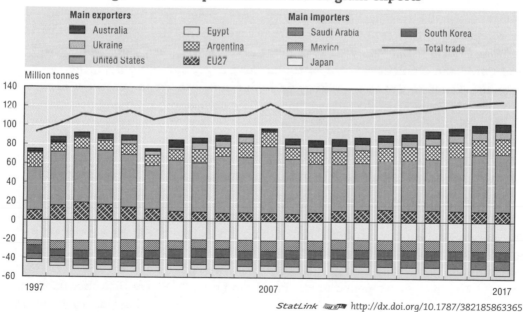

Source: OECD and FAO Secretariats.

StatLink ⬛⬛⬛ http://dx.doi.org/10.1787/382185863365

Main market developments: Rice

Productivity gains result in continued growth in global rice production

Despite more favourable prices and renewed government support in the development of the rice sector, global production is expected to expand at 1% per annum between 2008 and 2017, virtually the same pace as in the previous ten years, resulting in a 45 m tonnes increase to 475 m tonnes of milled rice, compared to the average 2005-07. The modest increase prospect mirrors expectations of an intensification of competition for resources coming from other crops but also from other sectors of the economy, which may thwart private and public initiatives to boost the sector. Growth in production is expected to stem from productivity gains, associated with an intensification of technologies, a greater reliance on water control, and dissemination of high performing varieties, while the area under rice is set to fall in absolute terms from 2011 onwards, largely influenced by cuts in Asia.

Despite a lingering tendency to reduce the area under rice, production in the developed countries is set to rebound, as yields reach new highs. Much of the production growth is expected to be sustained by an increase in the United States and a recovery in Australia, which more than compensate a policy-induced cut in Japan. The rebounding of production in Australia assumes a return to normal weather conditions, as the recurrence of drought in recent years and continuing water supply difficulties has raised questions over the long run sustainability of the sector.

Much of the expansion in world rice production would be concentrated in the developing countries, most of all in Asia (37 m tonnes) where Bangladesh, Cambodia, India, Indonesia, Myanmar, Thailand and Vietnam are foreseen to record sizeable increases. These compensate for a small decline in China, where the sector is anticipated to adjust to falling domestic consumption. Except for Myanmar, Cambodia and Laos, which still dispose of large swaths of land to expand cultivation, most Asian states are foreseen to cut the area planted to rice and to rely on yield gains to boost production. In Africa, the sector is expected to maintain a relatively strong pace of expansion, sustained by dynamic domestic demand, relying almost equally on area and yield increases. These results would be consistent with a renewed pledge from governments, for instance in Nigeria and Senegal, to achieve rice self-sufficiency in the next few years. Likewise, the Latin American and Caribbean countries, Brazil, Peru, but also Argentina, Colombia, the Dominican Republic, Ecuador, Guyana, Uruguay and Venezuela are set to achieve a fast pace of expansion, as higher world prices stimulate rice cultivation, reversing past trends, and yields. In contrast, the sector could suffer a contraction in Mexico, as rice from the United States enters its market unimpeded under NAFTA.

Changing diets in Asian countries affect per capita and total rice consumption

Unlike other cereals, little rice is used as feed and virtually none for transformation into biofuels. Rice remains a basic food commodity and its importance has extended beyond Asia into many African regions and many parts of LAC. However, fast income growth and the diversification of diets are expected to depress per capita rice consumption, especially among Asian countries, which would lower the world average from 57.3 kg in the base period to 56.5 kg per annum in 2017. On the other hand, rice is expected to make further inroads in African diets, where per capita consumption is set to rise from 22 kg to 24 kg over the ten year period, displacing traditional elements, like millet, maize or cassava, in both urban and rural areas. Reflecting the expected fall in per capita rice intake and slowing population growth, total rice consumption, all uses included, is projected to expand by 43 m tonnes compared to the base period over the next ten years, or less than 1% per annum, to reach 475 m tonnes. Because of the demographic distribution and the high per capita levels, rice utilisation is expected to increase by 32 m tonnes in Asia, to 404 million tonnes, and by around 8 m tonnes in Africa, to 30 m tonnes. Consumption in LAC is anticipated to rise by less than 3 m tonnes, to 22 m tonnes, while virtually no growth is anticipated for the developed countries as a whole.

Figure 5.7. **Per capita rice food consumption expected to decrease, total use increases**

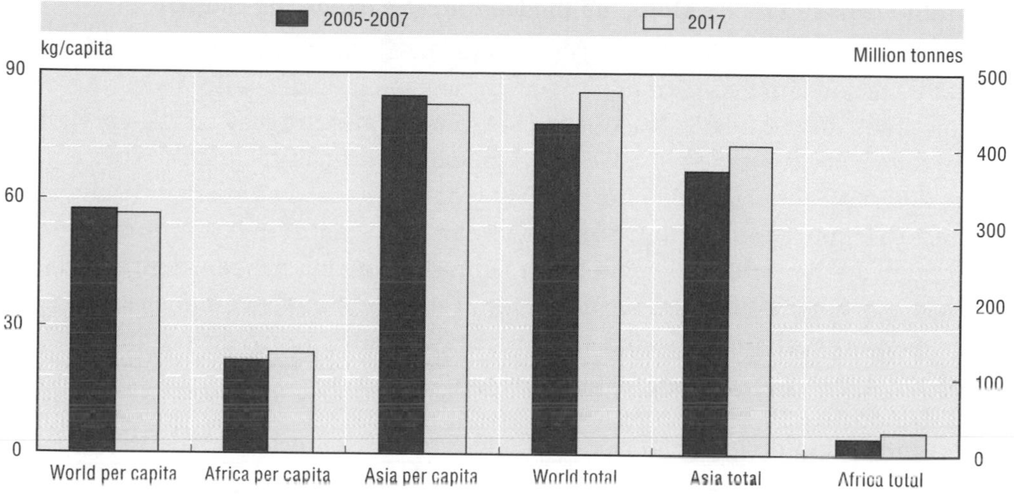

Source: OECD and FAO Secretariats.

StatLink http://dx.doi.org/10.1787/38226/402863

Trade in rice to increase vigorously, sustained by brisk imports by Africa and Asia

The international trade in rice has experienced a fast pace of expansion since the mid 1990s, a tendency expected to dominate also in the next ten years. Trade in rice is projected to grow by over 2% per annum from 30 m tonnes in the base period to 38 m tonnes by 2017. At that level, rice exchanged on world markets would represent 6% of world production, a rather low share, typical of a "thin" residual international market that caters principally for domestic needs.

Much of the expansion in world imports is anticipated to arise in Africa and in Asia. In Africa, the Ivory Coast, Ghana and Nigeria are expected to remain key players in the rice market, but increases are expected all across the continent, to the point that it may account for 32% of total rice imports in 2017, up from 29% in 2005-07. Asia, Indonesia, Iraq, the Democratic People's Republic of Korea, Saudi Arabia and Sri Lanka are raising their purchases of rice over the next ten years, despite the fact that many of them are pursuing expansionary production policies. However, the increases will be relatively modest, especially where governments retain their control over rice imports. In the rest of the region, the Islamic Republic of Iran, Malaysia and the Philippines are foreseen to cut imports, along with rising production. Imports to LAC are expected to rise by 3.5%, notably in Brazil and Chile, largely a reflection of rising consumption meeting stagnating production. The progressive opening of markets to rice from the United States under the US-Central America Free Trade Agreement also contributes to rising imports of Central American and Caribbean countries.

Imports by developed countries are projected to rise by about 1 m tonnes, boosted by increased purchases by the United States, the EU and South Africa. Free access granted to some least developed or ACP countries by the EU under the Everything-but-Arms initiative and, more recently, under new economic partnership agreements, is not expected to boost much the size of imports to the EU. Indeed, changes in trade and production policies in the past few years have tended to reduce the price premium that rice used to fetch on EU markets. Stringent rules of origin, quality standards and special safeguards will further limit the scope for stronger increases in EU rice imports.

Thailand to consolidate its status as the leading rice exporting country

Among exporters, Thailand is projected to sell over 12 m tonnes, or about one third of total trade, consolidating its current position as the main provider of rice to world markets. Vietnam, China, the United States, Australia, Argentina and Uruguay are also projected to increase their sales compared with 2005-07, while those from Egypt and Pakistan are set to decline, reflecting supply constraints and rising domestic needs. Exports by India are not expected to depart much from the base year level, as domestic production and consumption are projected to remain much in line. In general, the experience of 2008 has confirmed that external markets are, for many of the traditional rice suppliers, secondary to their own domestic market and that in case of tight supply, governments tend to respond by imposing restrictions on overseas sales.

Despite some rebuilding, global rice stocks to remain well below the levels in the 1990s

Since 1999, global rice stocks have been falling to the point that by 2007, they only represented 18% of domestic consumption, compared with 39% in 1999. Stocks held by the major exporting countries, including China and India, were also down, raising the potential for market price instability. Indeed, early in 2008, world prices soared amidst much reduced world rice reserves. A tendency to rebuild stocks is expected at the world level between 2008 and 2010, as concerns over supply availability and price volatility mount. By 2017, global rice stocks are projected to reach some 81 m tonnes, up 2.5 m tonnes from the level in 2007. Increases are concentrated in Brazil, India and Thailand. While remaining the largest holder of rice, China is expected to further cut its reserves, in line with consumption.

Figure 5.8. **World rice stocks to be partly rebuilt prices to fall after peak**

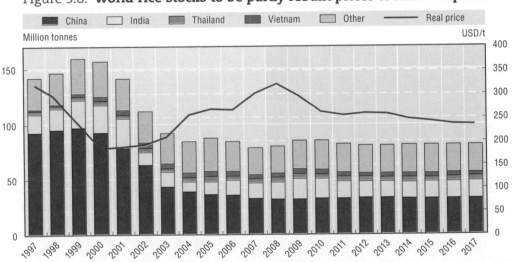

StatLink http://dx.doi.org/10.1787/382312026535

Source: OECD and FAO Secretariats.

OECD-FAO AGRICULTURAL OUTLOOK 2008-2017 – ISBN 978-92-64-04590-3 – © OECD/FAO 2008

International rice prices to strengthen in 2008 but to fall thereafter

International rice prices are anticipated to remain firm in 2008 and 2009, as countries rebuild their stocks. Weaker prices are projected as of 2010, although they are unlikely to fall below their 2006 level, mainly in reflection of expected higher costs. Given the lower size of buffer stocks, prices are likely to manifest much higher volatility than in the 1990s and early 2000s, as the market reacts sharply to supply or demand shocks.

Key issues and uncertainties

A growing link between energy and cereal markets

Ongoing developments in the still relatively new market for biofuels, coupled with high crude oil prices, are a major driving force in cereal market outcomes, particularly for maize in the US over the *Outlook* period. The growing demand for cereals as an input in ethanol production is one argument in favour of stronger prices for cereals than in the past decade. Since the profitability of biofuel production is strongly linked to energy prices, the demand for cereals will also become more dependent on energy prices than in the past. With higher energy prices cereal demand for biofuel production will increase. At the same time, high energy prices raise input cost for cereal production through higher costs for fertilisers, machinery fuels or other inputs, and this will lower gross margins in cereal production at the farm level. However, energy prices are not easy to predict and therefore constitute an important uncertainty for future cereal markets. Similarly, high current levels of support or mandates for biofuel production allow production to grow even in countries where this would otherwise not have been economically viable (*e.g.* the United States and the European Union). A change in these support policies could therefore change the picture of the *Outlook* considerably.

The importance of policies

Currently the EU is undertaking a so called "health check" of the Common Agricultural Policy, which is meant to fine-tune the 2003 CAP reform and to contribute to the discussion on future priorities in the field of agricultural policies. Without prejudging the outcome of this review, any change in policies and policy mechanisms are likely to influence EU and global agricultural markets. In addition, a new US Farm Bill is being negotiated in the US, a version having been approved by the US Congress and the Energy Security and Independence Act (ESIA) was passed in late 2007, which increases existing mandates for biofuels. None of these policy developments has been taken into account in the cereal market projections.

Multilateral negotiations about a new trade agreement within the Doha round are still some way from finding any consensus. Nevertheless, a successful conclusion of the negotiations could result in significant changes in policies affecting agricultural market access, export competition and domestic support. In the case of an agreement, there might also be noticeable indirect effects on cereal markets from changes in the policy environment for livestock and other crop markets.

Will there be increased supply variability?

The supply shortfalls of wheat in the recent two seasons were, in addition to increased demand, a major reason for higher observed prices. For example, Australia is a global player on world cereal markets, in particular for wheat. In the past decade Australia was responsible for about 15% of total wheat exports. In 2006 and 2007, Australia suffered from two severe consecutive droughts and as a result, the export share went down to 6% and 8%, respectively. This had strong impacts on international wheat prices. While such severe droughts were said to appear every 50 years, it is feared that the frequency of droughts will increase in future as Australia may increasingly suffer from climate change. This *Outlook* assumes that yield levels in Australia will return to levels in the past decade, but that their yield growth slows down. Given that water scarcity is also likely to become an issue in Australia, lower yields than expected in this *Outlook* cannot be excluded. But not only Australia has been facing higher yield fluctuations in recent years. Also the EU and the United States have experienced historically large variations in wheat production since 2000. This along with increasing production taking place in other more climate variable regions such as the CIS, contributes to potentially increasing volatility of global supply and hence prices and thus raising the uncertainties in cereal markets.

Climate change affects rice markets in particular

Climate change is of particular relevance to the rice sector because rice has been identified both as a major source of greenhouse gases and as a crop particularly vulnerable to changes in climatic conditions. Rice cultivation is responsible for high emissions of carbon dioxide (CO_2), methane (CH_4) and nitrous oxide (N_2O). The release of methane, a greenhouse gas 20 times more potential than CO_2, is of particular relevance to flooded rice fields, where it results from the decomposition of organic matter in absence of oxygen. Changes in climatic conditions could also have severe impacts on rice production. On the one hand, increased levels of CO_2 may have positive effects on rice yields (CO_2 fertilisation), but these benefits disappear when associated with increases in temperature. Other manifestations of climate change, in particular rising sea levels and increased frequency of extreme weather events, would also have severe impacts on rice production, especially in the lowlands and delta areas, which are the hubs of rice cultivation. Finally, climate change will affect other agricultural commodities as well, amongst other factors attributable to shifts in production zones.

ISBN 978-92-64-04590-3
OECD-FAO AGRICULTURAL OUTLOOK 2008-2017
© OECD/FAO 2008

Chapter 6

Oilseeds and Oilseed Products*

* All data are expressed on a marketing year basis (as defined in the glossary) unless stated otherwise. It is important to note that this discussion focuses on the following aggregates: oilseeds are rapeseed, soyabean and sunflower; oilseed meals are rapeseed meal, soyabean meal and sunflower meal; and vegetable oils are rapeseed oil, soyabean oil, sunflower oil and palm oil.

World market trends and prospects

Key market drivers

In 2007, the rise in oilseed, oil and meal prices that started in 2005 and intensified in 2006 continued with unabated vigour. During 2006, prices in the oilseed complex started to come under the influence of external factors: prices rose even though supplies were ample relative to demand and in spite of high levels of global stocks, both in absolute terms and compared to total consumption. The rise in prices was driven by the tightness in the related world feedgrain market: the unprecedented rise in maize prices provided incentives to shift land out of oilseeds, driving up oilseed and oilmeal prices. The price development was reinforced by the fact that both oilseeds and vegetable oils were also in demand for biodiesel production, particularly in the EU and some south-east Asian countries. Finally, the surge in ocean freight rates has also played a role. In 2007, prices moved at record levels as spillover effects from the related grain markets continued. Direct competition for land by maize and soybeans – both in demand by the feed as well as energy sector – resulted in shifts in land allocation to crops that led to an unprecedented fall in global meal availability. As to vegetable oil, utilisation as biofuel feedstock expanded steadily as well as demand for food uses, while global vegetable oil supplies tightened. Growing tightness of supplies called for steep reductions in inventories. Consequently, stock-to-use ratios fell to critical levels for both oils and meals, exacerbating the upward swing in prices.

Figure 6.1. Vegetable oil prices and oilseed prices to remain strong over the projection period

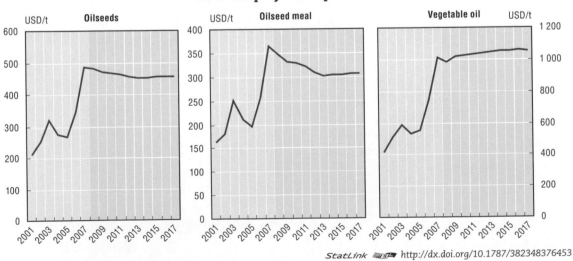

StatLink ⟶ http://dx.doi.org/10.1787/382348376453

Source: OECD and FAO Secretariats.

OECD-FAO AGRICULTURAL OUTLOOK 2008-2017 – ISBN 978-92-64-04590-3 – © OECD/FAO 2008

Assumptions of average weather, unchanged policies and a stable macroeconomic environment are behind a rather smooth evolution of oilseeds and oilseed product markets over the *Outlook* period. Oilseeds, vegetable oil and to a lesser extent oilseed meal markets will continue to expand, mainly because of strong demand for food and feed as income and population grow. In addition, growing vegetable oil use for biodiesel production is expected to drive expanding markets. In the course of the next decade, stock to use ratios for oilseeds and oilseed products are expected to remain low. The combination of these elements is supporting the projections for firm prices expressed in nominal terms (Figure 6.1). Increasing oilseed meal and dried distiller grains availability and some decline in other feedgrain prices later during the *Outlook* period mean decreasing meal prices over time. Over the projection period, prices of oilseeds, oilseed meal and vegetable oil, once corrected for inflation, are expected to decrease in real terms but to stay considerably above long term levels.

Main market developments

Sustained demand for vegetable oils

In 2007, supply stagnation and high prices led to reduced growth in global oils and fats consumption. Edible uses in countries in Asia and the EU have been most affected, whereas utilisation of vegetable oils for biofuel production grew further, driven by policy targets in some countries. Global vegetable oil demand is expected to rise by more than 40% in 2017, compared to the average level of 2005-07. Growth in global population and rising incomes continue to play an important role in vegetable oil markets. In developing countries, a 3.1% annual demand growth is expected for 80% driven by food use (Figure 6.2). Per-capita oil consumption is projected to grow by more than 1.9% and 0.8% annually in China and India, respectively. Combined with population growth this leads to a 8.7 million (m) tonne increase in vegetable oil use over the *Outlook* period, one fifth of the global increase. The divergence in average per capita consumption levels between developed countries and developing countries (in particular least developed nations) remains significant during the projection period.

Figure 6.2. **Demand for vegetable oil is growing**

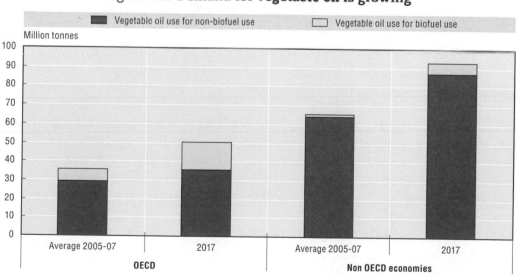

Source: OECD and FAO Secretariats.

StatLink ⬛⬛⬛ http://dx.doi.org/10.1787/382351238202

Stimulated by bioenergy mandates, vegetable oil use for biodiesel production should increase by 14 million tonnes over the *Outlook* period when compared to the level of 2005-07. The EU is expected to remain the dominant player with its use of vegetable oil for biodiesel production reaching almost 12.5 m tonnes, *i.e.* 9% of worldwide and 42% of domestic vegetable oil consumption, in 2017. Biodiesel industries are expected to develop in several countries worldwide. However, the EU is projected to account for more than half of global vegetable oil demand for biodiesel production over the projection period.

Within the OECD, vegetable oil consumption used for biodiesel production is expected to develop in Canada and Australia. After a strong increase between 2005 and 2007, vegetable oil use for biodiesel production in the US is projected to slightly decrease over the projection period because of lower margins in the biodiesel industry towards the end of the *Outlook* period. Outside the OECD, the emerging biodiesel production will increase the consumption of domestically produced palm oil in Indonesia and Malaysia and soyabean oil in Brazil. This new use of vegetable oil should reach almost 6 m tonnes by 2017.

Expansion in oilseed meal use to slow down in both developed and developing countries

In 2007, global meal consumption continued to expand, notwithstanding the on-going rise in prices. Constant demand growth was driven by continuously rising consumption of livestock products in Asia as well as by the exceptional worldwide shortage of feedgrains that induced feed industries to use more oilmeals. During the *Outlook* period, annual growth in meal consumption is projected at 3.4% and 0.9% in the developing and developed countries respectively. Global demand for protein meals is projected to be weaker than vegetable oil demand. Because meal and oil are produced in fixed proportions, this leads to a situation where the meal market is expected to be oversupplied in the short term. The OECD share in global oilseed meal consumption is projected to fall below 50%. Due to a slow-down of meat production growth in the European Union, China should become the dominant protein meal consumer in 2015. Indeed, the intensification of the Chinese livestock sector is responsible for 35% of the global increase in meal consumption. In 2017, dried distillers grains, a by-product of the rising ethanol production, are expected to replace almost 7% of oilseed meal consumption in the US compared to 2% on average over the period 2005-07. India's domestic demand for protein meals is continuously increasing over the projection period to more than 8 m tonnes in 2017 on account of the expanding dairy, livestock and poultry sectors.

When domestic meal consumption is expressed in meal use per tonne of non-ruminant meat production, the average projected consumption levels in developing and least developed countries remain significantly below those in developed countries. Because of this low feed intensity, developing countries continue to use only slightly more than 50% of the global protein meal consumption, despite their population share of over 80%. Feed intensity is projected to gradually increase in developing countries. Coupled with growing meat production, this is expected to slowly increase the share of protein meal consumed in these countries. Despite gradual improvements, least developed countries account for only about 1% of global non-ruminant meat production. This level of output requires just 0.5% of total protein meal used in the world.

The potential for oilseed and vegetable oil production increase is limited

While oilseed production continued to expand in 2006, an unprecedented decline in output occurred in 2007. This was largely on account of soybeans, the production of which dropped 6% (after expanding steadily in the preceding years), following the diversion of land from soybeans to maize in the US. Oilseeds lost out to grains also in China and CIS. Furthermore, the reductions in area were accompanied by yield declines due to unfavourable weather in several key growing regions. Prompt and substantial area and production increases in South America could only partly offset these falls. By the end of 2006, stocks had accumulated to record levels of about 12% of global consumption. Some 14 m tonnes of oilseeds were released from stocks in 2007 to compensate the production decline in a context of increasing crush demand. World oilseeds acreage and production are expected to recover in 2008 from their low 2007 levels because of relatively stronger oilseeds prices.

The projections show global oilseeds production rising by more than 25% in 2017 relative to the 2005-07 average, with Brazil alone providing 30% of the increase (Figure 6.3). The expansion of oilseeds production is limited to few regions, mainly South America and the EU. Brazil and Argentina are expected to confirm their leading role in global oilseeds supply with a combined share of global oilseed production of almost 38% in 2017. Brazil is expected to expand its production at a rate of almost 3.5% per annum. Area expansion – driven by high oilseeds and vegetable oil prices – should be the main contributor to production growth. Argentinean oilseeds area expansion should be relatively modest at 0.6% per annum. This, combined with slightly increasing yields, should imply an annual production growth of about 1.6%.

Despite a relatively stable OECD oilseed area at 50 m hectares throughout the projection period, some changes are expected in the geographical distribution of production mainly under the influence of biofuel development. Due to high oilseed prices (relative to competing arable crops), oilseeds acreage in the US should first recover from the low level recorded in 2007 but then decrease by 0.5% annually between 2009 and 2017. Oilseeds production in the European Union should increase by almost 3% per annum over the projection period. This expansion in oilseeds production is to a certain extent driven by the development of biodiesel, derived mainly from rapeseed oil. The rapeseed area is expected to increase in the former EU15. The new EU member countries are expected to contribute about 35% to the overall increase in EU oilseeds production because of yield improvements.

In China, production increases should continue to be driven by yield improvements rather than area expansion. Gains in yields are expected to lead to a growth in domestic production by an average rate of 1.6% per annum. China is expected to favour domestic production of coarse grains and imports of oilseeds to capture the value added from processing oilseeds into protein meals and vegetable oils domestically. The Chinese crushing capacity is expected to continue to grow at a rate of 3.5% per annum. India's oilseeds area is projected to continue to expand. Production is projected to grow to 20 m tonnes in 2017, based on moderate area expansion and yield improvements from the application of modern production technologies. India's oilseeds import tariffs continue to be prohibitive, barring any significant imports. The country's import requirements are satisfied by vegetable oil purchases.

Figure 6.3. **Growing world oilseed production**

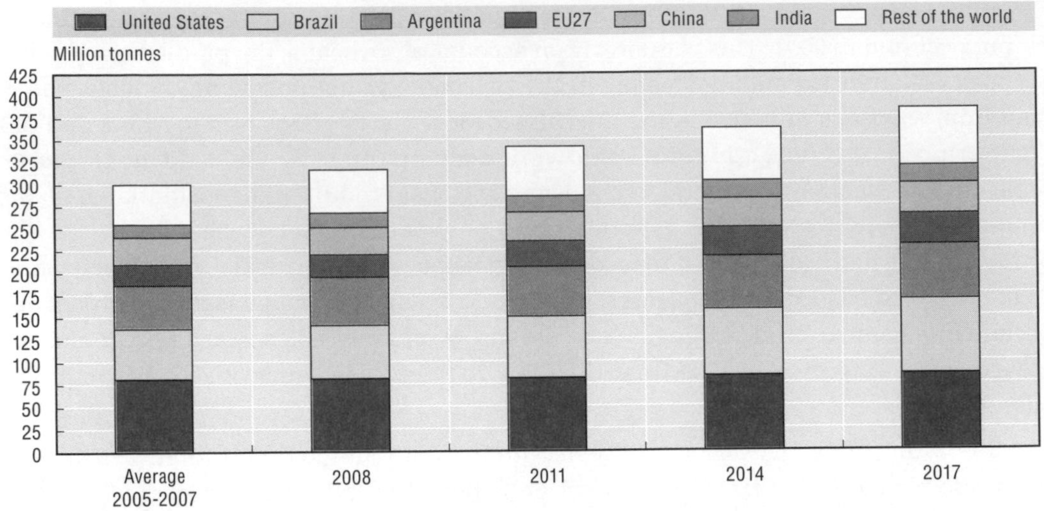

Source: OECD and FAO Secretariats.

As in the past, palm oil production will be clearly dominated by two countries, Malaysia and Indonesia. The share of palm oil produced in these two countries currently accounts for about one third of global vegetable oil output and is expected to grow further. In recent years, palm oil has surpassed soyabean oil as the leading vegetable oil in terms of quantities produced and consumed. Over the course of the baseline, the combined production of Malaysia and Indonesia is expected to expand by 18 m tonnes. Growth rates are expected to be lower in the future compared to recent years mainly because environmental constraints will restrict area expansion.

Brazil to become the leading oilseeds exporter

In 2007, trade growth in oilseeds and oilseed products was mostly driven by crop shortfalls in some major importing countries and by steadily rising demand in developing countries in Asia, in particular China, whose share in global imports of oilseeds and derived products reached about 25%. Due to the drop in US crop output, the importance of South America as a supplier of soybeans and derived products to the world market increased markedly in 2007. World oilseeds exports are expected to grow by almost 21 m tonnes over the *Outlook* period, compared to the period 2005-07. Brazil's share of global exports is expected to grow from 31% on average during the period 2005-07 to more than 40% in 2017. In 2009, Brazil should become the leading oilseeds exporter surpassing the United States, even though export growth is tempered by strong domestic demand for vegetable oil because of the development of the biodiesel sector.

In Argentina, the differential export tax system for oilseeds and oilseed products should continue to encourage domestic crush of seeds and exports of oilseed products. Domestic crushing is expected to increase by almost 25% over the projection period. This will not be enough to process all the domestic production and, as a result, oilseeds exports are anticipated to continue to represent 20% of production in 2017. US domestic demand for crushing is expected to grow at a rate of 1.3% per annum over the *Outlook* period. This, combined with an only slightly increasing oilseeds production over the projection period, is anticipated to lead to a contraction of the United States' share of global exports from 37%

OECD-FAO AGRICULTURAL OUTLOOK 2008-2017 – ISBN 978-92-64-04590-3 – © OECD/FAO 2008

on average over the period 2005-07 to around 22% in 2017. Canada should remain a strong oilseeds exporter.

Chinese oilseeds imports are expected to increase by almost 18 m tonnes accounting for 84% of the global increase in imports over the projection period, when compared to the 2005-07 period. This *Outlook* assumes that China will continue to expand its domestic oilseeds production and will keep expanding its crushing facilities to meet an increasing demand for oilseed meal and vegetable oil. In 2017, over 58% of Chinese oilseeds consumption should be met by imports.

The European Union should remain an important – but decreasing – importer of oilseeds, reflecting the impressive development of domestic rapeseed production. The European Union is assumed to increase domestic crush of oilseeds to meet the rising demand for oilseeds generated by a growing bio-diesel industry as well as by sustained demand for vegetable oils for food and for oilseed meal in animal rations.

Vegetable oil trade is influenced by the development of biodiesel

In terms of vegetable oil trade, palm oil and soybean oil continue to be the growth leaders. Trade in oilseed based biofuels or oils destined for the biofuel industry became more important in 2007 and this is expected to grow further. Argentina should continue to be the main exporter of oilseed oil with exports increasing at a rate of almost 2% per annum. The differential tax system in Argentina continues to favour the exports of soyabean oil in comparison to soybean seeds. However, the fiscal system is even more favourable for exporting biodiesel and significant investments in biodiesel producing capacities in Argentina could change the market picture for export supplies.

The use of vegetable oil for biodiesel production is also expected to develop in Malaysia, Indonesia and Brazil. The Indonesian Government is determined to counteract rising world market prices to control domestic cooking oil prices through variable export taxes. Despite the increasing export tax, shipments expanded in 2007 and are projected to reach 20 m tonnes in 2017 (Figure 6.4). Exports as a share of domestic production are expected to fall slightly because of the emerging biodiesel production. Palm oil in Malaysia has traditionally been used as raw material input in its oleo-chemical industry. Combined with the developing biodiesel sector, about 19% of Malaysia's palm oil production will be used by the domestic processing industry by 2017, up from 16% on average over the period 2005-07. In Brazil, oilseed oil shipments are expected to decrease as the use of domestically produced oil for biofuel production rises.

The expansion of EU oilseeds production and crush capacity is expected to lead to an increase in vegetable oil production of 20% over the *Outlook* period when compared to the average level of 2005-07. However to meet both industrial demand as well as traditional vegetable oil demand for food purposes, the EU is expected to more than double its imports over the course of the projection period. China is expected to continue to develop its domestic crushing industry. As a result Chinese vegetable oil imports should only increase by 0.7% per annum and the EU is expected to bypass China as the dominant vegetable oil importer in 2008.

More than half of India's additional vegetable oil needs should be supplied by domestic sources. Imports are projected to reach more than 6 m tonnes in 2017, solidifying India's position as the third largest vegetable oil importer in the world. Inflationary pressure from high food prices led the Government to initiate several differential duty reductions as a price control measure. The duty differential between palm and soyabean oils was narrowed by these reductions. India is expected to continue its variable tariff policy to control domestic oil prices and imports. In Pakistan, the oil produced from domestically produced and imported oilseeds will still only cover a small percentage of the domestic vegetable oil demand and vegetable oil imports are increasing as a consequence.

Figure 6.4. **Evolution of vegetable oil trade**

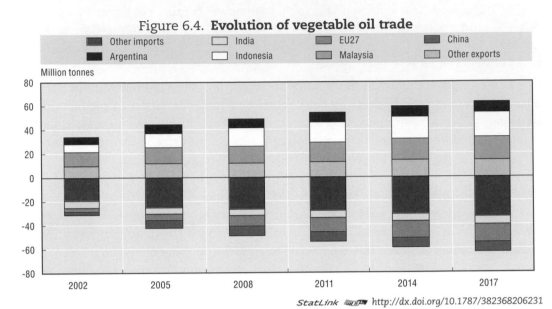

Source: OECD and FAO Secretariats.

StatLink http://dx.doi.org/10.1787/382368206231

Argentina and Brazil are the leading oilseed meal exporters

With regard to oilseed meals, almost the entire rise in global trade was on account of soybeans in 2007. EU imports increased as a result of surge in feedgrain prices. In 2007, the EU was the world's main buyer of oilseed meals and it is forecast to keep this position over the projection period. However, by 2017 the development of domestic rapeseed meal production should slightly reduce the dependency of the EU on imported protein meals. In China, meal demand will be satisfied by domestically produced oilseed meal (a considerable amount of which is derived from imported oilseeds) as well as through a sizeable expansion in meal imports.

Argentina and Brazil are the leading exporting countries, they should account for almost 70% of global exports throughout the projection period. Argentina is expected to remain by far the largest oilseed meal exporter. Indeed, a combination of factors such as investment in processing facilities, a differential export tax system and the small size of the domestic market are expected to lead to an increase in exports by almost 20% over the projection period. In 2007, India strengthened her role as a provider of oilseed meals within Asia, reflecting ample domestic crops and the recent rise in ocean freight rates that favoured nearby supply sources. India's domestic production is projected to expand over the projection period, but at a slower rate than consumption, resulting in a small reduction in exports by about 4% in the coming decade. Target markets for exports remain those Asian countries with growing livestock sectors such as the Philippines, Malaysia, Saudi Arabia and Egypt where Indian oilseed meals enjoy the competitive advantage of high protein content and biotech free status plus low freight costs.

OECD-FAO AGRICULTURAL OUTLOOK 2008-2017 – ISBN 978-92-64-04590-3 – © OECD/FAO 2008

Key issues and uncertainties

Development of biofuel market contingent on future policy measures

The *Outlook* starts in a period of soaring raw commodity prices. The strong increase in prices that commenced in the course of 2006 has been caused by the concomitant appearance of unusual weather conditions, strong demand growth and specific policy changes. In particular, global biofuel demand and production have grown significantly, stimulated by government support policies. This growth contributes increasingly to the surge in world prices of coarse grains and vegetable oils and, as a result, also of oilseeds and meals. Assumptions on biofuel developments in the *Outlook* are based on the continuation of the current policy set. During 2007, biofuel use targets and other measures to promote consumption have been established in numerous countries. In exporting countries in South America and South East Asia, where the private sector has invested in the production of biodiesel for exportation, the sector's viability is largely conditioned by the development of feedstock prices and how these compare to crude oil prices. Other countries, including China and India, are moving more cautiously as they have put food security as their first objective and thus restrict the use of edible crops for fuel production.

In a near future, the implementation of binding bioenergy directives in key supplying or consuming countries can be expected to increasingly affect the global market picture for oilseeds and other agricultural commodities. National bioenergy policies may be subject to changes over the coming years as governments take stock of the significant effects such measures have on domestic and international markets and on their economies and consumers. For instance, countries could face limitations regarding biofuel production from domestically grown food crops and international trade in biofuels or their feedstock is likely to grow. In addition, internationally recognised biofuel specifications and trade rules still need to be developed and policy makers will have to respond to consumer requests for environmentally and socially sustainable production of any feedstock used. Finally, if second generation biofuels and alternative forms of renewable energy would become more important over the *Outlook* period, the role of oilseeds and other basic food crops as biofuel feedstock would be reduced. Overall, the future course of technological innovations, the development of national bioenergy policies, the behaviour of private investors, together with the future evolution of crude oil prices, represent significant sources of uncertainty in projections for the global oilseed market.

Policy response to high food prices can affect the market

Sustained high international commodity prices can lead to lower levels of food consumption and cause price inflation. This is especially the case in developing economies where a high portion of household income is still spent on food. In particular food importing developing countries are concerned about the social consequences of rising prices for basic food staples. To mitigate the adverse effects of high prices, governments in several countries decided in the course of 2007 to introduce corrective policy measures. In numerous cases, governments lowered tariffs and introduced other measures to stimulate imports of oilseeds and vegetable oils. Direct support to consumers, release of government stocks and other consumption policies were also introduced, sometimes coupled with increased efforts to stimulate domestic oilseed production. Conversely, some exporting countries decided to introduce or raise export tariffs on domestically produced oilseeds and derived products or to otherwise restrict exportation. Indonesia has raised palm oil export tariffs and Argentina has further increased export taxes on oilseeds and oilseed products in an attempt to help contain or limit feed price rises to stimulate livestock production and to provide support to producers of key livestock foodstuffs so as to fight inflation on basic consumer foods. The immediate effect of most of these measures on domestic markets seems to have been limited, while prices have further strengthened in international markets. The longer term nature of these government interventions and the related market impacts remains an uncertainty in the *Outlook*.

With only few players dominating global supply, market instability can be expected to increase

The potential for further increases in the production of oilseeds and of palm oil is clearly concentrated in a few regions. The global market will depend heavily on South America (Brazil and Argentina) and Southeast Asia (Malaysia and Indonesia) for supplies. But the potential for further expansion of production in these areas could be increasingly constrained by resource and environmental limitations. In the case of Malaysia, future growth in palm oil output needs to be achieved almost entirely through yield improvements because of limited land availability. However, past productivity improvements have been modest and the reversal of this trend will largely depend on the development and adoption of genetically improved planting material and new varieties. Key environmental concerns facing oilseed production in the all these regions include the risk of soil degradation, water scarcity, loss of biodiversity and deforestation. With consumers becoming more concerned about these issues, oilseed and palm oil production and trade is likely to be confronted with new requirements in the future. First, voluntary attempts to certify sustainable practices of palm oil production are being made and similar initiatives are likely to follow with soyabean production. When and how such voluntary or mandatory schemes will impact production methods remains to be seen. Furthermore, given the size of production and exports in the countries in question, any weather anomalies, important shocks to their economies, or radical policy decisions could have huge consequences on markets and world prices for oilseeds and oilseed products. Also on the demand side, the trend towards concentration of consumption growth in relatively few countries, especially China and India, might lead to increased market instability, as any unexpected development in these countries would greatly affect the global market for oilseeds and oilseed products.

Genetic modification of crops can change the production context and consumption patterns

Another uncertainty comes from future developments of genetically modified (GM) crops. Past experience has shown that GM crops have the potential to modify productivity and production costs, thereby affecting competition between crops and, consequently, the overall composition of markets and pattern of trade. In years to come, more widespread use of genetic modification appears likely to modify crop traits according to particular product uses and consumer needs. However, in many countries the adoption of GM crops depends on policy decisions that are still evolving in response to the differing concerns of producers, processors, consumers and the wider society. Future decisions about introducing GM crops, as well as further research advances in this area, will remain of strategic importance for the sector in many developed and developing countries.

ISBN 978-92-64-04590-3
OECD-FAO AGRICULTURAL OUTLOOK 2008-2017
© OECD/FAO 2008

Chapter 7

Sugar

World market trends and prospects

Key market drivers

World sugar market fundamentals are bearish at the start of the long-term outlook. A near record sugar surplus has overhung the world sugar economy in 2006-07, and a similar situation is expected for 2007-08, as record sugar production continues to outstrip the more steady growth in global consumption. The surplus resulted in sharply lower world sugar prices in 2006-07 with a build-up of global ending stocks, an increasing stocks-to-use ratio that approached 53% and a trade surplus. In spite of the sugar glut, world sugar prices initially rallied in late 2007, but have subsequently weakened, reflecting a change in market sentiment and sugar price dynamics. Global sugar prices have been supported by speculative interest of hedge funds and commodity index funds that have invested massively in sugar futures markets (e.g. financial funds held a record number of over 265 000 *net long positions* in futures contracts February 2008, equivalent to about 13.3 mt of sugar, and up from 140 000 contracts three years earlier). This is partly because sugar has had the additional appeal of appearing cheap and undervalued relative to other commodities. A weaker US dollar has also lent some support to sugar prices by lowering the price of dollar denominated sugar imports in many countries and raising the cost of supply of efficient sugar producers such as Brazil and Australia.

A continuation of the sugar production cycle of booms followed by busts is expected in some countries of Asia such as India. Less rapid growth of cane production and milling capacity is projected for Brazil with rising sugar production costs in the near term and a more profitable alternative use and with further market and trade adjustments expected in the EU and North America. Along with steady growth in global sugar consumption and expanding demand for alternative products of sugar crops, such as for bio-ethanol, particularly in Brazil, these changes are expected to lift world sugar prices, in nominal terms, over the medium term. As the world market is brought into closer balance and excess sugar stocks drawn down, world indicator prices for raw and white sugar are projected to rise by 9% and 11%, respectively, in 2017-18 when compared to the average level of 2005-07, to reach USD 302/t for raw sugar and USD 379/t for white sugar. This will still represent a continuation of the decline in real terms over the projection period, however. The margin between raw and white sugar prices should narrow over the near term, given expectations of higher demand for raw sugar for further refining by an increasing number of large destination and toll refineries* in the Middle East and Asia, and then expand over following years as additional supplies of raw sugar come on stream. With reforms having reined back the EU as a major white sugar exporter, the white sugar premium in future years should reflect more the cost of further sugar refining.

---

* These refineries are being established in former import markets for white sugar to process raw sugar for domestic use and in some cases for export.

Main market developments

Growth in sugar cane crops boost global sugar production

World sugarcane **production** accounts for around 79% of global sugar production and its share is set to increase with rising yields and areas under production. The perennial nature of sugarcane tends to contribute to steady increases of cane and sugar output over time as producers increase plantings in response to higher prices, and with multiple harvests taken from a single planting (ratoon). The global harvested area of sugarcane is expected to increase by a further 20%, whereas the world sugar beet area declines by less than 1% by 2017-18, compared to the average for 2005-07. This is due mainly to lower beet area in the EU, following sugar policy reform, which more than offsets growth in other countries such as in the Russian Federation and Ukraine. World sugar production is projected at 189 million tonnes (mt) for 2017-18, some 27 mt or 17% above the average level for 2005-07. A key determinant of world sugar production trends is Brazilian cane production and its allocation between sugar and ethanol production over the medium term. With production in the OECD area relatively stable, other countries outside the OECD account for virtually all the increase in global sugar production to 2017-18. In fact, the non-OECD countries' share of global production rises from 77% in 2005-07 to 80% in 2017-18. Brazil is the largest sugar producer with expected output of 41 mt in 2017-18, and its share of world production rises from 20% to 22% over the ten-year period.

Figure 7.1. **World sugar prices to recover in near term**

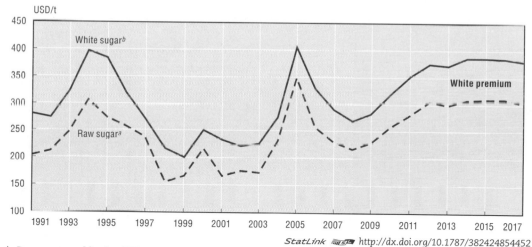

StatLink ᴬᴵˢᴾ http://dx.doi.org/10.1787/382424854452

a) Raw sugar world price, ICE sugar contract No. 11, New York f.o.b., bulk spot price, October/September.
b) Refined sugar price, London No. 5, f.o.b. Europe, spot price, October/September.
Source: OECD and FAO Secretariats.

Some of this growth is being driven by rapidly increasing demand for fuel ethanol, for which sugar crops are expected to be a major feedstock. The two largest ethanol producers are the United States and Brazil. The anticipated expansion in biofuel production in the United States stimulated by the new mandate is not yet taken into account in this *Outlook*. It is nevertheless clear that it will involve increased use of sugar beets as a feedstock, although maize will be by far the dominant source. In the case of Brazil, however, this growing alternative use for sugarcane has emerged as an extremely important determinant of growth in global sugar output and trade. According to the projections, the share of the sugarcane crop going to ethanol in Brazil is expected to increase from close to

Figure 7.2. **World sugar prices to trend down in real^c terms**

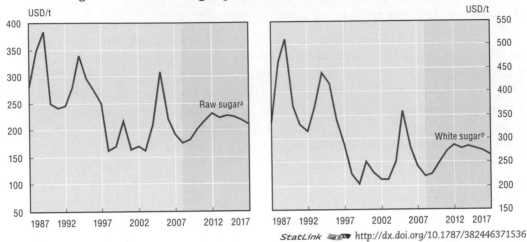

StatLink ⊶ http://dx.doi.org/10.1787/382446371536

a)   Raw sugar world price, ICE sugar contract No. 11, New York f.o.b., bulk spot price, October/September.
b)   Refined sugar price, London No. 5, f.o.b. Europe, spot price, October/September.
c)   Prices deflated by US GDP deflator (2000 = 1).

Source: OECD and FAO Secretariats.

Figure 7.3. **Larger sugarcane production to account for most of the additional sugar output**

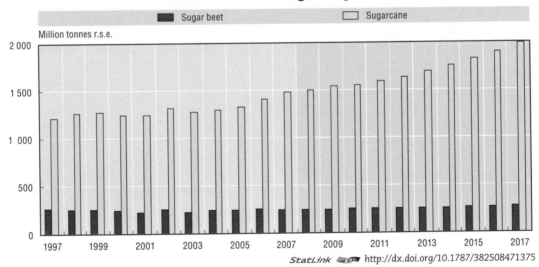

StatLink ⊶ http://dx.doi.org/10.1787/382508471375

Source: OECD and FAO Secretariats.

51% in 2005-07 to over 64% in 2017-18. Despite the growth in ethanol offtake from sugarcane, this is not expected to halt further expansion in sugar output in Brazil, as sugarcane production is projected to rise by over 35% between 2005-07 and 2017-18.

Outside the United States and Brazil, a number of sugar producing countries are currently embarking on, or reinvigorating existing renewable energy programmes, such as the EU, Japan, Malaysia, Indonesia, India, South Africa, Colombia, and the Philippines, particularly for use in the transport fuel sector. Most of these fledgling fuel ethanol programmes, however, are expected to use molasses or starch sources such as grains and cassava, in preference to raw sugarcane juice as the preferred feedstock. As molasses is produced as a by-product of the sugar refining process, molasses-based bio-ethanol production should not greatly impair sugar production in these countries and may even stimulate further growth in cane and sugar output. Furthermore, in some regions, such as the EU, specific sugar crops (industrial beets) are being separately designated and developed for non-food uses such as bio-ethanol production.

Steady consumption growth eventually eats away the global surplus

The relentless, year on year growth in sugar **consumption** remains the basic driver of the world sugar economy. Global sugar use has increased on averaged by over 2.3% per year in the 1998-2007 period in response to rapid increases in incomes and faster population growth in mainly the developing group of countries. Sugar consumption in the mature markets of OECD countries has shown less dramatic growth at less than 1% per annum in the same period. World sugar consumption is expected to continue to expand at a solid 1.5% per annum to 2017-18 with faster growth in the developing countries which averages over 1.9% per annum; albeit with considerable variation in per capita use between the different countries. The fastest growth in consumption is projected for the sugar deficit regions of Asia and the Pacific, where sugar consumption growth is significantly higher, at 2.1% per annum, than the world average. This is largely due to the emergence of higher growth in China, the most populous country but with comparatively low per capita sugar consumption by Asian and world standards. Overall, the developing world accounts for the lion's share of global consumption, with its proportion of global use increasing from 70% in 2005-07 to about 74% in 2017-18. These countries, thus, account for virtually all the increase in world sugar consumption (and production) over the projection period.

Figure 7.4. **Changing regional patterns of sugar consumption to 2017**

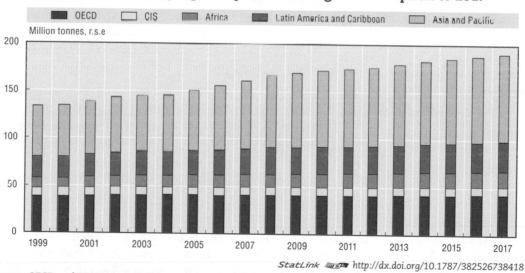

StatLink http://dx.doi.org/10.1787/382526738418

Source: OECD and FAO Secretariats.

World sugar **stocks** increased in 2006-07 with the recovery of global production and a similar situation of rising stocks is expected in 2007-08. The global sugar stocks-to-use ratio which averaged 49% in 2005-07, is expected to increase to nearly 53% in the near term. Notwithstanding some growth in total stock levels over the first half of the projection period, steady growth in sugar consumption ultimately results in the stocks-to-use ratio declining to around 44% in 2017-18.

Figure 7.5. **The global stock-to-use ratio to decline in the near term**

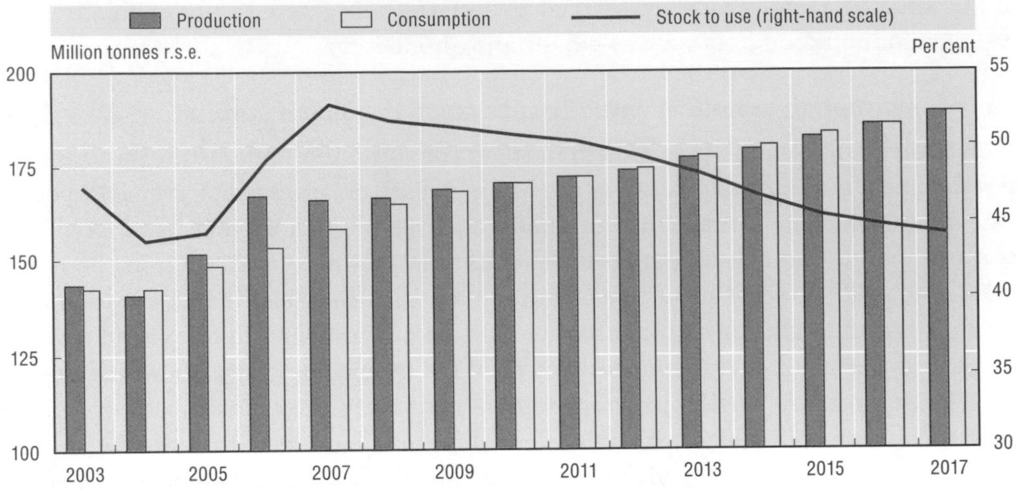

Legend: Production | Consumption | Stock to use (right-hand scale)

Million tonnes r.s.e. / Per cent

StatLink http://dx.doi.org/10.1787/382610602514

Source: OECD and FAO Secretariats.

OECD countries' global market shares to contract further

The OECD area currently accounts for around 23 to 26% of world sugar production and consumption. These shares have been declining over the last decade given the growing importance of the developing and transition countries in the world sugar market, and are projected to fall to around 20% for production and 23% for consumption, respectively, by 2017-18. On the production side, reform in the EU leads to a smaller domestic sugar industry, while stable consumption trends largely reflect the mature state of many OECD country sugar markets. Among the leading OECD producers, the wider adoption of smut resistant cane varieties, higher world prices, and a return to average seasonal conditions are expected to result in sugar production **in Australia** rising to 5.1 mt and sugar exports at nearly 4 mt in 2017-18.

The **European Union** which has currently the largest sugar industry in the OECD area is expected to downsize following the adoption of reforms in 2006 to the common market organisation (CMO) for sugar that are aimed at bringing production down to levels that are better aligned with internal demand and with the EU's external commitments (Box 7.1). As a result, sugar beet area for sugar production is expected to decline until 2011. Additional amounts of sugar beets, however, will be diverted to industrial purposes such as ethanol production over the medium term. In 2007-08, EU sugar production is expected to reach nearly 18 mt (raw value) and then progressively decline as quota is surrendered or cut to reach around 15.8 mt in 2017-18. With the expectation of lower internal market prices, and some substitution for existing HFCS use, sugar consumption rises moderately to 18.8 mt by the close of the projection period.

One outcome of the reforms is that the EU will have turned full circle from its initial position as a net sugar importer at the commencement of the CMO in 1968 to become the world's largest white sugar exporter in the following years to 2005-06, followed by a return to a net importer status and a sugar deficit region in 2006-07. This transformation essentially came about with the enforcement of lower WTO limits on subsidised exports at 1.374 mt per annum. Exports are expected to stabilise at this level to the close of the projection period. Total imports, however, are anticipated to increase to around 4.7 mt by 2017-18, driven mainly by preferential imports from the LDCs and the African,

OECD-FAO AGRICULTURAL OUTLOOK 2008-2017 – ISBN 978-92-64-04590-3 – © OECD/FAO 2008

Caribbean and Pacific (ACP) group of developing countries under the Everything But Arms (EBA) initiative and the Economic Partnership Agreements being negotiated by the EU to replace the Cotonou Agreement and expiring Sugar Protocol. As a consequence, the EU is on a pathway to becoming the world's largest sugar importer, surpassing the Russian Federation which currently occupies this position. As has been observed, this dramatic change in trade direction and status has had an important influence on world sugar price formation and the composition and pattern of international trade, particularly for white sugar. As a result, a considerable quantity of EU supplies, that were largely price-insensitive, are no longer being exported to world markets with the use of subsidies, and effectively depressing world prices. Instead, the situation has now been largely reversed with the EU becoming a large, price-insensitive importer that covers its needs at whatever level of the prevailing world price. However, the level of EU preferential imports remains an important uncertainty for the *Outlook*.

> ## Box 7.1. **EU sugar production downsising arrangements**
>
> The reform of the EU's Common Market Organisation (CMO) regime for sugar on 24 November 2005 includes a voluntary restructuring scheme to buy back surplus production quota. If, however, the restructuring scheme is unsuccessful in removing sufficient quota voluntarily from production by the payment of a fee, the Commission is mandated to apply an across the board "linear" quota cut in 2010, with no financial compensation. The restructuring scheme is intended to achieve the required structural rebalance of the sugar market by encouraging producers in high cost areas to give up quota and leave the industry in return for a (degressive) payment for surrendered quota.
>
> The quota reduction objective was set at 6 mt. In the first year of 2006-07, some 1.46 mt of quota were renounced covering sugar and inulin. However, for 2007-08, only 0.71 mt of sugar and isoglucose quota were renounced. Because the restructuring scheme was not working as planned, the EU Council revised the scheme in October 2007 by providing increased financial incentives of higher buy back rates for sugar companies and beet growers. These changes included fixing the percentage of aid given to growers and machinery contractors at 10% and an additional payment for growers who renounced their quota. The rule changes included setting up a two step process for surrendering quota in 2008-09. Under the new arrangements, sugar companies are given to the end of January 2008 to apply for quota renunciation, with a minimum set at the level of what they were forced to give up as part of the temporary preventive quota cut in 2007. The amount nominated by January 2008 has also to be agreed by the affected member states. To participate in a second step for quota surrender in 2008-09, companies are given until 31 March 2008 to offer at least the minimum of quota they had sold back to the Commission. If they do not, the Commission will advise them to what extent they risk an across the board, uncompensated quota cut in 2010. Some 2.5 mt of production quota was renounced in the first step for 2008-09 as well as 0.1 mt to apply from 2009-10. The Commission has indicated that the second round of voluntary quota surrender that closed on 31 March resulted in an additional 851 237 tonnes of quota (847 866 of sugar and 3 371 tonnes of iosoglucose) quota being renounced. Taking account of these latest offers and adding the production quota surrendered in earlier years, a total of nearly 5.7 mt will have been surrendered. The Commission is thus less than 310 000 tonnes short of its goal of 6 mt identified as necessary to ensure a balance market in 2010. If this outstanding amount is not renounced by 2010, the Commission will impose a compulsory reduction in sugar quotas across all member states without any compensation. One other factor in this

> ## Box 7.1. **EU sugar production downsising arrangements** (cont.)
>
> equation of achieving a balanced market in 2010, however, is whether sufficient quantities of imports will be forthcoming from the LDCs and DCs under preferential import arrangements to meet EU internal market requirements. While the EU remains an export destination with attractive prices given the depreciation of the US dollar that has largely offset the cut in support price under the reforms, these countries also have the choice of giving priority to domestic and regional markets or using cane for ethanol production, similar to the practice in Brazil. These alternatives would affect their sugar export availabilities

North America becomes a single sugar market under NAFTA

The **United States** and **Mexico** resolved their longstanding sweetener dispute in July 2006 and became one fully integrated market from 1 January 2008 under NAFTA. **Mexican** sugarcane production is projected to increase with sugar output growing to 6.9 mt by 2017-18. Increased use of HFCS in Mexico, largely sourced from imports, is expected to lead to higher exports of sugar to the United States in 2008 and following years. These exports, despite some continuing growth in Mexican sugar consumption, seek to take advantage of higher prices available in the United States as a result of the loan price support scheme for sugar. Mexican exports are expected to amount to around 15% of US consumption in 2017-18. In the **United States**, sugar production should increase with a continuation of longer term productivity trends. Some growth is also expected in sugar consumption with rising per capita use. Total sugar production from beet and cane crops is expected to increase to nearly 8 mt and consumption to 10.8 mt by 2017-18.

Japan and **Korea** remain significant importers of mainly raw sugar for domestic processing and consumption over the *Outlook* period. Korean sugar imports are projected to increase strongly and to grow by some 30% to over 2.1 mt in 2017-18, when compared to 2005-07, whereas imports by Japan decrease slightly over the same time span in line with slowing per capita consumption.

Figure 7.6. **EU sugar reform leads to lower production and exports**

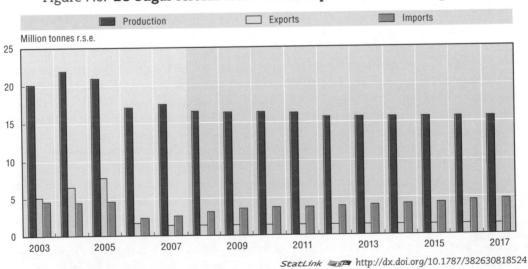

StatLink http://dx.doi.org/10.1787/382630818524

Source: OECD and FAO Secretariats.

OECD-FAO AGRICULTURAL OUTLOOK 2008-2017 – ISBN 978-92-64-04590-3 – © OECD/FAO 2008

Brazil dominates the South American and World scene

Brazil remains the largest sugar and ethanol producer as well as exporter in the world market for these commodities. Sugarcane production has increased rapidly in recent years, due to a combination of higher yields from improved varieties and increase planted area to accommodate the growth in sugar and ethanol production. Sugarcane production is projected to continue to grow rapidly over coming years but at a slightly lower rate that in the last decade. Approximately half of total annual sugarcane output in Brazil is directed toward ethanol production, with the centre-south region accounting for nearly 80% of all sugarcane feedstock. The share of sugarcane allocated to ethanol production is projected to rise to some 64% by 2017-18, to meet rising domestic demand and some growth in exports. Export opportunities for Brazilian ethanol as the lowest cost producer should increase to 2017-18, despite continuing import protection in several countries. The cane allocation share for ethanol production plays a key role in determining the size of annual sugar production and exports by Brazil to the world market and, thus, world sugar price formation. Despite increasing ethanol production projected at some 38 bn litres in 2017-18, sugar production is expected to increase as well to reach 41 mt, an increase of 28% above 2005-07 levels by 2017-18. Brazil's sugar consumption rises to just over 14 mt with growth of 1.3% per annum and exports reach 27 mt in 2017-18, accounting for more than 50% of world trade. Brazilian exports of high quality raw sugar are projected to increase more rapidly than those for white sugar in the period to 2017-18.

Argentinean production has benefited from high world prices and the devaluation of the currency back in 2002. Further investment in the sugar industry is expected to boost production which should reach just over 3.2 mt or some 32% above the average level for 2005-07 by the close of the projection period. Despite higher consumption, the rise in output allows increasing sugar exports that reach nearly 1.2 mt in 2017-18. Colombia is set to produce 3.1 mt of sugar in 2017-18, but supplies are expected to be tight in the light of increasing demand for ethanol.

Figure 7.7. **Sugar and ethanol production and exports to increase rapidly in Brazil**

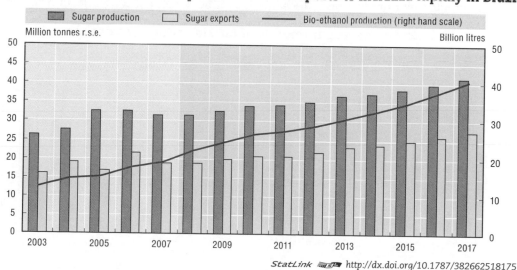

StatLink 🖳 http://dx.doi.org/10.1787/382662518175

Source: OECD and FAO Secretariats.

Figure 7.8. **Global sugar exports are increasingly dominated by Brazil**

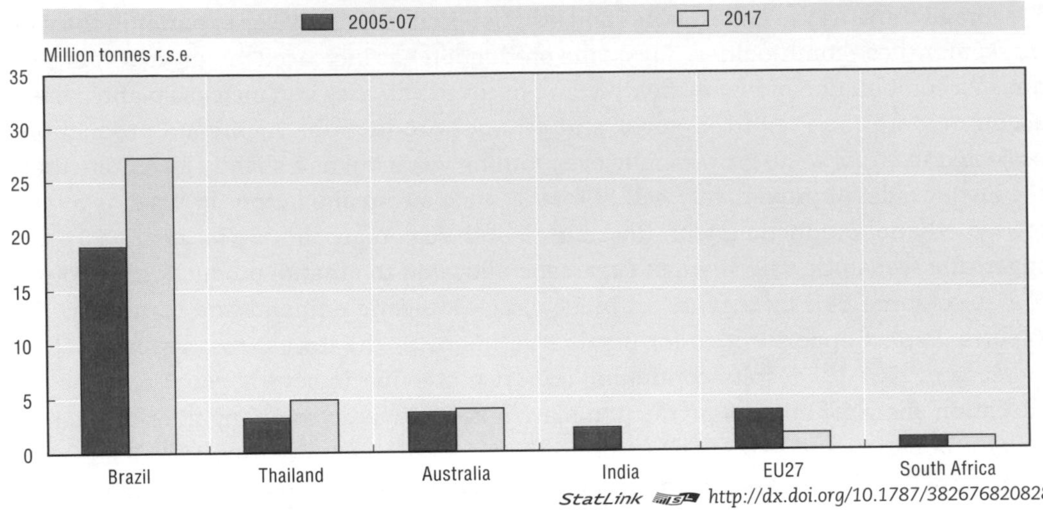

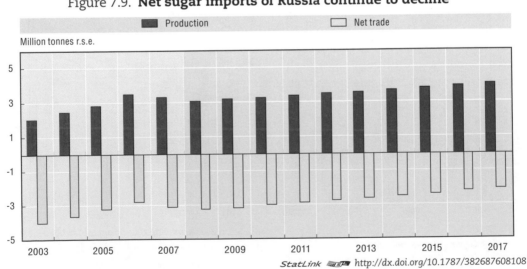

Source: OECD and FAO Secretariats.

Russia to become more self-sufficient in sugar

Outside of Asia, the **Russia** Federation and **Ukraine** have long been important players in the world sugar market. The Russian Federation is the world's leading sugar importer, having switched most of its imports from white to raw sugar for domestic off-season refining in the 1990s. Ukraine has returned to self-sufficiency in sugar, while **Russia**'s import requirements continue to fall steadily. Rapid growth in domestic beet production, stimulated by higher prices with tariff protection and increasing investment, has been a feature of the sugar industry in the Russian Federation in recent years. This trend is expected to continue over the medium term against a backdrop of stagnant demand and to result in further import substitution. Sugar production is projected to increase to 4 mt in 2017-18, and with only small growth in sugar consumption, raw sugar imports are anticipated to decline to just over 2.3 mt in the same period. Higher sugar beet yields are expected to lift sugar production in **Ukraine** to 3 mt by the end of the projection period, a

Figure 7.9. **Net sugar imports of Russia continue to decline**

Source: OECD and FAO Secretariats.

0.7 mt increase from 2005-07 average levels. Much uncertainty remains on the import side, as these could increase if Ukraine becomes a member of the WTO in 2008.

China is the main sugar producer in Far East Asia with both a sugarcane and sugarbeet sector. Sugar production in China has surged over the last two seasons in response to higher sugar prices. With some moderate increases in area harvested and yields, China's sugar production is expected to reach 15.7 mt in 2017-18, some 3 mt above the 2005-07 average level. Chinese sugar demand has been growing rapidly in the current decade, particularly for use in food products, preparations and beverages, with direct food consumption still relatively low in per capita terms in comparison to other countries in Asia. With tightening government controls on artificial sweeteners, sugar consumption in China is projected to increase by 1.5% per annum to reach just over 19 mt in 2017-18. This level of use would imply rising imports over the *Outlook* period.

Figure 7.10. **The EU and China emerge as the largest sugar importers**

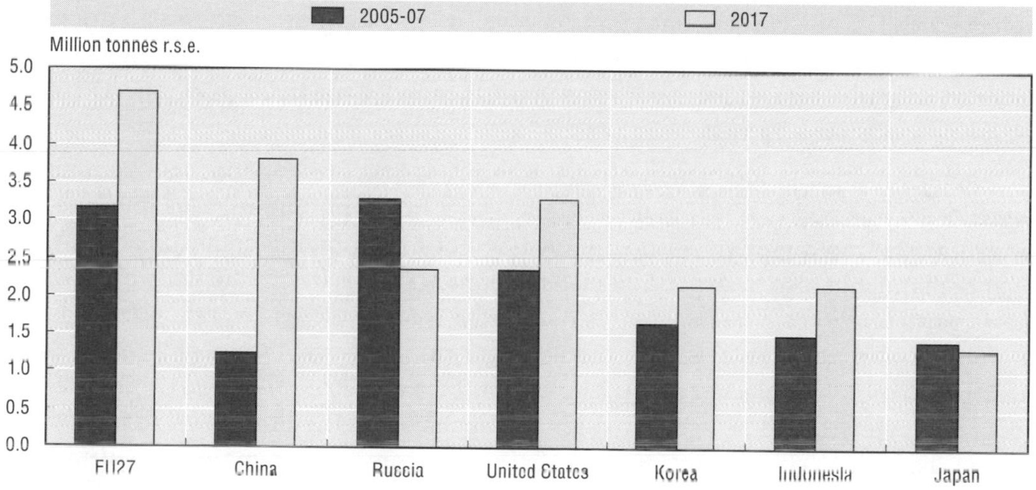

Source: OECD and FAO Secretariats.

Expansion in yields and moderate growth in cane plantings are expected to boost sugar production in **Indonesia** to 3.7 mt in 2017-18. The increase is attributed to remunerative returns and government institutional support. The industry is very much dependent on a government subsidy and the division between support levels in rice and sugar. Sugar consumption will remain strong, driven by population growth and high income elasticities. Indonesia as the second largest sugar importer after Russia is expected to further increase imports to 2.1 mt by the end of the projection period.

Sugar production in **Thailand** is projected at 7.7 mt in 2017-18, with a recovery in output following unfavourable weather conditions at the beginning of the *Outlook*. Production has been characterised by ups and downs over the last decade, as a result of changing policies and variability in growing conditions. Growth in sugar cane-based ethanol is expected to limit further expansion in sugar output. Sugar consumption is expected to increase by 27% between 2005-07 and 2017-18, because of higher use by households and the food and beverages industries. Sugar export should reach 4.8 mt, mainly in the form of raw sugar, with the bulk of the shipments likely to be directed to regional markets in the light of rising freights rates. Ethanol production is set to use about 3.3 mt of cane by 2017-18. Sugar production in the **Philippines** is projected to reach 2.8 mt in 2017-18, mainly reflecting moderate improvement in yields over the *Outlook* period, while consumption and sugar imports should total 2.3 mt and 94 kt, respectively.

India is traditionally the second largest sugar producer after Brazil, and an intermittent sugar trader on the world market. A feature of the Indian sugar market is a long established cycle that is characterised by a boom followed by a bust in sugar production. This arises in part because sugarcane prices, which tend to only rise over time, are fixed by the government to protect growers' incomes while sugar prices fluctuate, squeezing or inflating miller's margins, as sugar supplies increase or decline, and affecting their capacity to pay growers for their cane. The pronounced production cycle is expected to continue over the projection period, in the absence of a revenue sharing cane payment system. India is projected to produce 29 mt of sugar, corresponding to less than half a per cent growth over the projection period by 2017-18. Sugar consumption is foreseen to expand by more than 2.4% per annum. This is due to low domestic prices and expected economic growth, raising per capita consumption to 23.6 kg, slightly lower than the projected world per capita consumption level of 25.3 kg. Lower domestic prices are expected to encourage sugar intake at the expense of alternative local sweeteners such as jaggery and gur. Sugar exports are expected to reach 2.2 mt in 2008-09, and thereafter decline as stock levels retreat.

Aggregate sugar production in *Africa* is forecast to increase by about 1.83% per annum between 2005-07 and 2017-18, mainly due to gains in **Egypt**, **Sudan**, **Mozambique**, and **Tanzania**. The rapid growth is underpinned by not only growing domestic and regional sugar demand, but also by expansion plans to enhance capacity, productivity and exports. This is particularly the case for a number of *African Least Developed Countries (LDCs)*, as they gain duty and quota free access to the *EU* sugar market from 1 October 2009. In **Egypt**, sugar production is projected to grow by 0.3 mt, between 2005-07 and 2017-18, to 2.2 mt. Most of the growth will be accounted for by expansion in the area sown to beet, which reaches about 81 000 hectares by 2017-18. The beet sector is more dynamic and attracts the bulk of new investments in the sugar sector, while cane sugar production is stagnant due to limited area and water resources. Sugar consumption is projected to remain strong and to increase at the same rate as during the previous decade, sustained by population growth and expanded use of sugar in food processing.

Production in the *LDC* group as a whole is projected to reach nearly 4 mt, an increase of 33.8% over 2005-07. Driven by rehabilitation and expansion programmes, output in **Mozambique** and **Tanzania** is expected to increase by 5.4% and 5.5 % per annum, respectively. Sugar output is also projected to grow in **Zambia**, but at a slower pace to reach more than 320 000 tonnes in 2017-18. Sugar consumption in the *LDCs* group is projected to reach 8.1 mt by the close of the projection period, up 2.2 mt from the average level of 2005-07, and largely reflecting population growth. Much uncertainty remains as to the ability of the *LDC* countries to significantly increase export volumes given shortcomings in infrastructure, although efforts are being made to increase sugar storage capacity and reduce fobbing costs. Several key factors will have an impact on the profitability of the sugar industry in the *LDCs*. These include commitments to regional free trade agreements, that call for consolidated sugar policies and prices, changes to preferential agreements, notably with the EU, resulting in a quota and duty free access to the EU market, and the effect of the Economic Partnership Agreements (EPAs) between the EU and the ACP countries. The EPAs will replace the trade chapters of the 2000 Cotonou agreement, which has regulated the sugar trade between both parties. The EU has offered duty and quota free access to the ACP countries after 2015. However, the impact of this proposal on the ACP group, and individual countries within ACP in the light of the sugar price reforms underway in the EU, is still subject to much uncertainty.

Key issues and uncertainties

The sugar projections discussed in this chapter are a conditional scenario based on a number of assumptions regarding the future macroeconomic environment, a continuation of existing agricultural policies, average weather conditions, longer term productivity trends and the absence of market shocks. Should any of these assumptions change, the resulting set of sugar projections would also be different. For example, the projections for the United States are based on a continuation of the provisions of the 2002 *FSRI Act* for sugar which expired in 2007, but with replacement legislation still under negotiation in the US Congress. Should the provisions for sugar fundamentally change in the next Farm Bill, for example, along the lines of the version passed by the US House of Representatives in 2007, some significant differences would be observed in the projections for the United States. Major uncertainties for the sugar outlook are, thus, future changes in sugar policies as well as an eventual outcome of the current round of Doha multilateral trade negotiations in reducing support and further opening up sugar markets. The extent to which the current upsurge in renewable energy programmes by countries around the world will impact on future sugar crops use is another uncertainty for the *Outlook*. Fluctuations in exchange rates and movements in freight rates will also have implications for the export competitiveness of sugar industries. The Brazilian Real has been appreciating against the US dollar in 2007-08. Depending on the future direction of the Real/USD exchange rate this will determine the level at which world sugar prices, denominated in US dollars, are supported by Brazilian costs of sugar production. Finally, sharply higher speculative activity by hedge funds and commodity rebalancing by index funds in sugar futures markets can have an impact on physical cash market prices of sugar and their volatility.

Large EU import volumes will be required to balance the internal market

In the case of the European Union, a number of changes are being made to preferential import arrangements in coming years. These include the termination of the longstanding Sugar Protocol (SP) and SPS arrangement with the African, Caribbean and Pacific (ACP) countries in October 2009, and the removal of all duty and import restrictions on sugar imports from LDC countries under the Everything But Arms (EBA) initiative from 1 October 2009. In September 2002, the EU started negotiations on Economic Partnership Agreements (EPAs) with the 77 ACP countries to replace the Cotonou Agreement which expired in 2007. Although these negotiations are still continuing, the EPAs will eventually extend quota and duty free access to all ACP countries from 2015. This will allow additional quantities of sugar to enter the EU (see Figure 7.11). The projections assume the EU preferential imports under these various arrangements will increase over the period to 2017-18 to a level of 3.1 mt and this along with other imports will be an integral part of the exercise to balance the internal market given the planned reductions in quota production by 6 mt.

As noted previously, the reduction in EU quota production and beet areas for sugar production is almost a certainty under the existing reform arrangements (see Box 7.1). On the import side, however, the situation is far less certain. Given the expected growth in consumption in the sugar producing LDC and ACP developing countries, as well as developments underway in terms of known investments in sugar production capacity and in alternative uses of sugar crops for such things as ethanol production, the question arises as to whether these countries will have the sugar available to satisfy the EU's growing import requirements in coming years to ensure a stable internal market with lower market prices.

Figure 7.11. **Preferential imports to increase in the EU**

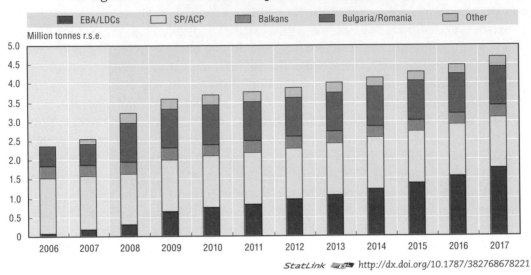

StatLink http://dx.doi.org/10.1787/382768678221

Source: OECD and FAO Secretariats.

For instance, governments in some of the most important African sugar producing and consuming countries have signed regional agreements to encourage trade amongst themselves and to exploit existing synergies. These free trade agreements (FTA) include commitments to deregulate the domestic sugar industries to ensure common trade policies and prices. In many cases, sugar was considered as a sensitive product and was allowed a waiver period before it would be subject to unrestricted trade. When these waivers come to end, and further integration of the sugar market is realised, it is expected that low cost producers will benefit from increased access to regional markets. This implies that low cost LDCs may face changing relative sugar export prices and may end up redirecting some or all of their EU destined sugar under the EBA initiative to more attractive regional markets. The extent to which volumes are diverted away from the EU and world markets is another uncertainty for the *Outlook*. What happens when not enough sugar is supplied under preferential imports to meet EU requirements, which will likely be highly price-insensitive? Normally the EU could turn to the world market to meet its additional needs in these circumstances. However, in periods of high world prices, this action may push world prices even higher and discourage additional preferential imports. Should supplies from EBA and former ACP countries prove to be highly variable from one year to the next, or increase less strongly than expected, this situation will add to the problems of achieving internal balance in the EU sugar market and, in turn, possibly generate more price volatility on world markets as other third-party sugar supplies are sought out.

Sugar versus ethanol in the developing countries

The results of the projections indicate that developing countries – outside Brazil – will divert close to 2.5% of world sugarcane area to ethanol production by 2017-18, up from 0.9%

OECD-FAO AGRICULTURAL OUTLOOK 2008-2017 – ISBN 978-92-64-04590-3 – © OECD/FAO 2008

in 2005-07. As a result, they will account for about 8.2% of global sugarcane-based ethanol production by 2017-18, compared to an average of 5.1% in 2005-07 (Figure 7.12). These projections reflect a conditional scenario based on a set of assumptions, including macroeconomic prospects, technological change, and trade policy. For instance, substitution of sugarcane for ethanol production rather than for sugar depends on the relative market returns of sugar *versus* ethanol. Also, the prospect of higher cane-based ethanol production suggests an increase in the degree of market flexibility for sugar producers in the developing countries. However, the degree to which producers make the necessary investment to diversify into the much larger energy market and take advantage of the growing demand for biofuel is still uncertain. This raises an important question for the *Outlook*: What would be the impacts on sugar market outcomes and prices if changes to the underlying assumptions implied an increase in cane-based ethanol production at the expense of sugar?

Figure 7.12. **Share of developing countries[a] in world sugarcane area devoted to ethanol**

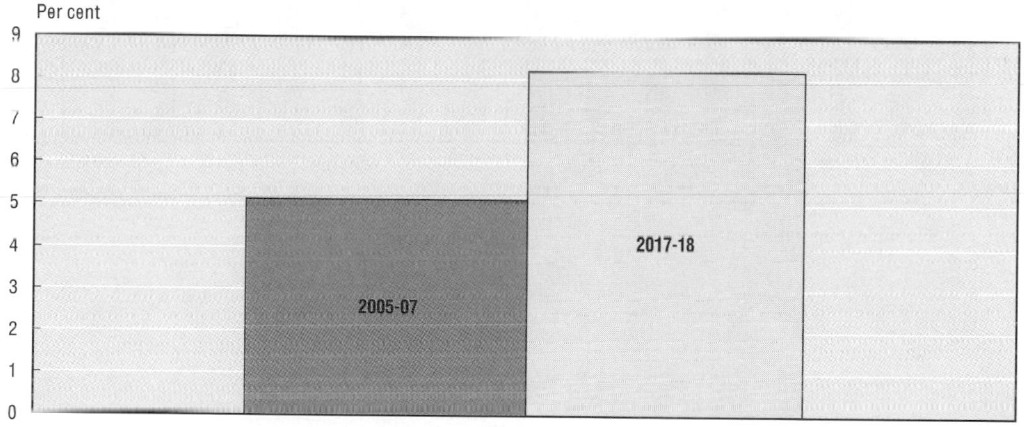

a) Brazil is not included.
Source: OECD and FAO Secretariats.

StatLink ⬛⬛⬛ http://dx.doi.org/10.1787/382811574725

The US price support system to come under increasing pressure

From 1 January 2008 all remaining restrictions on trade in sugar between Mexico and the United States were eliminated in conformity with NAFTA and the region became effectively a single market for sugar. As a consequence, sugar exports to the US from Mexico, together with those from third countries at the minimum access level of the WTO tariff quota and FTAs, rise to 3.3 mt by 2017-18. At this level, imports exceed the import volume trigger for suspending the marketing allotments program of the 2002 FSRI Act. Consequently, purchases by the Commodity Credit Corporation (CCC) of USDA are expected to be required in each projection year to 2017-18 to defend the US loan rate sugar price support system with domestic prices effectively driven down to minimum loan rate levels. The volume of these purchases will depend to some extent also on the volume of HFCS that is shipped to Mexico from the United States. These are projected to rise in the first three years of the *Outlook* period and then level off in following years. Should the imports of HFCS by Mexico continue to increase strongly beyond the near term, this will release additional Mexican sugar for export and add to US sugar programme costs. The US Administration has indicated it will take all steps necessary to minimise these programme costs. This might include the re-activation of the Payment in Kind (PIK) scheme which was last used in 2001 to dispose of unwanted CCC sugar stocks. Without some programme changes, however, the long-term sustainability of the existing US sugar price support system that provides a (high) floor price to the US, and the entire US-Mexico market after 2008, becomes questionable.

Figure 7.13. **US rising sugar imports, CCC stocks and HFCS exports**

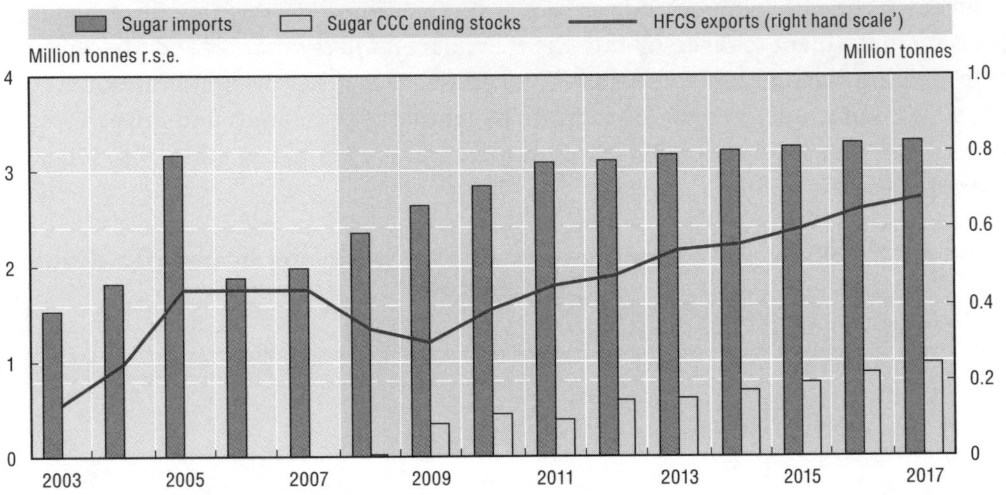

StatLink 🔗 http://dx.doi.org/10.1787/382826505088

Source: OECD and FAO Secretariats.

OECD-FAO AGRICULTURAL OUTLOOK 2008-2017 – ISBN 978-92-64-04590-3 – © OECD/FAO 2008

ISBN 978-92-64-04590-3
OECD-FAO AGRICULTURAL OUTLOOK 2008-2017
© OECD/FAO 2008

Chapter 8

Meat

World market trends and prospects

Key market drivers

In 2007, agricultural markets where characterised by unusually high prices: grain prices reached record highs, and prices for many dairy products were far above historic levels. Unlike these markets, most meat and livestock markets have not experienced comparable price hikes. This combination of high feed prices and relatively low meat prices has had an overall negative impact on profit margins of meat producers.

The lag in transmission of higher feed costs to increased livestock product prices can be partially explained by slow adjustment of production to changes in costs and the typical cyclical movement of prices for some types of livestock. For instance, pork markets in large producing countries such as the US, Canada and the European Union have been characterised by high levels of production and a concomitant cyclical decline in hog prices. In combination with other factors, such as a rapid currency appreciation, this has impeded increased input costs from being reflected in product prices. In addition to livestock prices lagging cost increases, production incentives for land-intensive livestock production, notably beef production, have been further reduced by the high relative profits that can currently be realised with crops and dairy products.

The relative profitability of the production of different types of meat is further affected by the availability of Distiller Dried Grains (DDGs) and other non-grain feeds (Box 8.1). DDGs are particularly apt for feeding ruminants and are available in large quantities as a by-product of ethanol production in the US. In this country, DDGs offset to some extent the impact of high cereals and oilseeds prices on production costs for beef, but only to a lower degree on those for pork and poultry. Also beef producers in the United States have an advantage over producers in countries like Canada, where DDGs supply is not expected to be abundant and cattle is finished on traditional feed rations.

Countries in which cattle is traditionally raised on grass and this grassland is not converted to arable land for legal, ecologic or economic reasons, can be expected to experience an increase in their relative competitiveness. Through continuing investment, education, improved transportation and other infrastructure improvements, as well as improved production technologies, production of meat and meat products has rapidly increased in many developing countries in recent years. As a result, some of them have been able to increase substantially their role in international meat markets. Brazil is an example of a country that has been successful in establishing itself as the largest meat exporter in a short time: from covering only 10% of world exports in 2000, it has achieved more than 30% in 2007. Given abundant land resources, capital and technology alongside with policy reforms in developed countries that decrease the incentive to produce meat, this trend is expected to continue at the cost of traditional meat exporters like the European Union.

Meat consumption will continue to be impacted by economic growth in large parts of the world and notably in emerging and developing countries. Higher incomes and

---

Box 8.1. **Distillers Grains**

Destillers Grains, often with solubles and in dried form (DDGs), represent an important by-product of grain-based ethanol production. The conversion process of cereals to ethanol only uses the starch, which in the case of corn accounts for 70% of the corn kernel. The other 30% of the kernel that include mainly protein, fat, minerals, and vitamins are used to produce DDGs, a valuable feed for livestock with high energy content. This feed can be used especially in the feed ratio of ruminants, and to a certain degree for non-ruminants as a substitute for grains and oil meal. DDGs became an important feedstuff in the recent years particularly in the US, the largest producer of grain-based ethanol and hence DDGs, but are increasingly relevant in other markets as well, including Canada and the EU.

However, given the size of the grain-based ethanol industry in the US relative to that of other countries, the US is projected to remain the largest producer of DDGs. Over the projection period, the production of DDGs is set to more than double in the US, reaching a level of over 41 mt in 2017, while the production quantities in the EU and in Canada reach levels around 8.5 mt and 2 mt, respectively, in 2017. These figures compare to cereal feed use quantities in the same year of 169 mt, 168 mt and 23 mt, respectively, in these countries, indicating the importance of taking into account properly this emerging feed stuff in the projections.

Based on research undertaken in the US, this *Outlook* assumes that 90% of the DDGs feed use is in the ruminant sector with the rest fed to non-ruminants (meat quality problems put limits on the share of DDGs in the feed ratios particularly for pig meat). While in the ruminant sector it is assumed that a unit of DDGs replaces 0.94 unit of coarse grains, but only 0.06 unit of oilseed meal, this ratio decreases to 0.70 to 0.30 unit in the non-ruminant sector. In consequence, 92% of the available DDGs substitute for coarse grains in the average feed ratios, and 8% for oil meal. In the US, the DDGs replace about 8% of the coarse grains in the feed ratio and 3% of oil meal already in the base period. These shares are projected to rise considerably to 17% and 7% respectively following the strong increase in US Ethanol production over the projection period. Given the smaller production levels of grain-based ethanol, DDGs shares in Canada and the EU remain significantly smaller but are increasing as well.

---

increased purchasing power in these countries will lead to staple foods of vegetable origin to be replaced by proteins of animal origin. With continued economic growth, protein demand in developing countries will increase especially for low priced foods such as poultry and eggs.

But consumer preferences are also changing in many developed countries. Demand for low calorie food products and changes in lifestyles which reduce the time consumers wish to spend on food preparation have been manifest in the past; and this is assumed to continue. Again, it is mainly poultry meat that complies with increased consumer demands for lean meat and ease of preparation.

Recent events, such as the import ban that the EU had temporarily posed on Brazilian beef following concerns on product safety, reveal that animal diseases are still an important driving force on world meat markets. Because of the highly unpredictable nature of animal disease incidents, this *Outlook* abstracts from any new animal disease outbreaks over the projection period. On the other hand, the animal disease induced segmentation of meat markets is assumed to continue.

Main market developments

Meat prices to evolve significantly

Given rising feed costs and strong meat demand in certain developing countries and emerging economies, meat prices are expected to rise above historic levels in the medium term. Non-ruminant production is particularly affected by high cereals and oilseeds prices as low-priced DDGs cannot easily be integrated into the feed ration. These higher input costs are expected to result in increased meat prices over the medium term.

Reflecting higher feed costs, but also sector adjustment and the ability of producers to pass part of the higher input cost on to consumers in the medium term, pork prices are expected to continue to exhibit cyclical movements but on higher average levels than in the past. Over the *Outlook* period, pork prices are expected to remain on average some 24% above the average of the last decade. In the short term, however, world pork prices are expected to remain low due to large hog supplies, widening the gap between the cost of producing pork and the price that producers receive for a finished pig.

Figure 8.1. **World prices for meat to strengthen**

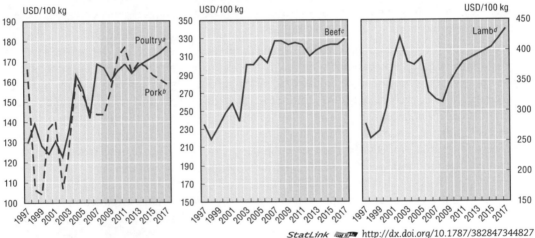

StatLink http://dx.doi.org/10.1787/382847344827

a) Wholesale weighted average broiler price, ready to cook, 12 cities, US.
b) Barrows and gilts, No. 1-3 Iowa/South Minnesota, US dress weight.
c) Choice steers, US, dress weight Nebraska.
d) New Zealand lamb schedule price all grade average, dressed weight.
Source: OECD and FAO Secretariats.

Feed costs also account for a large part of total cost of production for poultry. But when compared to production of pigmeat, the production cycle of poultry is relatively short and producers can react to changes in input costs and prices in a rather flexible manner. This became clear when prices rose from about 1.40 USD/kg in 2006 to almost 1.70 USD/kg in 2007. Over the projection period, poultry prices are expected to stay on high levels, averaging almost 20% above the average of the previous decade.

The share of feed grain in the total production costs of cattle is less than in the abovementioned non-ruminant meat production. In addition, DDGs can be used to substitute part of the protein in the feed ration for ruminants, offsetting some of the cost increase in other feedstuff. Nevertheless, cattle prices are also expected to be affected by higher feed costs. Additionally, low cattle inventories in the US, due to drought in recent years, hold up the beef price in the beginning of the projection period. The world beef price

OECD-FAO AGRICULTURAL OUTLOOK 2008-2017 – ISBN 978-92-64-04590-3 – © OECD/FAO 2008

over the projection period is estimated to average just under 18% above levels during the previous decade. The average beef price over the projection period remains approximately 3% higher than on average over 2005-07.

After some years of downward movement, world lamb prices dropped further in 2007. This effect can be explained by unusually high slaughter rates induced by lack of feed as a consequence of severe drought in Australia and New Zealand. However, strong international demand for lamb is expected to meet tight supplies, as sheep producers are expected to rebuild flock numbers and reduce slaughter. As this strong demand is expected to outpace production, recovery of lamb prices is anticipated for the next decade.

Despite high feed costs, world meat production continues to grow

Despite high feed costs and competition for land resources, world meat production is projected to grow over the *Outlook* period, though at slower pace than in the past decade. There was slow growth in world meat production from 2006 to 2007, mainly caused by a drop in Chinese pork production where the sector was much affected by massive pig slaughter following an outbreak of Porcine Reproductive and Respiratory Disease Syndrome (PRRS) and high feed prices. But global meat production resumes its growing trend again over the *Outlook* with an average growth rate of almost 2% per annum.

Figure 8.2. **Continued expansion in world meat production**

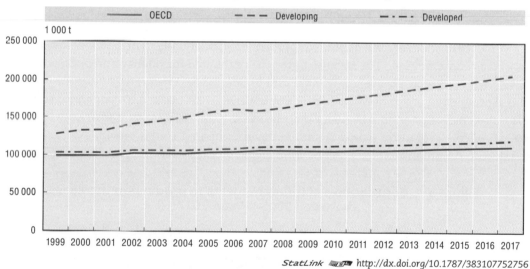

Source: OECD and FAO Secretariats.

StatLink http://dx.doi.org/10.1787/383107752756

Growth in meat production is unequally distributed across regions. While meat production in OECD countries is only projected to grow by less than 1% per annum, regions dominated by developing countries such as Africa, Latin America, the Caribbean and Asia and the Pacific are expected grow at rates between 20% and over 30% between the 2005-07 base period and 2017. As a result, the share of meat produced in developing countries will reach 63% of total meat produced around the globe. This picture is dominated by large, fast growing developing countries like Brazil, Argentina and China. Russia's meat production is also expected to grow by over 50% compared to the base period, followed by Brazil and Argentina with over 30%, and China with almost 30% growth when comparing 2017 to the base period.

Some of the gains will come from non-traditional meat-supplying areas of the world such as the Commonwealth of Independent States (CIS) or Sub Saharan Africa, which will account respectively for 6% and 3% of the increase in world meat production. However, as a whole, the rate of growth will be lower over the next decade compared with the previous one.

Figure 8.3. **Regional distribution of meat production increases between 2005-07 and 2017**

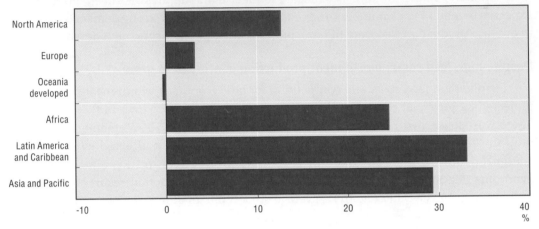

StatLink ⬛🖳 http://dx.doi.org/10.1787/383124858018

Source: OECD and FAO Secretariats.

The positive development of meat production is unequally distributed across regions as well as commodities.. The strongest growth is exhibited for poultry and pork, which are projected to grow at an average annual rate of nearly 2%. The growth rates for beef and sheep production are projected to be slightly lower, but still above 1.6% per annum over the projection period. It should be noted that the average annual growth rate of non-ruminant meat over the projection period is slowed down compared to the previous decade, while meat from ruminants exhibits higher annual growth rates as in the previous decade.

Figure 8.4. **Contribution of different meats to production increases between 2005-07 and 2017**

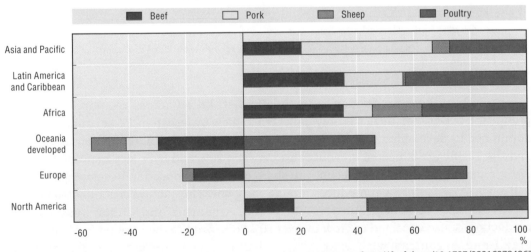

StatLink ⬛🖳 http://dx.doi.org/10.1787/383162784367

Source: OECD and FAO Secretariats.

OECD-FAO AGRICULTURAL OUTLOOK 2008-2017 – ISBN 978-92-64-04590-3 – © OECD/FAO 2008

Nevertheless, in Europe and North America, growth in poultry production accounts for around 50% of the production increase. In Australia and New Zealand, the structural change in the industry is even more noteworthy. In this region, production of all types of meat except poultry is lower in 2017 that it was on average over 2005-07.

The ranking changes when only the Asia and Pacific region is of interest. Then, pork has the highest share in additional meat production, followed by poultry, beef and sheep. It should be noted however, that this picture is dominated by China, where pork is traditionally the most important meat. In other developing regions like Latin America and Africa production will mirror consumption trends which favour poultry as the preferred meat.

Unequal development of consumption gains across countries and products

Fuelled by economic growth and changing dietary patterns, consumption of meat is projected to grow both in developed and developing countries in spite of higher projected meat prices over the next decade. The projected development of meat consumption differs significantly both in quantitative and qualitative terms between developed and developing countries.

In developed countries, the per capita consumption of meat is expected to grow only moderately from a little more than 64 kg in the base period to almost 70 kg in 2017. This increase in meat consumption is largely due to higher poultry consumption, which increases by more than 13% from the average of 2005-07 to 2017. Per capita intake of beef and pork remains rather stable over the Outlook period, while sheep meat consumption declines.

In developing countries, meat consumption growth is much more pronounced than in developed countries. Compared to the average of 2005-07, per capita meat consumption for this group of countries is expected to increase by almost 13% from 24 kg to more than 27 kg in 2017. For the reasons explained above, poultry accounts for the largest part of additional consumption.

Figure 8.5. **Composition of per capita meat consumption in 2017 compared to 2005-07**

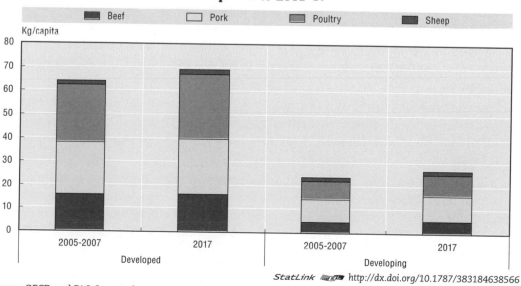

StatLink http://dx.doi.org/10.1787/383184638566

Source: OECD and FAO Secretariats.

Further analysis of the development of consumption at more disaggregated regional level also reveals variation in consumption trends across regions. In North America, almost three quarters of the consumption gains between the base period and 2017 originate from increased poultry consumption. In Europe, the consumption gains are almost equally distributed among poultry and pork, with sheep meat consumption declining compared to the base period. In the developed countries of Oceania, sheep meat consumption is expected to decline significantly, with poultry and beef dominating the overall growth in meat consumption.

Figure 8.6. **Shares of different meat types in growth of consumption**

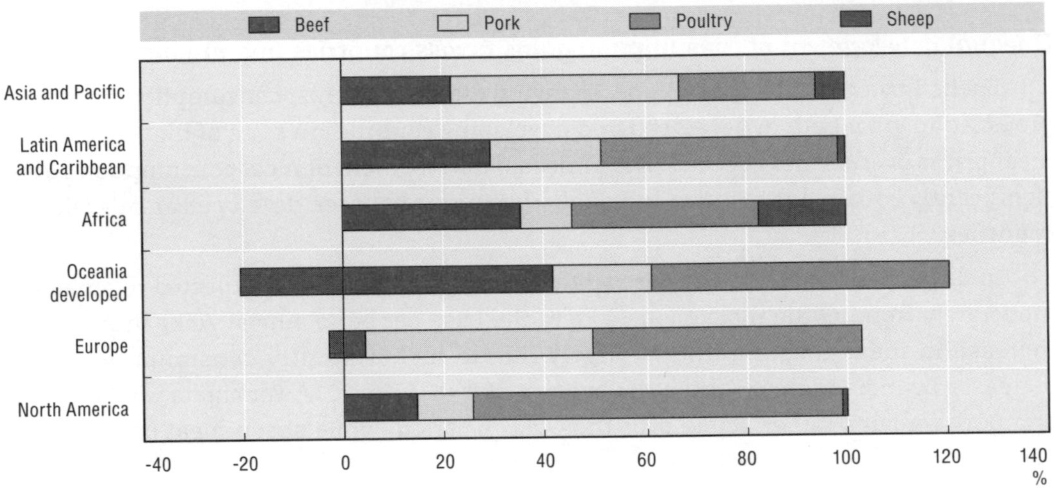

StatLink http://dx.doi.org/10.1787/383227245574

Source: OECD and FAO Secretariats.

In regions with more developing countries, consumption of all types of meat increases. In the case of Africa, growth is predominantly recorded for poultry and beef. In the Asia and Pacific region, it is pork meat that dominates the increase in consumption. Again, it should be noted that in this region, the largest market is China, where pork is traditionally the most important meat in the diet. In countries other than China in the Asia and Pacific region, poultry is the meat type that is expected to account for most of the additional meat consumption. The same holds true for Latin America, where additional consumption of poultry accounts for almost half of the additional meat consumption.

For the poorest countries in the world, the Least Developed Countries, the outlook for the availability of animal protein is not so bright. Despite firm income growth, simultaneous population growth leads to a nearly stable per capita consumption of meat.

Last, but not the least, another important source of protein intake comes from eggs, consumption of which rises in all developing regions of the world. With rising incomes, the demand for animal protein increases, and the efficient conversion of feed into eggs stimulates its consumption. In addition, as consumption of eggs grows, so does that of poultry meat in the form of slaughtered laying hens.

OECD-FAO AGRICULTURAL OUTLOOK 2008-2017 – ISBN 978-92-64-04590-3 – © OECD/FAO 2008

Figure 8.7. **Egg consumption in selected regions**

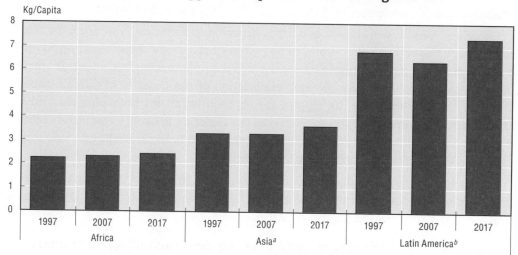

a) Excluding China.
b) Excluding Argentina and Brazil.

Source: OECD and FAO Secretariats.

StatLink ⬛⬛ http://dx.doi.org/10.1787/383281235288

Further growth in world meat trade

World meat trade is expected to continue to grow along the established increasing trend. From 21.9 m tonnes on average in 2005-07, it is projected to increase to 29.4 m tonnes in 2017. Apart from general sector development in some countries, policy changes and reopening of markets after animal disease-induced trade bans are some of the driving factors behind this development.

This growth in trade, however, is unevenly distributed across countries. Brazil and the US are expected to continue expanding their share in world meat exports, which, for the two countries taken together, is expected to increase from 47% in the 2005-07 base period to 57% in 2017. One of the reasons behind the growth in exports from Brazil is the fact that the European Union beef production is continuously declining, while consumption remains rather stable. The increasing gap is filled with imports mainly from Mercosur countries, and especially from Brazil, whose low production costs allow the import of significant quantities at full levy into the EU. With increasing demand and decreasing beef exports from the EU that traditionally supplied Russian markets, Russia has also become an important destination for beef from Brazil in recent years. Unlike many other exporting countries, Brazilian beef is nearly exclusively grass-fed. In a context of high feed grain prices, this could make Brazilian beef more competitive on international markets compared to grain-fed beef where consumers do not have a strong preference for the latter type of beef. In the case of the US, the export growth can partially be attributed to the progressively lifted trade bans that were put in place after the discovery of several cases of Bovine Spongiform Encephalopathy (BSE) in North America in 2003.

As a consequence of reduced beef production and exports, the share of meat exports from the EU in world meat trade is expected to further decrease. While the EU accounted for almost 11% on average of world meat exports over the years 2005-07, they are expected to lose market shares and cover less than 6% in 2017. Argentina has seen some rapid development of exports in the first half of this decade, but export restrictions have impeded the meat export sector from growing in recent years. The continuation of these policies and relatively stable beef production support this trend in the near future, until strongly increasing pork exports contribute towards trade volumes in the second half of the projection period.

Canada's share in world meat exports is expected to decrease from around 8% in the base period to under 6% in 2017. Continuing high feed prices, the expected continuation of the strong currency and increasing labour costs in the meat packaging industry contribute to this development. Moreover, the implementation of the Country of Origins Labelling (COOL)* by the United States, its biggest export destination for both pigmeat and beef, should result in a drop in slaughter volumes as the situation is likely to promote exports of live piglets for finishing in the US. The same logic should hold for beef and cattle exports that should shift in favour of exporting feeder cattle.

The export share of developing countries excluding Brazil and Argentina is expected to fall, despite an increase in meat exports from these countries from 5.7 million tonnes on average in 2005-07 to around 10.5 mt in 2017.

Figure 8.8. **Development of world meat exports (excluding live animals)**

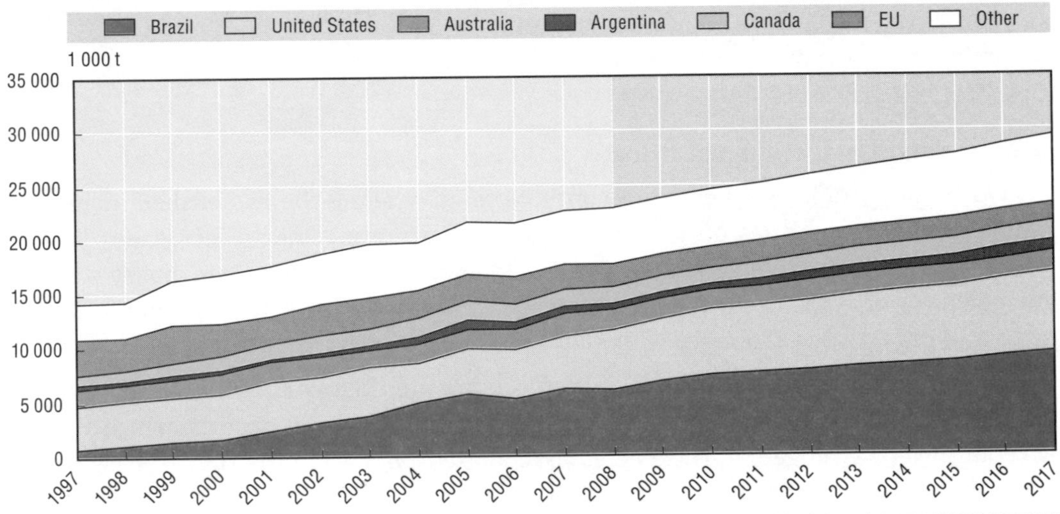

StatLink ⟶ http://dx.doi.org/10.1787/383313778118

Source: OECD and FAO Secretariats.

Russia projected to remain the leading net importer of meat over the Outlook period

Russia is set to remain the leading net meat importing country, though Russian meat imports remain rather stable over the projection period. Pork, beef and poultry imports into Russia are all constrained by tariff-rate quotas. For poultry the slightly expanded tariff-rate quota is expected to be binding. The tariff rate quotas for beef and pork have been overfilled in the past years, and a relatively stable degree quota overfill is also projected for the future. This limited import growth is explained as increasing demand for meats goes in parallel with expanded production.

As a result of decreasing population that offsets the effect of stable or declining domestic meat production, Japan's net imports of meat are expected to increase only moderately by around 5% comparing 2017 to the base period.

* The proposed rule would require that retailers specify the country of origin of perishable products including red meats. For the meat industry, this may imply the separation of meats of different origin during the production process, and therefore an additional cost. This in turn would give an incentive to purchase animals risen in the US instead of meat from Canada.

OECD-FAO AGRICULTURAL OUTLOOK 2008-2017 – ISBN 978-92-64-04590-3 – © OECD/FAO 2008

Korea is expected to significantly increase its position as a net importer of meat. Net meat imports are expected to roughly double from 584 kt on the 2005-07 average to 1.17 mt in 2017. For Korea, the net imports of both beef and pork more than double compared to the base period, while net imports of poultry increase by around 40% from the base period to 2017.

With growing population and rising income, growth of demand for meat outpaces production gains in Mexico. Meat imports are projected to increase by roughly 50% comparing the 2017 figure to the 2005-07 average. With over 640 kt in 2017, poultry remains the meat for which Mexico's net trade position is the weakest.

Figure 8.9. **Major meat net importing countries**

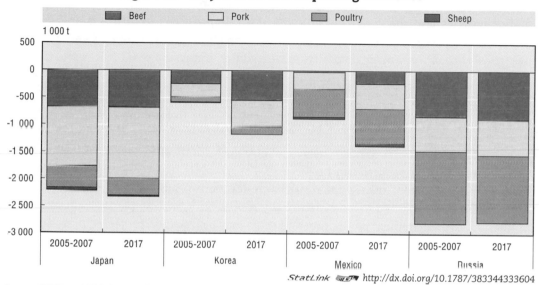

Source: OECD and FAO Secretariats.

StatLink ⟨⟨⟨ http://dx.doi.org/10.1787/383344333604

Despite favourable economic conditions, the import dependency of the Least Developed Countries will continuously increase over the Outlook period to reach more than 12% of total consumption.

Figure 8.10. **LDCs lose ground in trade for meat products**

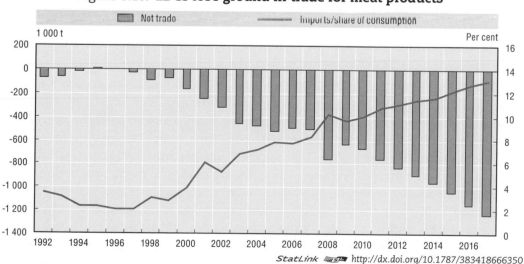

StatLink ⟨⟨⟨ http://dx.doi.org/10.1787/383418666350

Source: OECD and FAO Secretariats.

Key issues and uncertainties

Exchange rate developments, the continuation of current biofuel policies, weather conditions and the animal health situation are all factors that will condition the situation over this *Outlook* period. An unfavourable development of the Brazilian real could narrow the comparative advantage of the largest player on international meat markets. Outbreaks of animal diseases like Foot and Mouth disease, Blue Tongue or Avian Influenza could at any time occur and lead to unexpected developments on international meat markets. The continuation of support policies for biofuels and weather conditions will determine the availability and of grains and oilseeds for animal feeding.

The substitution of dairy farming or crop production is a very recent phenomenon in many countries and the extent to which this will happen in the future is still unclear. Substitution between these activities over the *Outlook* horizon will depend very much on the persistence of the current disparity between dairy, grains and meat prices and the cost of adaption to new production technologies that producers face, as well as agro-environmental legislation.

High food prices represent a challenge, especially for developing countries. In some cases, governments responded to the food price escalation by restricting exports of feedstuff or meat in order to raise the availability in the domestic market. In the long run, the effect of these measures can be adverse. For example, the measures the Argentine Government has taken to keep meat prices under control has reduced the incentive to produce beef; this resulted in land historically reserved for pasture being diverted to crop production. Growth in meat production and trade may be less than projected in this *Outlook* if more countries introduce such trade restricting measures in the future.

Trade policies will continue to play an important role on meat markets in the future. The end of the Russian ban on meat imports from Poland can be assumed to trigger additional export opportunities for Polish meat producers. In the case that the Russian Federation joins the WTO, changes in its overall trade policies and consequently international meat trade patterns can be expected. The conclusion of the US-Korea Free Trade Agreement is expected to provide significant export opportunities for US meat exporters. Last but not least, a conclusion of the Doha Round of multilateral trade negotiation would bring about increased market access, thereby fostering international meat trade. Sanitary requirements, however, will ultimately determine whether any increase in market access can *de facto* be used or not. The evolution of reciprocal sanitary agreements, therefore, along with tariff reduction, will play a crucial role in shaping world meat trade through this *Outlook* period.

The development of Chinese agricultural and trade policies presents a major uncertainty. During the sharp drop in pork production in 2007 caused by PRSS, pork imports to China were not sufficient to keep prices down. This can partly be explained by strict sanitary requirements for pork imports into China, which deterred many countries from exporting to this destination. Chinese meat imports have been growing, but at the same time, the Chinese Government is boosting domestic meat production. It has announced significant investment in mass immunisation and insurance schemes for pigs, in an effort to improve the production incentives. Today, it remains to be seen if these measures will be sufficient to satisfy the increasing demand for meat through increased domestic production, or whether China will become a more significant meat importer in the future.

The impact of meat production on the environment should not be ignored. Currently the livestock sector rates among the three most significant contributors to environmental problems, such as land degradation, climate change, air pollution, water shortage and pollution as well as loss of biodiversity. The growth in competitive livestock production that could help to supply developing countries' increased demand for meat can only be achieved with improved technical efficiency. This requires proper animal husbandry: feeding, housing, health and breeding practices. Processing and adding value to animal products will increase the returns to the producer and help in providing a safe product for the consumer. In order to allow for growth of the meat sector, especially in developing countries, government actions are required to improve access to credit, inputs and latest production technology. Education, improved transportation and infrastructure should be developed to connect developing countries agriculture to the domestic and international markets.

ISBN 978-92-64-04590-3
OECD-FAO AGRICULTURAL OUTLOOK 2008-2017
© OECD/FAO 2008

Chapter 9

Dairy

World market trends and prospects

Key market drivers

In recent editions of this report, the key driving forces identified as conditioning the medium-term evolution of the global dairy industry have been strong demand growth, largely in developing countries, within the context of restrained supply from traditional OECD exporters. The main drivers on the demand side in developing countries are a sustained growth in population, a rapid pace of urbanisation, and higher per capita income growth than has been experienced in decades. Consumption of milk and dairy products varies vastly by country/culture, but is rising nearly everywhere, exhibiting the highest growth rates among agricultural food commodities. Supplies from traditional OECD exporters have slowed, either due to supply constraints and/or policy reforms that have reduced production and export incentives. These fundamental factors remain the same in the projections provided in this *Outlook*.

New, and more spectacular in this projection, is the major issue of how the global dairy industry will react to the unprecedented price spike experienced in 2007. This spike was already on top of the historically high nominal prices of 2005 and 2006, and has led many to consider that the dairy industry has entered a new "world", where international markets have suddenly become profitable, and not simply a dumping ground for excess supplies, as it had a reputation for in the past. High international prices of dairy products have sent strong signals for supply response from both traditional and emerging exporters. More importantly, they have also filtered through into developing countries, creating incentives for investment, expansion and restructuring in net importing countries, and challenging the interface of formal and informal markets. Such price incentives may encourage technology as a factor to reshape the industries of these countries, creating supply potential that will enable future production growth and improved domestic marketing linkages, positioning these countries in a stronger competitive position in their local markets.

The supply response to higher prices must also face the fact of higher costs induced by both higher feed and higher energy prices. These affect production, processing and distribution of milk products, and will encourage the competitiveness of pasture based systems. They also will affect trade, as higher transportation costs put local production at greater advantage. In addition to these market forces, dairy policies will continue to have a critical impact on the evolution of world dairy markets. These policies include high tariffs and tariff quotas which restrain import demand. They also include continuation of supply management arrangements in the European Union, but also in Canada, Japan and Norway. But conditioning policies are not confined to OECD countries. Some key emerging suppliers, such as Argentina, apply export taxes, other policies include variable tariff regimes, and fixed producer or consumer prices. The current policies are assumed to continue over the *Outlook*, conditioning domestic responses to international market developments.

Main market developments

World dairy prices fall after a spectacular increase, but remain firm over the entire Outlook period

International dairy prices increased spectacularly in 2007, recording particularly strong gains in the first half of the year. On a year over year basis, world butter prices increased by 66%, cheese prices by 50% while those for milk powders soared by more than 90%. The end of forward fixed-price contracts in the summer obliged buyers to purchase at much higher prices which resulted in an equally spectacular jump in retail prices, putting dairy in the headlines around the world.

This tight situation on the market is linked to continuing solid demand for dairy products in important dairy markets such as the European Union, the United States, Russia, Mexico, North Africa, the Middle East and also in rapidly growing economies of the Pacific Rim where an expanding middle class population is consuming more sophisticated processed foods. On the other hand, milk production has declined in Australia, Argentina and the EU and was hindered elsewhere by rapidly increasing production costs – rising oil and feed prices. The situation has been to some extent aggravated by policy decisions in certain countries to tax or ban exports. Speculation in the face of extremely low global dairy stock levels has also contributed to the sharp climb in prices. Moreover, stronger currencies vis-à-vis the US dollar mitigated the producer price gains in local currencies while at the same time facilitated higher demand by importers, thus driving world price higher in USD terms.

During the price spike, prices of skim milk powder were the first to shoot up reflecting the largely residual function of SMP in the dairy product processing system. Prices of WMP followed suit with some delay, and those of butter and cheese tagged along yet later. In September 2007, prices started to ease, particularly for powders (mainly SMP and whey powders) as food manufacturers looked for cheaper substitutes. Demand also started to abate as higher prices filtered through to consumers. World butter and cheese prices are however expected to stay firm in 2008, keeping the long term relative dairy product value ratios in line.

All dairy prices are expected to weaken somewhat over the next two years as supply, with some lag, reacts to the strong price incentives. While prices are anticipated to decline from current high levels, it is expected that they will remain firm over the entire Outlook and stay at about 100-150 USD per100kg, or 65% to 75%, higher compared to the previous decade (Figure 9.1). In real price terms, the well-established longer term declining trend was reversed radically last year. Over the Outlook, the prices in real terms are expected to resume a modest declining trend, albeit from a much higher level than in the past: over the next decade, dairy prices in real terms average 20% to 40% higher as compared to those of the last decade (Figure 9.2).

Milk production growth on trend over the Outlook

World milk production is expected to increase by 142 million tonnes between 2007 and 2017 with an average annual growth rate of 1.8%. The growth rate is marginally lower when compared to the period 1998-2007 (2% per annum) mainly due to slower milk production growth in China. Although the expansion in milk production in China is expected to slow down as a result of increasingly pervasive water and feed limitations,

Figure 9.1. **Prices to remain firm over the projection period**

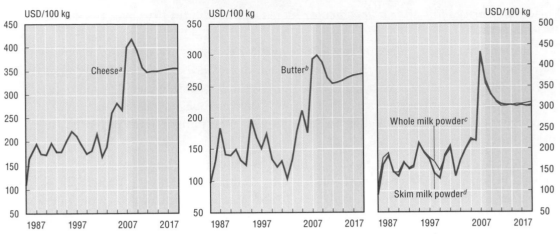

a) F.O.B. export price, cheddar cheese, 39% moisture, Oceania.
b) F.O.B. export price, butter 82% butterfat, Oceania.
c) F.O.B. export price, WMP 26%, Oceania.
d) F.O.B. export price, not fat dry milk, 1.25% butterfat, Oceania.

StatLink ᴍᴤ▶ http://dx.doi.org/10.1787/383428357736

Source: OECD and FAO Secretariats.

Figure 9.2. **Prices in real terms 20% to 40% above historical averages**

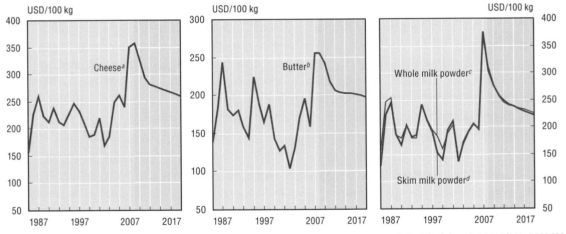

StatLink ᴍᴤ▶ http://dx.doi.org/10.1787/383473036301

a) F.O.B. export price, cheddar cheese, 39% moisture, Oceania, deflated by US GDP 2002 = 1.
b) F.O.B. export price, butter 82% butterfat, Oceania, deflated by US GDP 2002 = 1.
c) F.O.B. export price, WMP 26%, Oceania, deflated by US GDP 2002 = 1.
d) F.O.B. export price, not fat dry milk, 1.25% butterfat, Oceania, deflated by US GDP 2002 = 1.

Source: OECD and FAO Secretariats.

China is still expected to register the highest growth over the projection period – increasing milk output by more than 4% annually.

The overwhelming majority (82%) of additional milk will be produced outside the OECD area. China, India, Pakistan, Argentina and Brazil account for half of the global milk production gains. The rest of the additional milk (18%), produced in the OECD countries, comes mainly from Oceania and the US (12%).

The impacts of high milk prices partly offset by increased input costs

Milk producers are expected to see relatively high milk prices but they will also be confronted with higher input costs (land prices, feed, energy, replacement heifers) and increased opportunity costs to move into alternative productions; these latter pressures will vary considerably by country. Nevertheless, the *outlook* is for milk production to increase over the medium term, particularly over the next several years, as in net terms, profitability will be higher than in the past. Pasture based production systems are projected to grow more rapidly, while those depending on grain inputs will grow less. For many developing countries growth in milk production will exceed that of the recent past. This might not be the case for developed countries although the situation is country and region specific (Figure 9.3).

- *United States* – the trend of declining cow numbers, recently reversed, is going to continue over the *Outlook* but the production is expected to remain on trend despite higher costs as a lower average age of the dairy herds boosts yields. Production grows by nearly 1% annually – a growth covering more than 40% of additional milk production in the OECD area over the *Outlook*.

- *New Zealand* – production is projected to increase by 2.6% annually, a lower growth rate than seen in the 1990s despite strong international prices. This is mainly due to higher costs (land prices) and increased environmental concerns. While the New Zealand industry is becoming gradually more capital intensive with increased production costs, it nevertheless retains its dominant position on the global markets over the *Outlook*.

- *Australia* – after falling by more than 5% in one year, Australian milk production is expected to grow on average by 2.6% annually. Recent widespread rain brought more optimism about the dairy industry potential under strong international prices. The trend towards larger farms and increased efficiency is the main driver in the future.

- *European Union* – milk production in the EU has declined marginally in 2007 with deliveries staying below the quota level. A dry summer, increased costs and only slow transmission of high international prices to domestic milk producers (owing largely to contractual arrangements) are some of the reasons behind the weak production. Over the *Outlook* period, production is expected to largely (although not to the full extent) follow the milk reference quantities, increased in 2008 by 2%.

- *Argentina* – milk production is expected to grow by more than 3% and recover quickly from the recent 8% tumble linked to adverse weather conditions. The potential for even stronger expansion is hindered by government-imposed export taxes, and to some extent, by the high cereals and oilseeds profitability. As a result of fierce land competition farmers might be gradually moving to a more intensive dairy production system, focusing on improved genetics and nutrition.

- *India* – milk production in India is projected to grow 2.4% per annum and add a further 27 mt to India's large milk production base, further consolidating its position as the world's largest dairy industry. This growth is underpinned by strong domestic demand, fuelled by high income growth which will generate positive market conditions to sustain expansion. Increasingly, expansion will derive from milk cows as opposed to buffalo cows. Yield increases are expected to account for the majority of production gains, as improved management and technology adjustments continue over the *Outlook*.

Figure 9.3. **Milk production growth from 2005-07 to 2017**

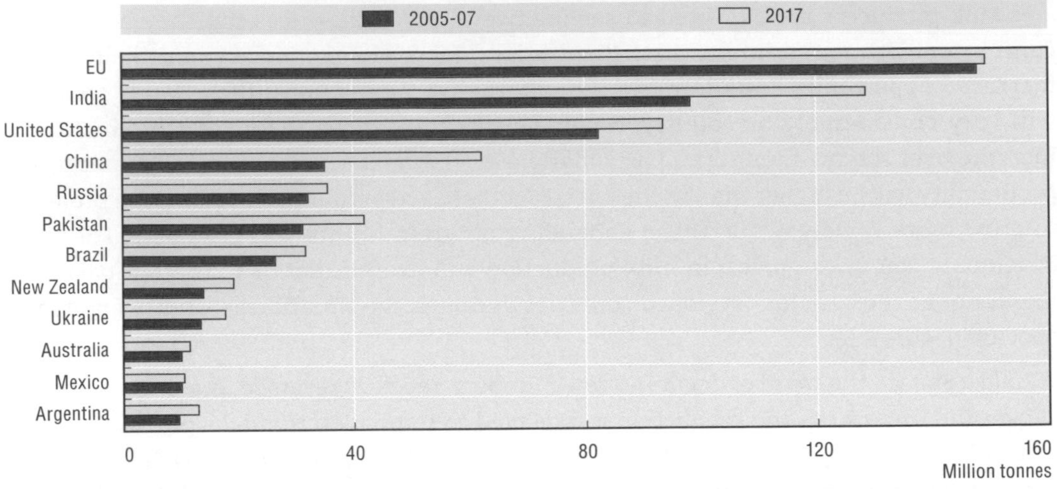

StatLink http://dx.doi.org/10.1787/383481571626

Source: OECD and FAO Secretariats.

Production gains are foreseen in other Latin American countries that are of a similar order as those in Argentina. For example, production in **Uruguay** is expected to grow by 3.7% annually over the *Outlook*. High prices also provide the incentive for stronger milk production growth in Africa (3.1% per annum). In Eastern Europe, **Ukraine's** production would grow just below 3% annually, providing the potential to increase the country's presence on world markets.

Production and trade to increase mainly for butter and WMP

Most of the additional milk production is expected to be processed into dairy products. In developing countries, however, fresh fluid milk and fluid milk products will retain by far its dominant share of domestic milk markets. World production of butter increases by 30% from the 2005-07 average level. More than three quarters of additional butter is expected from India with New Zealand adding an extra 5%.

The main driving force for whole milk powder production is its use for reconstitution in milk production deficit areas and in low-production seasons. Over the *Outlook* all the additional production of WMP – up 23% – is expected to come from developing countries as gains in Oceania are negated by reductions in Europe. China and Argentina account for 57% and 23% of extra WMP production respectively. SMP and cheese production is expected to grow by 19% and 18% respectively. The US deliver more than 40% of the additional global SMP production. More than half of the global gains in cheese production come from the EU (38%) and the US (19%).

World export markets will continue to be dominated by few major players

Despite the recent slowdown in trade growth, world exports are expected to increase for all products with cheese trade growing the fastest – by 36% over the projection period. Nevertheless, WMP remains the most important dairy product in international trade with nearly half of all WMP production traded.

Over the projection period developing countries and emerging economies are expected to increase their presence on global markets, but only very few are able to affect significantly the shares of traditional OECD exporters. Ukraine is expected to increase its presence on the export markets mainly for cheese while Argentina is emerging as a dominant player on the WMP market, more than doubling its exports over the projection period. Uruguay may also more than double its exports of all dairy products, albeit from a smaller base.

Exports of SMP from the US are expected to grow by 60% making the US the largest SMP exporter ahead of New Zealand, whose exports will increase by 40% from the 2005-07 period (Figure 9.4). EU exports of cheese remain relatively stable but those of WMP are expected to be reduced by a half, while butter and SMP exports attain only 20-30% of the level of the historic period-average used as a benchmark for this projection (Figure 9.5).

Figure 9.4. **United States overtake New Zealand in SMP exports**

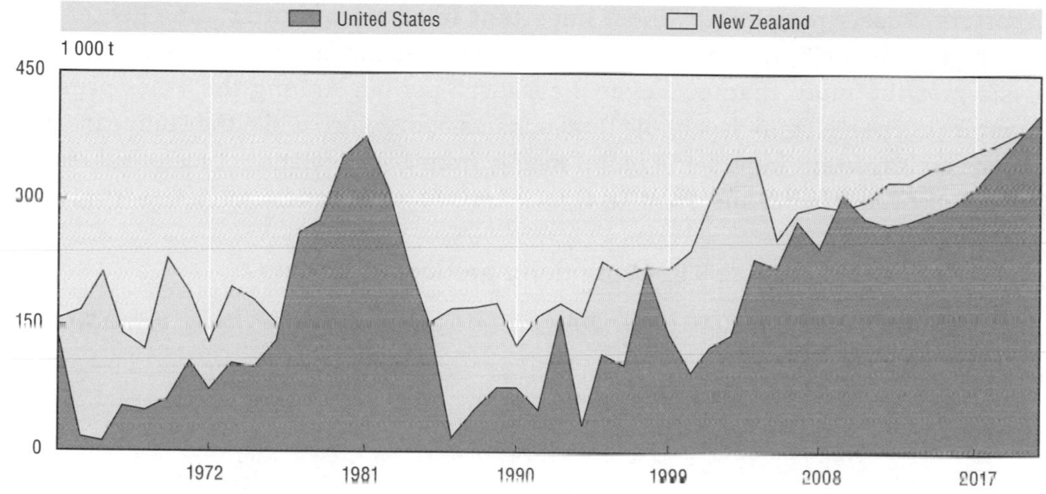

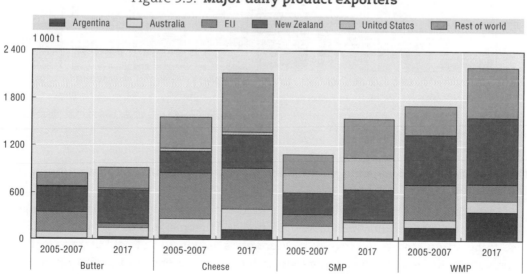

StatLink http://dx.doi.org/10.1787/383484/11445

Source: OECD and FAO Secretariats.

Figure 9.5. **Major dairy product exporters**

StatLink http://dx.doi.org/10.1787/383506811731

Source: OECD and FAO Secretariats.

Global imports to be sustained through solid demand mainly from Asia

Driven by milk reconstitution needs, global imports of skim milk powder and whole milk powder will grow by 3-3.5% annually over the medium term, and they will grow most in Asia. Growing employment opportunities for women in that region contribute to the higher demand for milk via baby food formulas. Currently, Asia imports 58% and 53% of global skim milk powder and whole milk powder trade respectively. These shares will grow to 60% and 58%.

Import markets will remain fragmented compared to those for exports. The six largest importers of dairy products cover only less than 50% of the world market. (Less than 30% for WMP) (Figure 9.6). Algeria, Saudi Arabia, Nigeria and China are among the most important WMP importers while Mexico, the Philippines and Malaysia are leading SMP importers. Russia remains the most important importer of butter and cheese. With consumption driven by increasing incomes, it is expected that imports of these products to Russia grow by more than 60% over the *Outlook* period. Among the other principal importers of cheese figure Japan, the United States and Mexico while the European Union remains an important importer of butter mainly from New Zealand for historical reasons and market access quota allocation.

Figure 9.6. **Major dairy product importers**

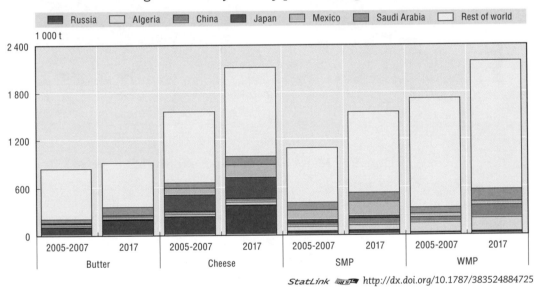

StatLink http://dx.doi.org/10.1787/383524884725

Source: OECD and FAO Secretariats.

Growing income and appetite for milk and dairy products drives consumption over the Outlook

Developing countries are the engine behind the global milk and dairy consumption gains. The main driver there remains population and income growth. However, demand is also to be stimulated by a range of new products, expansion of cold storage facilities, improved shelf life and product marketing, increasing presence of western retail chains and fast food catering. Consumption of dairy products in the area outside of OECD is expected to increase by 20-40% over the *Outlook*. The fastest growth in per capita consumption is expected in China where milk and dairy product consumption increases by 40-60%.

OECD-FAO AGRICULTURAL OUTLOOK 2008-2017 – ISBN 978-92-64-04590-3 – © OECD/FAO 2008

The consumption of dairy products in the OECD area should increase only modestly with the main drivers being nutrition and health concerns. The strongest growth is exhibited for fresh dairy products and cheeses. The popularity of the "*probiotic*" diet is boosting consumption of yoghurts and fermented milk drinks. Dairy products are increasingly enriched with vitamins, proteins and other health improving functionalities (*i.e.* combating high cholesterol levels, improving sleep). Cheese consumption is propelled mainly through cheese use as an ingredient in food products such as pizzas, hamburgers, sandwiches and ready-to-eat-meals, but also through increased variety of speciality cheeses and consumers' desire to try new products.

Consumption of dairy products remains affected by income profiles and product attributes

OECD countries continue to dominate cheese consumption and maintain their three quarter share of the world total while other countries consume more than 80% of global WMP consumption. OECD cheese consumption is expected to increase by 16% over the *Outlook* period while consumption for butter remains stable as a drop in the EU is compensated by increases in the US.

In countries outside the OECD area, demand growth is expected for all dairy products with butter consumption growing the strongest (48%), followed by WMP (43%) over the *Outlook* (Figure 9.7). Strong growth for butter comes primarily from increased demand for butter and ghee in India and a recovery in butter consumption in Russia. The growth in consumption remains region-specific and varies highly among products (Figure 9.8). In general, higher income growth, urbanisation, and the changing demographic pyramid are contributing to higher per capita demand for value added dairy products. Dairy products remain among the agricultural commodities for which production and consumption exhibit the highest growth rates.

Figure 9.7. **Outlook for global dairy product consumption**

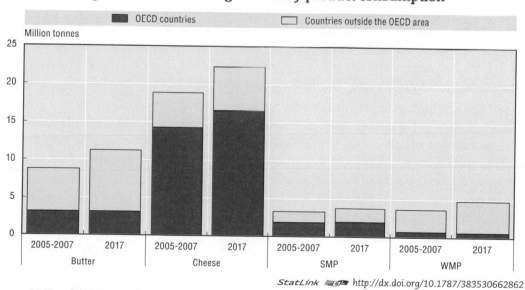

StatLink http://dx.doi.org/10.1787/383530662862

Source: OECD and FAO Secretariats.

Figure 9.8. **Sustained growth for butter and cheese consumption over 2008-2017**

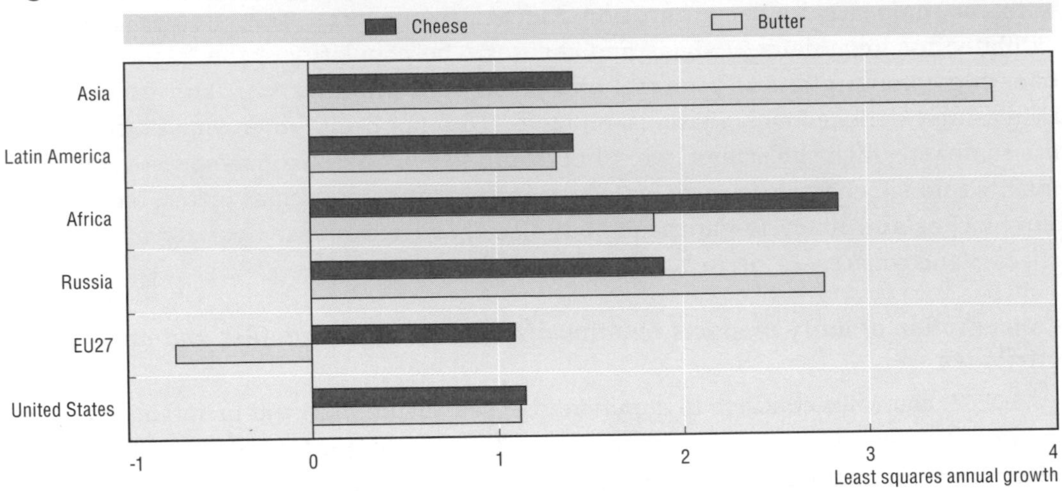

StatLink ᵐˢᵖ http://dx.doi.org/10.1787/383533262056

Source: OECD and FAO Secretariats.

Key issues and uncertainties

The price projections presented in this *Outlook* reflect the usual assumptions of stability in weather as well as in economic and policy conditions. Actual price outcomes can nevertheless exhibit significant annual variations in their average trend in any one year. This is particularly pertinent for dairy markets which are traditionally very thin. Consequently, a small change in the supply/demand balance of milk may have a substantial impact on the volume and prices of traded dairy products.

Not surprisingly, weather, economic conditions and the evolution in policies remain among the key factors influencing the dairy outlook. For example, a slowdown in global economic growth, compared to that assumed in this *Outlook*, would moderate international dairy prices. In addition, exchange rate developments could have an important influence as world dairy trade is typically denominated in US dollars, whereas the supplies of world exports depend mostly on the currencies of Oceania, Europe and South America. A severe drought in an important dairy-producing region could also have a critical impact on the *Outlook*, further strengthening the prices.

The uncertainties mentioned above form an integral part of the dairy markets and they all played a role in the recent international dairy price spike. However, the issue for the forthcoming period relates to the likelihood of fundamentally changing variations in these factors. In other words, the ups and down in prices will always exist (see Figure 9.1), the question is whether the amplitude will change.

It should be said, that although the recent international dairy price climb was indeed impressive, the market developments were quietly pointing in this direction. Dairy stocks have already been drained gradually over several years especially in the EU and the US. Then, food security fears and speculations in the face of extremely low global dairy stock levels ignited the dairy market fever. But, has the global market changed fundamentally? At the moment it is premature to judge, but, for example, the volume of traded commodity futures and options has recently risen sharply and financial investors and funds have been adding agricultural commodities into their investment portfolios. It could be expected that investment capital will exert more influence on commodity prices and play an increasingly

OECD-FAO AGRICULTURAL OUTLOOK 2008-2017 – ISBN 978-92-64-04590-3 – © OECD/FAO 2008

important role for global commodity markets in coming years. The jury is still out whether these developments add to price volatility, but the possibility should not be excluded. If the future would be for increasing price volatility, dairy farming might have to resemble a dynamic business with increased risk exposure. The question for the *Outlook* then is how well farmers will be able to cope with these new conditions and what assistance in risk management will be provided to them.

The weather related uncertainties, inseparable from the agricultural production process, present a major challenge in assessing risk and returns on investment into dairying. It follows that the adverse weather that recently plagued many important dairy producing regions represents perhaps the single most important factor for the *Outlook*. Could the latest spell of bad weather be considered accidental or was it a first sign of systematic changes linked to global warming altering the weather pattern around the world? Or, with the question posed in other terms: Is modern agriculture – overstraining land, overusing water – more prone to collapse and correspondingly less immune to normal weather fluctuation? Clearly, discussion on the subject of climate change and the potential of further production increases in the presence of water and other environmental limitations will intensify in the future.

Higher milk prices may give rise to further research, which will likely provide avenues to increase output. Productivity gains stimulated by increased automation of the production process, improved feed efficiency, improved health and longevity of cattle and the ability to improve productivity via GM technology, could be some of the alternatives. Although technological change will be key for the dairy markets outlook, these advances will be weighed against the increased awareness of animal welfare, threat of pollution and environmental degradation from livestock production. In many of the more developed regions, there is an increasing emphasis on the negative side effects of animal production.

Livestock production currently contributes 18% to the global warming effect. It produces about 9% of total carbon dioxide (CO_2) emission, 37% of methane and 65% of nitrous oxide. The situation is likely to worsen in the future as production gradually becomes more intensive (crop based). Moreover, livestock is among the largest sources of water pollution, mainly coming from animal wastes, antibiotics and hormones, fertilisers for feed crops and sediments from eroded pasture (FAO 2006). It can be expected that environmental and other civil society concerns will be increasingly translated into more demanding private standards by the retail sector (carbon footprint, animal welfare) and in changes in government legislations (*e.g.* regulations of greenhouse gas emissions, stringent nitrate directives and manure management regulations) (OECD 2004).

In conclusion, future responses by countries to high prices remain conditioned by extensive policy intervention and by internal food security concerns, but also increasingly by environmental constraints linked to high livestock populations, water availability and competition for pasture land. Increasingly, higher production response in many countries will come from higher yields as opposed to larger cattle numbers. Moreover, supply response will depend on the extent to which international product prices are being transmitted to local markets. A key issue for the dairy outlook is the ability of the industry to balance the market for perishable milk in the presence of greater price volatility and low global stock levels of dairy products.

References

FAO (2006), *Livestock's long shadow*, FAO, Rome.

OECD (2004), *Agriculture, Trade and the Environment: The Dairy Sector*, OECD Committee for Agriculture, Paris.

ISBN 978-92-64-04590-3
OECD-FAO AGRICULTURAL OUTLOOK 2008-2017
© OECD/FAO 2008

Methodology

This section provides information on the methodological aspects of the generation of the present *Agricultural Outlook*. It discusses the main aspects in the following order: First, a general description of the agricultural baseline projections and the Outlook report is given. Second, the compilation of a consistent set of the assumptions on macroeconomic projections is discussed in more detail. A third part presents an important model element that has been improved for this Outlook, *i.e.*, the representation of production costs in the model's supply equations.

The generation of the OECD-FAO Agricultural Outlook

The projections presented and analysed in this document are the result of a process that brings together information from a large number of sources. The use of a model jointly developed by the OECD and FAO Secretariats, based on the OECD's Aglink model and extended by FAO's Cosimo model, facilitates consistency in this process. A large amount of expert judgement, however, is applied at various stages of the *Outlook* process. The *Agricultural Outlook* presents a single, unified assessment, judged by the OECD and FAO Secretariats to be plausible given the underlying assumptions, the procedure of information exchange outlined below and the information to which they had access.

The starting point of the *Outlook* process is the reply by OECD countries (and some non-member economies) to an annual questionnaire. Through these questionnaires, the OECD Secretariat obtains information from these countries on future commodity market developments and on the evolution of their agricultural policies. This information is supplemented by the FAO Secretariat for its members which are not part of the OECD. External sources, such as the World Bank and the UN, are also used to complete the view of the main economic forces determining market developments. This part of the process is aimed at creating a first insight into possible market developments and at establishing the key assumptions which condition the *Outlook*. The main economic and policy assumptions are summarised in the Macroeconomic and policy assumptions chapter and in specific commodity tables of the present report. The main macroeconomic variables assumed for the *Outlook* period are based on the December 2007 medium term projections of the OECD's Economics Department for OECD countries, and on the Global Economic Prospects 2008 of the World Bank for other countries. While sometimes different from the macroeconomic assumptions provided through the questionnaire replies, it has been judged preferable to use just two consistent sources for these variables. The sources and assumptions for the macroeconomic projections are discussed in more detail further below.

As a next step, the modelling framework jointly developed by the OECD and FAO Secretariats is used to facilitate a consistent integration of this information and to derive an initial set of global market projections (baseline). In addition to quantities produced, consumed and traded, the baseline also includes projections for nominal prices (in local currency units) for the commodities concerned. Unless otherwise stated, prices referred to in the text are also in nominal terms. The data series for the projections is drawn from

OECD and FAO databases. For the most part information in these databases has been taken from national statistical sources. For further details on particular series, enquiries should be directed to the OECD and FAO Secretariats.

The model provides a comprehensive dynamic economic and policy-specific representation of major world producing and trading countries for the main temperate-zone commodities as well as rice and vegetable oils. The World Sugar Model, formerly a standalone model separate from Aglink, was revised during the year and fully integrated into the Aglink-Cosimo modelling system. From the integrated model, a set of long-term baseline projections for world and OECD sugar markets, covering raw and white (or refined) sugar was developed. In addition, comprehensive and fully integrated biofuel models have been developed for several OECD member countries as well as for a range of developing countries.*

The Aglink and Cosimo country and regional modules are all developed by the OECD and FAO Secretariats in conjunction with country experts and, in some cases, with assistance from other national administrations. The initial baseline results are compared with those obtained from the questionnaire replies and issues arising are discussed in bilateral exchanges with country experts. On the basis of these discussions and of updated information, a second baseline is produced. The information generated is used to prepare market assessments for cereals, oilseeds, meats, dairy products and sugar over the course of the outlook period, which are discussed at the annual meetings of the Working Group on Meat and Dairy Products and the Working Group on Cereals, Animal Feeds and Sugar of the OECD Committee for Agriculture. Following the receipt of comments and final data revisions, a last revision is made to the baseline projections. The revised projections form the basis of a draft of the present Agricultural Outlook publication, which is discussed by the Working Party on Agricultural Policies and Markets of the Committee for Agriculture, in May 2008, prior to publication. In addition, the Outlook will be used as a basis for analysis presented to the FAO's Committee on Commodity Problems and its various Intergovernmental Commodity Groups.

The Outlook process implies that the baseline projections presented in this report are conditioned by those developed by OECD countries and other participating economies. It also reconciles inconsistencies between individual country projections through the use of a formal modelling framework. The review process ensures that judgement of country experts is brought to bear on the projections and related analyses. However, the final responsibility for the projections and their interpretation rests with the OECD and FAO Secretariats.

Sources and assumptions for the macroeconomic projections

Population estimates from the 2006 Revision of the United Nations Population Prospects database provide the population data used for all countries and regional aggregates in the Outlook. For the projection period, the medium variant set of estimates was selected for use from the four alternative projection variants (low, medium, high and constant fertility). The UN Population Prospects database was chosen because it represents a comprehensive source of reliable estimates which includes data for non-OECD developing countries. For consistency reasons, the same source is used for both the historical population estimates and the projection data.

---

* For details on the modeling of biofuels in Aglink-Cosimo and a detailed analysis of the market impacts of biofuel policies, see OECD/IEA Economic Assessment of Biofuel Support Policies (forthcoming).

The other macroeconomic series used in the Aglink-Cosimo model are real GDP, the GDP deflator, the private consumption expenditure (PCE) deflator, the Brent crude oil price (in US dollars per barrel) and exchange rates expressed as the local currency value of 1 US dollar. Historical data for these series in OECD countries are consistent with those published in the *OECD Economic Outlook No. 82*, December 2007 and in the *OECD Main Economic Indicators*. Assumptions made about the future paths of all these variables apart from exchange rates, are based on the recent (November 2007) medium-term macroeconomic projections of the OECD Economics Department and extended from 2014 by holding the 2013 to 2014 annual growth rate constant for the remaining years to 2017. Exchange rates for OECD countries were extended to 2017 from the 2008 projections using the simple assumption of constant rates in real terms.

For non-member economies, historical and projection data for these macroeconomic series were obtained from the World Bank 2008 Global Economic Prospects of November 2007.

The model uses indices for real GDP, consumer prices (PCE deflator) and producer prices (GDP deflator) which are constructed with the base year 2000 value being equal to 1. The assumption of constant real exchange rates implies that a country with higher (lower) inflation relative to the United States (as measured by the US GDP deflator) will have a depreciating (appreciating) currency and therefore an increasing (decreasing) exchange rate over the projection period, since the exchange rate is measured as the local currency value of 1 US dollar.

The world oil price assumption underlying this year's agricultural outlook is based on that published in the *OECD Economic Outlook No. 82* (December 2007).

The representation of production costs in Aglink-Cosimo

Changes in production costs are an important variable for farmers' decisions on crop and livestock production quantities, in addition to output returns and, if applicable, policy measures.

While supply in Aglink-Cosimo is largely determined by gross returns, production costs are represented in the model in the form of a cost index used to deflate gross production revenues. In other words, supply equations in the model in most cases depend on gross returns per unit of activity (such as returns per hectare or the meat price) relative to the overall production cost level as expressed by the index. Consequently, equations for harvested areas in crop production and for livestock production quantities take the following general forms:

$$AH = f\left(\frac{RH}{CPCI}\right); \; QP = f\left(\frac{PP}{CPCI}\right)$$

with: AH area harvested (crop production); RH returns per hectare (crop production); CPCI commodity production cost index; QP production quantity (livestock production); PP producer price (livestock production).

Among others, energy prices, increased by rising crude oil prices, have fostered attention to agricultural production costs in agricultural commodity models. Energy prices can significantly impact on international markets for agricultural products as production costs for both crops and livestock products are highly dependent on energy costs. Fuels for tractors and other machinery, as well as heating and other forms of energy are directly used in the production process. In addition, other inputs such as fertilisers and pesticides, have a high energy content, and costs for these inputs are driven to a significant extent by energy prices. It is therefore important to explicitly consider energy prices in the representation of production costs.

The production cost indices employed in Aglink-Cosimo – one each for crops and for livestock products, respectively, to account for the different shares of input groups in total production costs – is constructed from three sub-indices representing non-tradable inputs, energy inputs, and other tradable inputs, respectively. While the non-tradable sub-index is approximated by the domestic GDP deflator, the energy sub-index is affected by changes in the world crude oil price and the country's exchange rate. Finally, the tradable sub-index is linked to global inflation (approximated by the US GDP deflator) and the country's exchange rate. This relationship is shown in the following equation:

$$CPCI_{r,t}^{I} = CPCS_{r,t}^{NT,I} * GDPD_{r,t}$$
$$+ CPCS_{r,t}^{EN,I} * \left(XP_{t}^{OIL} * XR_{r,t}\right) / \left(XP_{bas}^{OIL} * XR_{r,bas}\right)$$
$$+ \left(1 - CPCS_{r,t}^{NT,I} - CPCS_{r,t}^{EN,I}\right) * XR_{r,t} / XR_{r,bas} * GDPD_{USA,t}$$

with: $CPCI^{I}$ commodity production cost index for commodity group I

$CPCS^{NT,I}$ share of non-tradable input in total base commodity production costs for commodity group I

$CPCS^{EN,I}$ share of energy in total base commodity production costs for commodity group I

$GDPD$ deflator for the gross domestic product

XP^{OIL} world crude oil price

XR nominal exchange rate with respect to the US Dollar

I commodity group (crops, livestock products)

r,t region and time index, respectively

bas   base year (2000) value

Detailed data on the composition of production costs are available for Argentina, New Zealand and the United States. These data, available from the Secretariat on request, suggest non-tradable and energy shares in crop production costs as shown in the table below. Given that detailed data on other countries are not available, the respective crop production cost shares for Argentina are applied for all non-OECD countries, those for New Zealand are applied also for Australia, and the shares found for the US are applied for all other OECD countries/regions. As no data on livestock production shares are available for Argentina, the shares found for the US are applied to all countries/regions with the exception of New Zealand and Australia.

Production cost shares for:		Argentina	New Zealand	United States
Crop production	Non-tradable	47%	66%	67%
	Energy	43%	27%	25%
	Other tradable	10%	7%	8%
	Applied for:	*All non-OECD countries/regions*	*New Zealand, Australia*	*All other OECD countries/regions*
Livestock production	Non-tradable	n.a.	77%	97%
	Energy	n.a.	23%	3%
	Other tradable[1]	n.a.	1%	0%
	Applied for:	—	*New Zealand, Australia*	*All other countries/regions*

1. Excludes tradable feed.

Methodology and limitations of partial stochastic analysis

In the context of the 2008 *OECD-FAO Agricultural Outlook*, partial stochastic simulations based on yields and macroeconomic variables have been undertaken. The assumptions of normal weather and stable macroeconomic environment are replaced by a range of yield results and macroeconomic variables constructed according to the procedure presented below.

Limitations of partial stochastic analysis

The results of multiple simulations are multiple outcomes for each market variable in each year. The aim of carrying such an analysis is to widen the range of relevance of Outlook results. It is of particular interest for studying markets where agricultural policies in place may have asymmetric effects. It is also useful when trying to identify at least partially the uncertainties embedded in the deterministic point projections. The analysis presented in the report takes into account the uncertainties around macroeconomic and weather assumptions and their consequences on the evolution of agricultural commodity markets in the coming decade. The evolution of markets in the future is likely to differ from the deterministic scenario because of unexpected developments or shocks in the underlying assumptions.

Partial stochastic projections aim to take into account more possibilities of evolution but obviously do not imply that one of the stochastic scenarios will be the "real" one. There are serious limitations to partial stochastic analysis that need to be well understood when looking at the results. Indeed partial stochastic analysis has only a partial coverage of uncertainties; it focuses on exogenous uncertainties linked to climate and macroeconomic evolution. There are several other sources of uncertainty in the benchmark projections. In particular, there is an empirical uncertainty on the estimation of the parameters used in the agricultural commodity model jointly developed by the OECD and the FAO and an endogenous uncertainty on the functioning of agricultural markets. Despite these limitations, the information that partial stochastic analysis brings is of interest for better assessing the evolution of agricultural commodity markets than just looking at a deterministic baseline.

Procedure used to conduct partial stochastic simulations: simulations of yields

The deterministic benchmark projections presented in the 2008 *Agricultural Outlook* are based on a "normal" weather assumption, *i.e.* no shock in crop yield due to weather shocks is taken into account and no assumption is made on possible climate change (*i.e.* variation from average weather). For the partial stochastic analysis, 350 different sets of crop yields for all crop and all countries studied in the *Agricultural Outlook* over the coming ten years have been simulated. For each crop, a random deviation from the deterministic baseline is generated for every year of projections and for every simulation. This random deviation takes into account long term trends in yields for the different crops and historical deviations from long term trends. This implies that for every crop, a random distribution of 350 sets of medium term projections of its associated yield is obtained. In a given year, the average yield value is equal to the yield value in the deterministic baseline and its random deviation corresponds to historical random deviations from long term yields.

Procedure used to conduct partial stochastic simulations: simulations of macroeconomic variables

The deterministic benchmark projections in the *2008 Agricultural Outlook* are based on an assumption of a stable macroeconomic environment assumption. In the partial stochastic analysis conducted on the *2008 Outlook* numbers, 350 different sets of correlated macroeconomic projections for the world oil price, exchanges rates, GDP and price indices for OECD and non-OECD economies are generated. The 350 different sets of macroeconomic variables projections are obtained thanks to the use of a simple macroeconomic model. This simple macroeconomic model explains econometrically macroeconomic variables in function of their past values and/or of the past or actual values of other macroeconomic variables in the given country or in other major economies. This model is calibrated on historical data. The macroeconomic projections are the combination of the outcomes of the calibrated model and random draws of historical deviations from the calibrated model.

Procedure used to conduct partial stochastic simulations: stochastic outcomes

The 350 sets of medium term projections for yield and macroeconomic variables are put together to create 350 sets of assumptions that are taken as input to the joint OECD-FAO modelling system Aglink-Cosimo. This results in 350 resolutions of the model to get 350 sets of medium-term projections. The process of getting the stochastic outcomes is summarised by the following table.

Procedure used to conduct partial stochastic analysis

Yields	Macroeconomic variable
1/ Identify long term trend	1/ Construction of a simple macroeconomic model
2/ Define historical errors	2/ 350 draws based on historical errors
3/ 350 draws based on errors and trend	3/ Input errors into the macroeconomic model
4/ Input as shocks to the model	4/ Input macroeconomic variables into the model
350 resolutions of the model to get 350 sets of medium term projections	

Interesting lessons can be drawn from partial stochastic analysis when looking at the distributions of medium term projections and at the relation between these distributions and assumptions on yields or macroeconomic variables evolution.

ISBN 978-92-64-04590-3
OECD-FAO AGRICULTURAL OUTLOOK 2008-2017
© OECD/FAO 2008

ANNEX A

Statistical Tables

Table A.1. **Economic assumptions**

Calendar year[a]		Average 2002-06	2007 est.	2008	2009	2010	2011	2012	2013	2014	2015	2016	2017
REAL GDP[b]													
Australia	%	3.2	4.3	3.5	3.0	3.2	3.2	3.1	3.0	2.8	2.8	2.8	2.8
Canada	%	2.7	2.6	2.4	2.7	2.7	2.2	2.1	2.2	2.1	2.1	2.1	2.1
EU15	%	1.6	2.6	1.9	2.0	2.0	1.9	1.8	1.8	1.8	1.8	1.8	1.8
Japan	%	1.7	1.9	1.6	1.8	1.5	1.2	1.2	1.2	1.2	1.2	1.2	1.2
Korea	%	4.8	4.9	5.2	5.1	4.7	4.2	4.0	3.9	3.9	3.9	3.9	3.9
Mexico	%	2.8	3.0	3.6	4.3	4.2	4.0	4.0	4.0	4.0	4.0	4.0	4.0
New Zealand	%	3.5	3.4	1.9	2.1	2.2	2.2	2.2	2.2	2.2	2.2	2.2	2.2
Norway	%	2.4	3.4	3.6	2.4	1.7	1.7	2.0	2.1	2.0	2.0	2.0	2.0
Switzerland	%	1.7	2.7	2.0	2.0	1.7	1.4	1.4	1.4	1.5	1.5	1.5	1.5
Turkey	%	7.2	5.1	5.4	5.7	5.5	5.5	5.5	5.5	5.5	5.5	5.5	5.5
United States	%	2.7	2.2	2.0	2.2	2.7	2.6	2.4	2.4	2.4	2.4	2.4	2.4
Argentina	%	4.9	7.8	5.7	4.7	3.4	3.2	3.1	3.0	2.9	2.9	2.9	2.8
Brazil	%	2.8	4.8	4.5	4.5	3.9	3.6	3.6	3.6	3.5	3.5	3.4	3.5
China	%	10.1	11.3	10.8	10.5	8.2	8.2	8.2	8.2	8.2	8.2	8.2	8.2
India	%	7.7	7.7	7.2	6.9	6.7	6.4	6.1	5.9	5.6	5.3	5.3	5.3
Russia	%	6.5	7.5	6.5	6.0	5.4	5.4	5.4	5.4	5.4	5.4	5.4	5.4
South Africa	%	4.4	5.0	5.1	5.3	5.2	5.2	5.2	5.2	5.2	5.2	5.2	5.2
OECD[c, d]	%	2.3	2.5	2.2	2.3	2.4	2.3	2.2	2.2	2.2	2.2	2.2	2.2
PCE DEFLATOR[b]													
Australia	%	2.1	2.5	2.9	2.5	2.5	2.5	2.5	2.5	2.5	2.5	2.5	2.5
Canada	%	2.7	1.6	1.4	1.7	1.9	2.0	2.0	2.0	2.0	2.0	2.0	2.0
EU15	%	2.1	1.9	2.4	2.1	1.9	1.8	1.8	1.8	1.8	1.8	1.8	1.8
Japan	%	−0.8	−0.5	0.1	0.3	0.5	0.6	0.9	1.0	1.1	1.1	1.1	1.1
Korea	%	2.9	2.4	2.8	3.0	3.0	3.0	3.0	3.0	3.0	3.0	3.0	3.0
Mexico	%	5.1	3.7	3.7	3.4	3.2	3.2	3.2	3.2	3.2	3.2	3.2	3.2
New Zealand	%	1.6	1.6	2.2	2.0	2.0	2.1	2.1	2.1	2.1	2.1	2.1	2.1
Norway	%	1.6	0.5	2.5	2.1	2.1	2.0	2.0	2.0	2.0	2.0	2.0	2.0
Switzerland	%	0.9	0.9	1.5	1.4	1.0	0.8	0.8	0.8	0.8	0.8	0.8	0.8
Turkey	%	17.4	8.5	6.5	4.5	7.5	7.5	7.5	7.5	7.5	7.5	7.5	7.5
United States	%	2.4	2.5	2.4	1.7	1.9	1.9	1.9	1.9	1.9	1.9	1.9	1.9
Argentina	%	12.7	8.6	11.1	11.3	4.7	4.8	4.7	4.6	4.6	4.6	4.5	4.5
Brazil	%	7.7	4.0	4.1	4.2	3.7	4.4	4.4	4.4	4.4	4.4	4.4	4.4
China	%	1.8	4.6	3.9	3.0	2.6	2.8	2.9	3.1	3.1	3.0	2.9	3.0
India	%	4.1	6.2	5.5	4.5	5.8	5.8	5.8	5.8	5.8	5.8	5.8	5.8
Russia	%	6.5	10.4	8.9	7.6	5.5	5.2	4.9	4.7	4.4	4.2	4.0	3.8
South Africa	%	4.4	5.9	5.7	5.2	5.4	5.4	5.4	5.4	5.4	5.4	5.4	5.4
OECD[c, d]	%	2.4	2.2	2.4	2.0	2.1	2.2	2.2	2.2	2.3	2.3	2.3	2.3

For notes, see end of the table.

Table A.1. **Economic assumptions** (cont.)

Calendar year[a]		2007 est. (million)	2008	2009	2010	2011	2012	2013	2014	2015	2016	2017
POPULATION												
Australia	%	20.6	1.04	1.00	0.97	0.97	0.97	0.96	0.95	0.94	0.93	0.92
Canada	%	32.6	0.92	0.90	0.88	0.87	0.86	0.85	0.84	0.83	0.82	0.80
EU27	%	491.7	0.22	0.18	0.16	0.14	0.13	0.11	0.09	0.08	0.07	0.05
Japan	%	127.8	0.01	−0.02	−0.05	−0.09	−0.12	−0.15	−0.18	−0.21	−0.24	−0.28
Korea	%	48.3	0.36	0.34	0.31	0.28	0.24	0.21	0.18	0.15	0.13	0.09
Mexico	%	102.9	1.13	1.19	1.18	1.12	1.06	1.01	0.96	0.93	0.90	0.88
New Zealand	%	4.1	0.94	0.86	0.83	0.82	0.82	0.81	0.78	0.77	0.77	0.72
Norway	%	4.7	0.62	0.62	0.61	0.61	0.63	0.60	0.60	0.59	0.61	0.59
Switzerland	%	7.5	0.39	0.37	0.37	0.36	0.37	0.34	0.34	0.35	0.34	0.35
Turkey	%	73.9	1.29	1.27	1.24	1.21	1.18	1.14	1.11	1.08	1.04	1.01
United States	%	299.4	0.99	0.97	0.96	0.94	0.93	0.91	0.89	0.88	0.86	0.85
Argentina	%	39.1	0.90	0.89	0.88	0.96	0.94	0.93	0.92	0.90	0.88	0.88
Brazil	%	188.6	1.14	1.12	1.10	1.29	1.25	1.22	1.18	1.14	1.11	1.07
China	%	1 324.1	0.63	0.62	0.62	0.64	0.67	0.69	0.69	0.68	0.66	0.63
India	%	1 151.8	1.50	1.47	1.44	1.41	1.38	1.35	1.32	1.28	1.25	1.22
Russia	%	142.5	−0.53	−0.53	−0.54	0.46	−0.47	−0.47	−0.49	−0.50	−0.52	−0.53
South Africa	%	48.3	0.61	0.53	0.47	0.44	0.42	0.40	0.39	0.39	0.39	0.39
OECD[c]	%	1 213.5	0.57	0.55	0.53	0.51	0.49	0.47	0.45	0.44	0.42	0.40
World	%	6 607.1	1.19	1.18	1.16	1.6	1.5	1.14	1.13	1.11	1.09	1.07

Calendar year[a]		Average 2002-06	2007 est.	2008	2009	2010	2011	2012	2013	2014	2015	2016	2017
EXCHANGE RATE													
Australia	AUD/USD	1.47	1.19	1.20	1.21	1.23	1.24	1.25	1.27	1.28	1.29	1.31	1.32
Canada	CAD/USD	1.32	1.07	1.07	1.07	1.08	1.08	1.09	1.09	1.10	1.11	1.11	1.12
European Union	EUR/USD	0.87	0.73	0.73	0.73	0.74	0.74	0.74	0.74	0.74	0.74	0.74	0.74
Japan	JPY/USD	115.0	117.4	114.7	112.8	111.2	109.6	108.3	107.0	105.9	104.8	103.6	102.5
Korea	'000 KRW/USD	1.11	0.93	0.92	0.91	0.92	0.92	0.93	0.94	0.94	0.95	0.96	0.97
Mexico	MXN/USD	10.70	10.95	11.15	11.30	11.45	11.57	11.70	11.82	11.94	12.07	12.19	12.32
New Zealand	NZD/USD	1.67	1.36	1.39	1.39	1.40	1.40	1.41	1.41	1.42	1.42	1.43	1.43
Argentina	ARS/USD	3.02	3.10	3.30	3.40	3.45	3.52	3.61	3.68	3.75	3.83	3.91	3.99
Brazil	BRL/USD	2.66	1.90	1.90	2.00	2.04	2.09	2.13	2.18	2.22	2.27	2.32	2.37
China	CNY/USD	8.20	7.57	7.20	6.84	6.53	6.43	6.35	6.30	6.26	6.23	6.20	6.18
India	INR/USD	45.74	41.50	40.00	39.50	41.78	44.19	46.75	49.45	52.30	55.33	58.52	61.90
Russia	RUR/USD	29.3	26.4	26.1	26.1	27.2	28.1	28.7	28.7	29.5	30.1	30.7	31.3
South Africa	ZAR/USD	7.64	7.22	7.17	7.33	7.72	8.14	8.58	9.05	9.54	10.06	10.60	11.18
WORLD OIL PRICE													
Brent crude oil price	USD/barrel	42.30	72.30	90.00	90.00	91.10	92.80	94.60	96.40	98.20	100.10	102.00	104.00

a) For OECD member countries, historical data for population, real GDP, private consumption expenditure deflator and exchange rate were obtained from the *OECD Economic Outlook*, No. 82, December 2007. For non-member economies, historical macroeconomic data were obtained from the World Bank, November 2007. Assumptions for the projection period draw on the recent medium term macroeconomic projections of the OECD Economics Department, projections of the World Bank, responses to a questionnaire sent to member country agricultural experts and for population, projections from the United Nations World Population Prospects Database, 2006 Revision (medium variant). Data for the European Union are for the euro area aggregates.
b) Annual per cent change. The price index used is the private consumption expenditure deflator.
c) Excludes Iceland.
d) Annual weighted average real GDP and CPI growth rates in OECD countries are based on weights using 1995 GDP and purchasing power parities (PPPs).
est.: estimate.
Source: OECD and FAO Secretariats.

StatLink ⊞≊ http://dx.doi.org/10.1787/383781634100

Table A.2. **World prices**[a]

		Average 02/03-06/07	07/08 est.	08/09	09/10	10/11	11/12	12/13	13/14	14/15	15/16	16/17	17/18
WHEAT													
Price[b]	USD/t	167.8	318.6	267.0	233.6	225.9	229.7	231.0	231.2	230.2	230.9	231.6	230.6
COARSE GRAINS													
Price[c]	USD/t	113.2	181.3	185.3	185.0	189.0	188.4	178.5	173.0	173.2	170.9	166.6	164.6
RICE													
Price[d]	USD/t	262.3	361.0	390.6	367.9	330.7	326.7	337.2	340.3	335.6	333.8	332.5	334.5
OILSEEDS													
Price[e]	USD/t	293.4	485.8	481.9	470.6	468.3	464.2	455.8	452.4	453.2	455.6	457.6	457.2
OILSEED MEALS													
Price[f]	USD/t	219.5	365.7	348.2	331.5	328.4	321.6	308.4	302.6	303.4	304.0	305.8	307.0
VEGETABLE OILS													
Price[g]	USD/t	587.5	1 015.1	986.9	1 017.9	1 026.3	1 031.2	1 043.8	1 048.0	1 050.9	1 055.9	1 060.3	1 055.1
SUGAR													
Price, raw sugar[h]	USD/t	237.1	229.3	216.0	228.0	257.6	280.4	304.5	298.0	307.1	309.6	308.2	301.7
Price, refined sugar[i]	USD/t	291.2	289.1	268.1	280.8	317.8	351.8	374.5	371.3	384.9	385.0	383.4	379.1
BEEF AND VEAL													
Price, EU[j]	EUR/100 kg dw	256.5	276.0	275.3	279.2	281.2	282.9	285.9	288.8	295.0	300.4	303.2	305.9
Price, USA[k]	USD/100 kg dw	291.0	327.1	327.2	323.1	325.4	322.7	310.7	317.1	320.5	322.9	323.1	328.7
Price, Argentina[l]	USD/100 kg dw	120.7	151.7	143.3	142.3	138.6	138.1	136.2	138.1	143.1	144.5	147.9	147.5
PIG MEAT													
Price, EU[m]	EUR/100 kg dw	131.3	130.6	148.5	149.6	149.8	147.7	150.8	149.7	147.5	150.5	148.4	151.6
Price, USA[n]	USD/100 kg dw	137.3	143.5	143.5	156.0	172.3	176.9	164.6	169.8	167.5	163.2	160.8	158.8
Price, Brazil[o]	USD/100 kg dw	78.0	109.4	147.7	153.6	151.4	145.7	148.2	150.2	149.9	149.0	151.1	153.0
POULTRY MEAT													
Price, EU[p]	EUR/100 kg rtc	101.5	111.7	115.9	118.5	120.9	117.7	115.7	120.3	121.4	122.5	123.6	124.8
Price, USA[q]	USD/100 kg rtc	144.1	168.4	166.8	160.6	165.6	168.7	164.2	167.9	170.1	171.9	174.0	177.3
Price, Brazil[r]	USD/100 kg pw	95.1	143.8	156.0	137.7	137.4	140.1	140.3	143.4	146.2	148.1	149.7	152.8
SHEEP MEAT													
Price, New Zealand[s]	NZD/100 kg dw	379.0	318.8	313.2	344.6	365.8	379.9	386.1	392.4	398.8	405.3	420.1	435.6
BUTTER													
Price[t]	USD/100 kg	161.6	293.8	300.6	290.1	265.6	256.1	257.1	259.8	264.4	268.1	269.6	271.8
CHEESE													
Price[u]	USD/100 kg	234.6	402.2	418.9	393.9	359.6	349.9	350.4	351.7	354.1	355.6	357.3	358.0
SKIM MILK POWDER													
Price[v]	USD/100 kg	191.2	431.6	355.2	331.2	314.4	308.3	305.8	304.7	303.4	304.2	303.9	304.6
WHOLE MILK POWDER													
Price[w]	USD/100 kg	192.1	416.7	365.7	333.5	311.3	303.6	303.4	304.6	306.6	308.0	309.6	311.0
WHEY POWDER													
Wholesale price, USA[x]	USD/100 kg	54.1	133.8	92.1	87.9	93.3	96.1	100.9	102.4	104.2	108.9	111.0	114.3
CASEIN													
Price[y]	USD/100 kg	577.0	1 029.5	956.7	804.6	807.4	752.6	784.2	755.0	776.6	757.0	772.4	759.3

For notes, see end of the table.

OECD-FAO AGRICULTURAL OUTLOOK 2008-2017 – ISBN 978-92-64-04590-3 – © OECD/FAO 2008

Table A.2. **World prices**[a] (cont.)

		Average 02/03-06/07	07/08 est.	08/09	09/10	10/11	11/12	12/13	13/14	14/15	15/16	16/17	17/18
ETHANOL													
Price[z]	USD/hl	31.4	42.0	53.0	55.6	54.0	53.7	53.6	52.9	52.8	52.7	52.0	51.3
BIODIESEL													
Price[aa]	USD/hl	83.8	94.7	98.6	105.2	105.8	103.4	104.2	104.8	105.3	106.3	106.3	105.5

a) This table is a compilation of price information presented in the detailed commodity tables further in this annex. Prices for crops are on marketing year basis and those for meat and dairy products on calendar year basis (e.g. 07/08 is calendar year 2007).
b) No. 2 hard red winter wheat, ordinary protein, USA f.o.b. Gulf Ports (June/May), less EEP payments where applicable.
c) No. 2 yellow corn, US f.o.b. Gulf Ports (September/August).
d) Milled, 100%, grade b, Nominal Price Quote, NPQ, f.o.b. Bangkok (August/July).
e) Weighted average oilseed price, European port.
f) Weighted average meal price, European port.
g) Weighted average price of oilseed oils and palm oil, European port.
h) Raw sugar world price, ICE Inc. No. 11, f.o.b. stowed Caribbean port (including Brazil), bulk spot price.
i) Refined sugar price, London No. 5 , f.o.b. Europe, spot.
j) Producer price.
k) Choice steers, 1 100-1 300 lb lw, Nebraska – lw to dw conversion factor 0.63.
l) Buenos Aires wholesale price linier, young bulls.
m) Pig producer price
n) Barrows and gilts, No. 1-3, 230-250 lb lw, Iowa/South Minnesota – lw to dw conversion factor 0.74.
o) Producer price.
p) Weighted average farm gate live chickens, first choice, lw to rtc conversion of 0.75, EU15 starting in 1995.
q) Wholesale weighted average broiler price 12 cities.
r) Weighted average wholesale price of differents cuts.
s) Lamb schedule price, all grade average.
t) f.o.b. export price, butter, 82% butterfat, Oceania.
u) f.o.b. export price, cheddar cheese, 39% moisture, Oceania.
v) f.o.b. export price, non-fat dry milk, 1.25% butterfat, Oceania.
w) f.o.b. export price, WMP 26% butterfat, Oceania.
x) Edible dry whey, Wisconsin, plant.
y) Export price, New Zealand.
z) Brazil, Sao Paulo (ex-distillery).
aa) Central Europe FOB price net of biodiesel tariff.
est.: estimate.
Source: OECD and FAO Secretariats.

StatLink 🔗 http://dx.doi.org/10.1787/383803078767

Table A.3. **World trade projections**

IMPORTS			Average 2002-06	2007 est.	2008	2009	2010	2011	2012	2013	2014	2015	2016	2017
Wheat	World trade	kt	109 363	111 003	121 070	115 943	116 958	118 354	120 578	120 885	122 913	124 106	125 294	126 465
	OECD	kt	24 907	25 144	26 484	24 906	24 424	24 152	24 818	24 698	24 853	24 913	25 070	25 127
	Developing	kt	85 114	87 062	96 495	92 824	94 400	95 863	97 699	97 976	99 778	100 858	101 793	102 849
	Least Developed Countries	kt	10 445	10 590	13 271	11 822	11 853	12 292	12 710	12 809	13 009	13 173	13 369	13 605
Coarse grains	World trade	kt	105 924	119 616	111 697	111 197	111 423	112 858	114 921	116 832	119 567	122 072	125 101	126 943
	OECD	kt	49 923	59 088	49 298	50 523	50 116	49 694	49 646	50 033	50 097	50 593	51 179	51 448
	Developing	kt	73 297	76 900	79 529	78 276	78 858	80 639	83 000	84 940	87 352	90 165	92 497	94 151
	Least Developed Countries	kt	2 553	2 057	2 287	2 506	2 655	2 885	3 156	3 409	3 692	3 715	4 025	4 277
Rice	World trade	kt	29 641	31 245	30 844	31 901	32 486	33 422	34 414	35 167	36 090	36 791	37 485	38 082
	OECD	kt	4 242	4 436	4 463	4 510	4 793	4 812	4 861	4 954	5 116	5 252	5 421	5 475
	Developing	kt	25 171	26 568	26 014	27 091	27 371	28 225	29 152	29 829	30 655	31 273	31 874	32 440
	Least Developed Countries	kt	6 279	7 051	7 516	8 319	8 201	8 083	8 170	8 552	8 770	9 055	9 199	9 374
Oilseeds	World trade	kt	71 937	83 620	80 052	82 152	83 945	85 127	86 578	88 186	90 512	92 514	94 802	97 488
	OECD	kt	33 788	34 199	30 982	30 855	31 084	30 188	29 397	29 141	29 427	29 751	30 261	31 280
	Developing	kt	45 609	57 178	56 601	59 084	60 808	62 997	65 395	67 367	69 555	71 317	73 205	74 999
	Least Developed Countries	kt	238	270	261	264	277	295	310	323	337	352	368	383
Oilseed meals	World trade	kt	52 056	61 773	64 787	66 941	69 238	70 192	71 501	72 734	73 614	74 249	74 866	75 329
	OECD	kt	32 007	35 142	36 685	37 228	37 263	37 179	37 222	37 299	37 081	36 586	36 054	35 181
	Developing	kt	20 873	27 347	29 091	30 619	32 902	34 061	35 422	36 535	37 680	38 993	40 142	41 555
	Least Developed Countries	kt	271	408	444	494	510	535	567	604	626	642	659	678
Vegetable oils	World trade	kt	38 655	45 805	48 889	50 596	52 408	54 340	56 270	58 012	59 616	61 029	62 238	63 175
	OECD	kt	9 275	11 883	14 075	15 495	16 874	17 547	18 434	19 290	19 831	20 480	20 833	21 141
	Developing	kt	29 182	33 768	34 623	34 755	35 136	36 349	37 333	38 176	39 182	39 902	40 706	41 290
	Least Developed Countries	kt	3 316	3 875	4 001	4 118	4 264	4 413	4 563	4 721	4 883	5 049	5 213	5 390
Sugar	World trade	kt	46 908	44 096	48 656	50 624	51 560	51 916	52 588	53 901	54 780	56 260	57 842	59 657
	OECD	kt	11 261	10 130	10 911	11 764	12 120	12 481	12 631	12 845	13 023	13 239	13 495	13 768
	Developing	kt	30 732	30 589	33 960	35 257	36 108	36 484	37 220	38 500	39 438	41 002	42 633	44 405
	Least Developed Countries	kt	3 513	3 702	3 821	4 045	4 247	4 409	4 430	4 657	4 705	4 872	5 040	5 283
Beef[a]	World trade	kt	6 232	7 071	7 675	7 594	7 789	8 075	8 442	8 707	9 033	9 250	9 529	9 787
	OECD	kt	3 536	3 478	3 692	3 853	3 930	4 052	4 216	4 317	4 407	4 444	4 441	4 509
	Developing	kt	2 393	2 977	3 313	3 223	3 328	3 489	3 649	3 770	3 996	4 118	4 323	4 497
	Least Developed Countries	kt	102	135	219	188	201	214	232	249	263	277	294	305
Pigmeat[a]	World trade	kt	4 263	4 798	5 184	5 408	5 507	5 615	5 757	5 909	6 065	6 208	6 410	6 601
	OECD	kt	2 407	2 544	2 608	2 712	2 832	2 922	3 000	3 069	3 136	3 190	3 282	3 368
	Developing	kt	1 464	1 818	2 060	2 295	2 305	2 290	2 367	2 442	2 541	2 630	2 764	2 883
	Least Developed Countries	kt	44	57	70	71	82	95	101	112	121	132	139	153
Poultry	World trade	kt	7 635	8 568	8 827	9 277	9 682	9 778	9 977	10 258	10 409	10 544	10 831	11 102
	OECD	kt	2 021	2 150	2 326	2 205	2 416	2 277	2 336	2 427	2 442	2 387	2 391	2 377
	Developing	kt	4 248	4 906	5 131	5 537	5 835	5 968	6 150	6 393	6 509	6 652	6 949	7 238
	Least Developed Countries	kt	420	453	479	542	571	587	596	593	594	617	632	652
Butter	World trade	kt	738	735	745	761	778	800	817	835	856	875	897	916
	OECD	kt	144	144	138	137	138	139	138	137	136	134	133	133
	Developing	kt	436	458	443	457	471	482	490	500	512	522	534	544
	Least Developed Countries	kt	12	14	14	20	21	22	24	26	29	31	33	35
Cheese	World trade	kt	1 418	1 564	1 623	1 680	1 732	1 799	1 854	1 902	1 949	1 995	2 046	2 113
	OECD	kt	754	778	792	809	833	857	881	903	925	948	971	994
	Developing	kt	567	618	626	656	693	721	742	770	795	824	851	896
	Least Developed Countries	kt	17	20	14	24	31	28	29	34	35	37	37	40
Whole milk powder	World trade	kt	1 382	1 400	1 625	1 661	1 723	1 785	1 856	1 924	1 984	2 049	2 126	2 197
	OECD	kt	85	76	77	78	78	78	78	78	78	78	78	79
	Developing	kt	1 312	1 331	1 545	1 583	1 645	1 706	1 779	1 847	1 908	1 973	2 038	2 107
	Least Developed Countries	kt	124	139	153	164	176	187	197	208	220	232	245	259

For notes, see end of the table.

OECD-FAO AGRICULTURAL OUTLOOK 2008-2017 – ISBN 978-92-64-04590-3 – © OECD/FAO 2008

Table A.3. **World trade projections** (cont.)

IMPORTS			Average 2002-06	2007 est.	2008	2009	2010	2011	2012	2013	2014	2015	2016	2017
Skim milk powder	World trade	kt	1 220	1 207	1 192	1 217	1 236	1 270	1 319	1 367	1 418	1 463	1 510	1 549
	OECD	kt	211	210	213	216	209	212	216	219	220	224	227	230
	Developing	kt	1 081	1 052	1 038	1 064	1 092	1 125	1 172	1 219	1 266	1 311	1 357	1 395
	Least Developed Countries	kt	56	32	32	33	35	37	39	41	43	45	47	49

For notes, see end of the table.

Table A.3. **world trade projections** (cont.)

EXPORTS			Average 2002-06	2007 est.	2008	2009	2010	2011	2012	2013	2014	2015	2016	2017
Wheat	World trade	kt	109 363	111 003	121 070	115 943	116 958	118 354	120 578	120 885	122 913	124 106	125 294	126 465
	OECD	kt	71 994	64 315	81 900	75 891	75 752	76 396	77 232	75 394	75 600	74 946	74 731	74 776
	Developing	kt	19 101	18 735	19 856	18 486	18 860	18 866	19 895	20 738	21 288	21 799	22 419	22 663
	Least Developed Countries	kt	145	88	71	55	56	56	57	57	58	58	59	59
Coarse grains	World trade	kt	105 924	119 616	111 697	111 197	111 423	112 858	114 921	116 832	119 567	122 072	125 101	126 943
	OECD	kt	72 984	86 515	76 856	72 763	72 300	73 485	76 506	77 500	79 184	81 871	84 160	84 694
	Developing	kt	28 286	32 390	29 258	29 547	27 888	27 932	27 850	29 240	29 845	30 025	30 368	31 359
	Least Developed Countries	kt	2 007	3 547	3 591	3 656	4 119	4 035	3 739	3 712	3 628	3 152	3 059	3 084
Rice	World trade	kt	29 641	31 245	30 844	31 901	32 486	33 422	34 414	35 167	36 090	36 791	37 485	38 082
	OECD	kt	3 991	3 814	3 647	4 204	4 340	4 115	4 238	4 437	4 607	4 712	4 800	4 905
	Developing	kt	24 544	26 540	27 167	27 676	28 124	29 284	30 153	30 707	31 459	32 055	32 660	33 152
	Least Developed Countries	kt	537	1 652	1 825	1 336	1 432	1 768	2 188	2 023	2 210	2 255	2 439	2 213
Oilseeds	World trade	kt	71 937	83 620	80 052	82 152	83 945	85 127	86 578	88 186	90 512	92 514	94 802	97 488
	OECD	kt	35 321	35 086	35 024	32 612	32 586	31 097	29 875	29 789	30 089	30 347	30 356	30 479
	Developing	kt	33 134	41 996	42 741	46 122	47 386	49 826	52 277	53 959	55 708	57 372	59 433	61 682
	Least Developed Countries	kt	18	18	34	29	28	27	25	23	21	20	19	18
Oilseed meals	World trade	kt	52 056	61 773	64 787	66 941	69 238	70 192	71 501	72 734	73 614	74 249	74 866	75 329
	OECD	kt	8 795	10 656	9 842	11 348	12 375	12 660	13 174	13 343	13 302	13 090	12 931	12 567
	Developing	kt	45 705	50 494	52 415	52 999	54 120	54 784	55 716	56 601	57 504	58 335	59 039	59 833
	Least Developed Countries	kt	18	19	19	19	19	20	20	20	20	20	21	21
Vegetable oils	World trade	kt	38 655	45 805	48 889	50 596	52 408	54 340	56 270	58 012	59 616	61 029	62 238	63 175
	OECD	kt	2 579	2 631	2 308	2 459	2 696	2 897	3 220	3 459	3 607	3 642	3 735	3 718
	Developing	kt	35 859	42 512	44 085	45 549	46 984	48 545	50 008	51 352	52 702	53 928	54 921	55 741
	Least Developed Countries	kt	81	96	89	90	91	93	94	95	96	97	98	99
Sugar	World trade	kt	48 322	49 287	48 656	50 624	51 560	51 916	52 588	53 901	54 780	56 260	57 842	59 657
	OECD	kt	10 299	5 735	5 813	6 340	6 639	7 005	7 160	7 534	7 683	7 752	7 854	7 845
	Developing	kt	36 247	41 731	41 193	42 836	43 625	44 029	44 611	45 619	46 209	47 563	49 079	50 873
	Least Developed Countries	kt	566	688	708	810	847	851	861	877	912	934	969	1 011
Beef[a]	World trade	kt	6 232	7 071	7 675	7 594	7 789	8 075	8 442	8 707	9 033	9 250	9 529	9 787
	OECD	kt	3 427	3 291	3 300	3 212	3 216	3 298	3 436	3 508	3 607	3 631	3 644	3 714
	Developing	kt	3 286	4 136	4 284	4 452	4 657	4 899	5 189	5 394	5 634	5 848	6 167	6 384
	Least Developed Countries	kt	2	2	3	3	11	3	3	3	3	3	3	3
Pigmeat[a]	World trade	kt	4 263	4 798	5 184	5 408	5 507	5 615	5 757	5 909	6 065	6 208	6 410	6 601
	OECD	kt	3 468	3 854	3 979	4 160	4 247	4 273	4 312	4 402	4 486	4 551	4 684	4 789
	Developing	kt	1 225	1 380	1 461	1 575	1 601	1 680	1 779	1 843	1 918	2 000	2 075	2 154
	Least Developed Countries	kt	0	0	4	1	2	1	1	1	1	2	2	2
Poultry	World trade	kt	7 635	8 568	8 827	9 277	9 682	9 778	9 977	10 258	10 409	10 544	10 831	11 102
	OECD	kt	3 716	3 877	3 961	3 962	4 123	4 113	4 231	4 340	4 325	4 301	4 341	4 355
	Developing	kt	4 094	4 974	4 822	5 272	5 513	5 617	5 696	5 868	6 035	6 192	6 439	6 695
	Least Developed Countries	kt	7	11	10	10	10	10	11	11	12	12	13	13
Butter	World trade	kt	738	735	745	761	778	800	817	835	856	875	897	916
	OECD	kt	749	616	537	545	560	573	582	586	599	608	617	627
	Developing	kt	66	104	113	121	124	132	140	147	156	165	172	180
	Least Developed Countries	kt	1	1	3	1	1	1	1	1	1	1	1	1
Cheese	World trade	kt	1 418	1 564	1 623	1 680	1 732	1 799	1 854	1 902	1 949	1 995	2 046	2 113
	OECD	kt	1 194	1 232	1 213	1 245	1 267	1 288	1 302	1 311	1 308	1 311	1 313	1 320
	Developing	kt	176	234	289	281	296	315	345	376	413	450	486	527
	Least Developed Countries	kt	0	0	0	0	0	0	1	0	0	0	0	0
Whole milk powder	World trade	kt	1 382	1 400	1 625	1 661	1 723	1 785	1 856	1 924	1 984	2 049	2 126	2 197
	OECD	kt	1 231	1 140	1 043	1 056	1 093	1 107	1 134	1 154	1 166	1 184	1 200	1 219
	Developing	kt	442	449	545	571	597	644	690	736	783	830	879	929
	Least Developed Countries	kt	3	4	4	5	5	6	7	7	8	8	9	9

For notes, see end of the table.

OECD-FAO AGRICULTURAL OUTLOOK 2008-2017 – ISBN 978-92-64-04590-3 – © OECD/FAO 2008

Table A.3. **world trade projections** (cont.)

EXPORTS			Average 2002-06	2007 est.	2008	2009	2010	2011	2012	2013	2014	2015	2016	2017
Skim milk powder	World trade	kt	1 220	1 207	1 192	1 217	1 236	1 270	1 319	1 367	1 418	1 463	1 510	1 549
	OECD	kt	951	907	881	851	848	860	880	898	930	968	1 015	1 053
	Developing	kt	121	108	140	171	191	202	212	222	231	245	257	269
	Least Developed Countries	kt	2	1	1	1	1	1	1	1	1	1	1	1
Biofuel[b]	Ethanol world trade	mn l	6 363	4 752	4 613	5 998	6 237	5 175	5 478	6 366	7 065	7 831	8 842	10 384
	Biodiesel world trade	mn l	563	1 554	1 790	2 360	2 491	2 296	2 104	2 011	1 999	2 034	2 115	2 187

a) Excludes trade of live animals.
b) Sum of all positive net trade positions.
est.: estimate.
Source: OECD and FAO Secretariats.

StatLink 🔗 http://dx.doi.org/10.1787/383803202427

Table A.4. **Main policy assumptions for cereal markets**

Crop year[a]		Average 02/03-06/07	07/08 est.	08/09	09/10	10/11	11/12	12/13	13/14	14/15	15/16	16/17	17/18
ARGENTINA													
Crops export tax	%	20	20	27	27	27	27	27	27	27	27	27	27
Rice export tax	%	10	10	10	10	10	10	10	10	10	10	10	10
CANADA													
Tariff-quotas[b]													
Wheat	kt	350	350	350	350	350	350	350	350	350	350	350	350
in-quota tariff	%	1.1	1.1	1.1	1.1	1.1	1.1	1.1	1.1	1.1	1.1	1.1	1.1
out-of-quota tariff	%	62	62	62	62	62	62	62	62	62	62	62	62
Barley	kt	399	399	399	399	399	399	399	399	399	399	399	399
in-quota tariff	%	0.7	0.7	0.7	0.7	0.7	0.7	0.7	0.7	0.7	0.7	0.7	0.7
out-of-quota tariff	%	58	58	58	58	58	58	58	58	58	58	58	58
EUROPEAN UNION[c, d]													
Cereal support price[e]	EUR/t	101	101	101	101	101	101	101	101	101	101	101	101
Cereal compensation[f, g]	EUR/ha	209	31	31	31	31	31	31	31	31	31	31	31
Rice support price[h]	EUR/t	210	150	150	150	150	150	150	150	150	150	150	150
Compulsory set-aside rate	%	10	10	0	10	10	10	10	10	10	10	10	10
Set-aside payment[g]	EUR/ha	209	31	31	31	31	31	31	31	31	31	31	31
Direct payment for rice	EUR/ha	592	470	470	470	470	470	470	470	470	470	470	470
Wheat tariff-quota[b]	kt	3 184	3 780	3 780	3 780	3 780	3 780	3 780	3 780	3 780	3 780	3 780	3 780
Coarse grain tariff-quota[b]	kt	3 409	3 469	3 469	3 469	3 469	3 469	3 469	3 469	3 469	3 469	3 469	3 469
Subsidised export limits[b]													
Wheat	mt	15.4	15.4	15.4	15.4	15.4	15.4	15.4	15.4	15.4	15.4	15.4	15.4
Coarse grains[i]	mt	10.8	10.8	10.8	10.8	10.8	10.8	10.8	10.8	10.8	10.8	10.8	10.8
JAPAN													
Wheat support price[j]	'000 JPY/t	133	120	120	120	120	120	120	120	120	120	120	120
Barley support price[k]	'000 JPY/t	114	0	0	0	0	0	0	0	0	0	0	0
Wheat tariff-quota	kt	5 740	5 740	5 740	5 740	5 740	5 740	5 740	5 740	5 740	5 740	5 740	5 740
in-quota tariff	'000 JPY/t	0.0	0.0	0.0	0.0	0.0	0.0	0.0	0.0	0.0	0.0	0.0	0.0
out-of-quota tariff	'000 JPY/t	55	55	55	55	55	55	55	55	55	55	55	55
Barley tariff-quota	kt	1 369	1 369	1 369	1 369	1 369	1 369	1 369	1 369	1 369	1 369	1 369	1 369
in-quota tariff	'000 JPY/t	0	0	0	0	0	0	0	0	0	0	0	0
out-of-quota tariff	'000 JPY/t	39	39	39	39	39	39	39	39	39	39	39	39
Rice tariff-quota[l]	kt	682	682	682	682	682	682	682	682	682	682	682	682
in-quota tariff	'000 JPY/t	0	0	0	0	0	0	0	0	0	0	0	0
out-of-quota tariff	'000 JPY/t	341	341	341	341	341	341	341	341	341	341	341	341
KOREA													
Wheat tariff	%	5.9	5.4	5.4	5.4	5.4	5.4	5.4	5.4	5.4	5.4	5.4	5.4
Maize tariff-quota	kt	6 102	6 102	6 102	6 102	6 102	6 102	6 102	6 102	6 102	6 102	6 102	6 102
in-quota tariff	%	1.7	1.7	1.7	1.7	1.7	1.7	1.7	1.7	1.7	1.7	1.7	1.7
out-of-quota tariff	%	406	404	404	404	404	404	404	404	404	404	404	404
Barley tariff-quota	kt	53	54	54	54	54	54	54	54	54	54	54	54
in-quota tariff	%	23	23	23	23	23	23	23	23	23	23	23	23
out-of-quota tariff	%	362	359	359	359	359	359	359	359	359	359	359	359
Rice quota[l]	kt	195	205	205	205	205	205	205	205	205	205	205	205
in-quota tariff	%	5	5	5	5	5	5	5	5	5	5	5	5
MERCOSUR													
Wheat tariff	%	11	10	10	10	10	10	10	10	10	10	10	10
Coarse grain tariff	%	8	8	8	8	8	8	8	8	8	8	8	8
Rice tariff	%	11	10	10	10	10	10	10	10	10	10	10	10

For notes, see end of the table.

OECD-FAO AGRICULTURAL OUTLOOK 2008-2017 – ISBN 978-92-64-04590-3 – © OECD/FAO 2008

Table A.4. **Main policy assumptions for cereal markets** (cont.)

Crop year[a]		Average 02/03-06/07	07/08 est.	08/09	09/10	10/11	11/12	12/13	13/14	14/15	15/16	16/17	17/18
MEXICO													
Wheat NAFTA tariff	%	0.3	0.0	0.0	0.0	0.0	0.0	0.0	0.0	0.0	0.0	0.0	0.0
Fidelist social program	MXN mn	176	0	0	0	0	0	0	0	0	0	0	0
Tortilla consumption subsidy	MXN mn	0	0	0	0	0	0	0	0	0	0	0	0
Maize tariff-quota	kt	2 501	2 501	2 501	2 501	2 501	2 501	2 501	2 501	2 501	2 501	2 501	2 501
in-quota tariff	%	50	50	50	50	50	50	50	50	50	50	50	50
out-of-quota tariff	%	195	194	194	194	194	194	194	194	194	194	194	194
Barley tariff-quota	kt	5	5	5	5	5	5	5	5	5	5	5	5
in-quota tariff	%	50	50	50	50	50	50	50	50	50	50	50	50
out-of-quota tariff	%	116	115	115	115	115	115	115	115	115	115	115	115
UNITED STATES													
Wheat loan rate	USD/t	101.8	101.0	101.0	101.0	101.0	101.0	101.0	101.0	101.0	101.0	101.0	101.0
Maize loan rate	USD/t	77.2	76.8	76.8	76.8	76.8	76.8	76.8	76.8	76.8	76.8	76.8	76.8
Prod. flex. contract payment													
Wheat	USD/t	16.9	16.9	16.9	16.9	16.9	16.9	16.9	16.9	16.9	16.9	16.9	16.9
Maize	USD/t	10.3	10.3	10.3	10.3	10.3	10.3	10.3	10.3	10.3	10.3	10.3	10.3
CRP areas[m]	mha	6.2	7.1	6.7	6.6	6.4	6.3	6.4	6.4	6.6	6.8	7.0	7.1
Wheat	mha	2.9	3.6	3.4	3.3	3.2	3.2	3.2	3.2	3.3	3.4	3.5	3.6
Coarse grains	mha	3.3	3.5	3.3	3.2	3.2	3.1	3.1	3.2	3.2	3.4	3.5	3.5
Subsidised export limits[b]													
Wheat	mt	14.5	14.5	14.5	14.5	14.5	14.5	14.5	14.5	14.5	14.5	14.5	14.5
Coarse grains	mt	1.6	1.6	1.6	1.6	1.6	1.6	1.6	1.6	1.6	1.6	1.6	1.6
Wheat EEP payment[n]	USD/t	0.0	0.0	0.0	0.0	0.0	0.0	0.0	0.0	0.0	0.0	0.0	0.0
CHINA													
Wheat support price	CNY/t	0	0	0	0	0	0	0	0	0	0	0	0
Coarse grains support price	CNY/t	0	0	0	0	0	0	0	0	0	0	0	0
Rice support price	CNY/t	0	0	0	0	0	0	0	0	0	0	0	0
Wheat tariff-quota	kt	9 286	9 636	9 636	9 636	9 636	9 636	9 636	9 636	9 636	9 636	9 636	9 636
in-quota tariff	%	2.3	2.3	2.3	2.3	2.3	2.3	2.3	2.3	2.3	2.3	2.3	2.3
out-of-quota tariff	%	66.4	65.0	65.0	65.0	65.0	65.0	65.0	65.0	65.0	65.0	65.0	65.0
Coarse grains tariff	%	2	2	2	2	2	2	2	2	2	2	2	2
Maize tariff-quota	kt	6 795	7 200	7 200	7 200	7 200	7 200	7 200	7 200	7 200	7 200	7 200	7 200
in-quota tariff	%	3.7	3.7	3.7	3.7	3.7	3.7	3.7	3.7	3.7	3.7	3.7	3.7
out-of-quota tariff	%	43.9	41.7	41.7	41.7	41.7	41.7	41.7	41.7	41.7	41.7	41.7	41.7
Rice tariff-quota	kt	4 921	5 320	5 320	5 320	5 320	5 320	5 320	5 320	5 320	5 320	5 320	5 320
in-quota tariff	%	2.3	2.3	2.3	2.3	2.3	2.3	2.3	2.3	2.3	2.3	2.3	2.3
out-of-quota tariff	%	53.2	51.7	51.7	51.7	51.7	51.7	51.7	51.7	51.7	51.7	51.7	51.7
INDIA													
Input subsidy rate coarse grains[o]	INR/t	1 452	1 254	1 254	1 254	1 254	1 254	1 254	1 254	1 254	1 254	1 254	1 254
Input subsidy rate rice[o]	INR/t	729	641	641	641	641	641	641	641	641	641	641	641
Input subsidy rate wheat[o]	INR/t	1 854	1 772	1 772	1 772	1 772	1 772	1 772	1 772	1 772	1 772	1 772	1 772
Minimum support price													
Maize	INR/t	5 190	5 400	5 400	5 400	5 400	5 400	5 400	5 400	5 400	5 400	5 400	5 400
Rice	INR/t	5 190	5 700	5 700	5 700	5 700	5 700	5 700	5 700	5 700	5 700	5 700	5 700
Wheat	INR/t	6 300	6 400	6 400	6 400	6 400	6 400	6 400	6 400	6 400	6 400	6 400	6 400

For notes, see end of the table.

Table A.4. **Main policy assumptions for cereal markets** (*cont.*)

Crop year[a]		Average 02/03-06/07	07/08 est.	08/09	09/10	10/11	11/12	12/13	13/14	14/15	15/16	16/17	17/18
Wheat export subsidy	INR/t	1 940	1 941	1 941	1 941	1 941	1 941	1 941	1 941	1 941	1 941	1 941	1 941
Wheat tariff	%	88	88	88	88	88	88	88	88	88	88	88	88
Maize tariff	%	50	50	50	50	50	50	50	50	50	50	50	50
Rice tariff	%	30	30	30	30	30	30	30	30	30	30	30	30
Barley tariff	%	100	100	100	100	100	100	100	100	100	100	100	100

a) Beginning crop marketing year.
b) Year beginning 1 July.
c) Prices and payments in market Euro.
d) EU farmers also benefit from the Single Farm Payment (SFP) Scheme, which provides flat-rate payments independent from current production decisions and market developments. For the accession countries, payments are phased in with the assumption of maximum top-ups from national budgets up to 2011 through the Single Area Payment (SAP) and from 2012 through the SFP. Due to modulation, between 2.7% and 4.6% of the total SFP will go to rural development spending rather than directly to the farmers in the 15 former member states. From 2013, 4.6% of the total SFP will go to rural development spending in the accession countries.
e) Common intervention price for soft wheat, barley, maize and sorghum.
f) Compensatory area payments.
g) Actual payments made per hectare based on program yields.
h) Subject to a purchase limit of 75 000 tonnes per year.
i) The export volume excludes 0.4 mt of exported potato starch. The original limit on subsidised exports is 10.8 mt.
j) Government purchase price, domestic wheat.
k) Government purchase price, barley, 2nd grade, 1st class.
l) Husked rice basis.
m) Includes wheat, barley, maize, oats and sorghum.
n) Average per tonne of total exports.
o) Indian input subsidies consist of those for electricty, fertiliser and irrigation.
Note: The source for tariffs and Tariff Rate Quotas is AMAD (Agricultural market access database). The tariff and TRQ data are based on Most Favoured Nation rates scheduled with the WTO and exclude those under preferential or regional agreements, which may be substantially different. Tariffs are simple averages of several product lines. Specific rates are converted to *ad valorem* rates using world prices in the Outlook. Import quotas are based on global commitments scheduled in the WTO rather than those allocated to preferential partners under regional or other agreements. For Mexico, the NAFTA in-quota tariff on maize and barley is zero, while the tariff-rate quota becomes unlimited in 2003 for barley and 2008 for maize.
est.: estimate.
Source: OECD and FAO Secretariats.

StatLink 🛬 http://dx.doi.org/10.1787/383821625435

Table A.5. **World cereal projections**

Crop year[a]		Average 02/03-06/07	07/08 est.	08/09	09/10	10/11	11/12	12/13	13/14	14/15	15/16	16/17	17/18
WHEAT													
OECD[b]													
Production	mt	250.8	234.2	283.3	272.8	271.6	276.8	280.7	281.1	283.5	285.7	287.9	290.5
Consumption	mt	205.4	205.7	212.6	218.9	222.0	225.6	228.7	231.8	234.3	236.4	239.0	241.3
Closing stocks	mt	54.6	39.3	54.6	57.4	55.6	54.6	54.2	52.9	51.4	50.7	49.9	49.4
Non-OECD													
Production	mt	345.7	368.2	375.8	372.9	376.0	376.8	381.9	386.5	388.3	392.3	394.7	398.9
Consumption	mt	406.5	415.8	422.9	423.4	428.3	429.5	432.8	436.0	438.7	441.9	444.8	448.1
Closing stocks	mt	128.1	115.7	124.1	124.6	123.6	123.3	124.9	126.1	126.4	126.9	126.5	126.9
WORLD[c]													
Production	mt	596.5	602.4	659.2	645.7	647.5	653.7	662.7	667.6	671.8	678.0	682.6	689.4
Consumption	mt	611.9	621.5	635.5	642.3	650.3	655.0	661.5	667.7	673.0	678.3	683.7	689.4
Closing stocks	mt	182.7	155.0	178.6	182.0	179.2	177.9	179.1	179.0	177.9	177.6	176.4	176.4
Price[d]	USD/t	167.8	318.6	267.0	233.6	225.9	229.7	231.0	231.2	230.2	230.9	231.6	230.6
COARSE GRAINS													
OECD[b]													
Production	mt	508.6	567.2	567.8	576.2	590.1	601.2	608.1	611.8	617.4	625.3	630.2	637.2
Consumption	mt	488.7	546.7	549.8	556.1	563.2	571.9	577.6	581.9	585.5	591.4	595.4	600.8
Closing stocks	mt	102.1	79.9	70.3	68.2	72.9	78.4	82.0	84.4	87.2	89.8	91.7	94.8
Non-OECD													
Production	mt	456.3	491.9	507.3	514.6	523.1	534.1	539.9	545.5	551.7	562.0	571.3	579.5
Consumption	mt	482.2	516.6	532.0	542.8	547.9	553.3	564.4	573.3	582.4	591.3	602.2	611.3
Closing stocks	mt	126.3	123.7	125.7	119.8	117.2	121.8	124.2	123.9	122.2	124.1	126.2	127.7
WORLD[c]													
Production	mt	964.9	1 059.1	1 075.0	1 090.8	1 113.3	1 135.2	1 148.0	1 157.4	1 169.0	1 187.3	1 201.5	1 216.7
Consumption	mt	970.9	1 063.4	1 082.6	1 098.9	1 111.1	1 125.1	1 142.0	1 155.3	1 168.0	1 182.7	1 197.6	1 212.1
Closing stocks	mt	228.3	203.6	196.1	188.0	190.1	200.3	206.2	208.3	209.3	213.9	217.8	222.4
Price[e]	USD/t	113.2	181.3	185.3	185.0	189.0	188.4	178.5	173.0	173.2	170.9	166.6	164.6
RICE													
OECD[b]													
Production	mt	22.2	21.0	21.9	22.3	22.3	21.9	21.8	21.9	21.9	21.9	21.8	21.7
Consumption	mt	22.8	23.0	22.6	22.6	22.6	22.6	22.5	22.5	22.5	22.4	22.4	22.4
Closing stocks	mt	6.8	5.3	5.4	5.3	5.4	5.4	5.3	5.2	5.1	5.1	5.0	5.0
Non-OECD													
Production	mt	387.5	410.8	416.9	424.2	426.4	429.0	434.0	437.6	442.2	446.9	450.4	453.2
Consumption	mt	399.2	416.5	415.1	418.1	426.2	431.8	434.4	437.0	441.4	445.9	449.7	452.8
Closing stocks	mt	85.7	73.6	74.5	80.3	80.1	76.6	75.6	75.7	76.0	76.5	76.6	76.4
WORLD[c]													
Production	mt	409.7	431.8	438.8	446.5	448.7	450.9	455.9	459.5	464.1	468.7	472.2	475.0
Consumption	mt	422.0	439.5	437.8	440.8	448.8	454.4	456.9	459.4	463.8	468.4	472.1	475.2
Closing stocks	mt	92.5	78.8	79.9	85.6	85.5	81.9	80.9	80.9	81.2	81.5	81.6	81.4
Price[f]	USD/t	262.3	361.0	390.6	367.9	330.7	326.7	337.2	340.3	335.6	333.8	332.5	334.5

a) Beginning crop marketing year.
b) Excludes Iceland but includes the 8 EU members that are not members of the OECD.
c) Source of historic data is USDA.
d) No. 2 hard red winter wheat, ordinary protein, USA f.o.b. Gulf Ports (June/May), less EEP payments where applicable.
e) No. 2 yellow corn, US f.o.b. Gulf Ports (September/August).
f) Milled, 100%, grade b, Nominal Price Quote, NPQ, f.o.b. Bangkok (August/July)
est.: estimate.
Source: OECD and FAO Secretariats.

StatLink 🔗 http://dx.doi.org/10.1787/383822472634

Table A.6. **Wheat projections**

Crop year[a]	PRODUCTION (kt)			Growth[b] (%)		IMPORTS (kt)			Growth[b] (%)		EXPORTS (kt)			Growth[b] (%)	
	Average 2005-07 est.	2008	2017	1998-2007	2008-17	Average 2005-07 est.	2008	2017	1998-2007	2008-17	Average 2005-07 est.	2008	2017	1998-2007	2008-17
WORLD	608 070	659 171	689 357	0.46	0.67	110 255	121 070	126 465	0.79	0.82	107 941	121 070	126 465	0.51	0.82
DEVELOPED	317 250	357 754	373 162	0.15	0.72	22 583	24 575	23 616	0.21	0.00	90 330	101 214	103 802	0.29	0.53
NORTH AMERICA	77 976	89 472	84 268	−1.56	−0.25	2 686	2 747	3 288	−1.06	2.19	44 427	43 077	42 204	0.10	0.15
Canada	23 689	24 744	26 320	−0.81	0.99	26	25	22	−11.27	−0.69	16 426	15 656	15 675	−0.09	0.78
United States	54 287	64 728	57 948	−1.90	−0.78	2 661	2 722	3 266	−0.84	2.21	28 001	27 422	26 529	0.08	−0.21
EUROPE	130 809	147 772	157 811	−0.22	1.04	8 332	9 664	8 422	4.82	−0.44	12 970	18 892	12 993	−4.93	−3.61
EU(27)	126 735	143 633	152 874	−0.12	1.01	6 472	7 683	6 716	5.49	−0.18	12 785	18 752	12 838	−4.85	−3.66
CIS	89 463	92 596	101 862	4.19	1.18	4 676	4 881	4 914	−5.17	0.04	22 350	21 368	31 374	13.82	4.20
Russian Federation	46 867	48 006	51 773	5.40	0.97	1 048	1 181	1 214	−12.03	0.18	11 154	12 319	15 159	32.21	3.30
Ukraine	15 403	14 883	17 768	−1.31	2.17	71	0	0	−16.95	0.00	3 773	814	6 147	5.50	15.55
OCEANIA DEVELOPED	16 173	25 141	26 477	−5.92	0.40	389	397	395	10.66	−0.01	10 432	17 746	17 101	−7.82	−0.45
Australia	15 868	24 834	26 170	−6.02	0.41	0	0	0	0.00	0.00	10 432	17 746	17 101	−7.82	−0.45
New Zealand	305	307	307	−1.31	0.00	389	397	395	10.66	−0.01	0	0	0	21.66	0.00
OTHER DEVELOPED	2 829	2 773	2 745	0.69	−0.36	6 499	6 887	6 596	0.80	−0.42	151	130	130	7.90	0.00
Japan	881	901	936	5.30	0.41	5 455	5 618	5 216	−0.37	−0.84	0	0	0	0.00	0.00
South Africa	1 947	1 872	1 809	−1.07	−0.74	1 044	1 269	1 381	8.91	1.34	151	130	130	7.90	0.00
DEVELOPING	290 820	301 417	316 195	0.79	0.62	87 673	96 495	102 849	0.95	1.01	17 611	19 856	22 663	1.64	2.22
AFRICA	20 285	20 750	26 449	4.86	2.82	28 619	31 899	34 169	1.91	0.88	966	713	1 620	15.21	9.10
NORTH AFRICA	18 766	18 939	24 200	4.94	2.84	17 686	19 837	19 127	0.22	−0.42	400	183	480	12.81	10.49
Algeria	2 650	3 025	4 459	8.17	4.31	5 000	4 819	3 712	0.96	−2.50	0	0	0	0.00	0.00
Egypt	7 946	7 485	8 898	3.11	2.06	7 300	8 488	8 961	1.89	0.34	0	0	0	−13.69	0.00
SUB-SAHARAN AFRICA	1 518	1 811	2 248	3.95	2.60	10 932	12 062	15 042	5.15	2.77	566	530	1 140	17.09	8.56
LATIN AMERICA and CARIBBEAN	24 615	25 564	30 075	1.66	2.12	20 207	22 821	20 868	1.28	−0.37	9 072	10 200	13 315	0.27	3.69
Argentina	13 895	15 164	18 679	0.12	2.79	0	0	0	0.00	0.00	7 891	9 309	12 088	−0.74	3.88
Brazil	4 318	3 819	4 533	8.45	1.88	6 517	7 730	4 907	−0.82	−2.92	219	0	0	11.80	0.00
Chile	1 526	1 255	1 202	0.15	−0.35	780	1 352	1 387	4.71	1.17	0	0	0	−24.58	0.00
Mexico	3 253	3 399	3 387	−0.49	0.12	3 624	3 866	3 561	4.33	−1.49	415	402	415	4.04	0.15
Uruguay	555	783	895	6.04	1.36	23	0	0	−21.07	0.00	125	221	336	8.55	2.38
ASIA and PACIFIC	245 920	255 103	259 672	0.41	0.26	38 847	41 775	47 813	0.12	1.78	7 572	8 943	7 728	2.59	−0.81
Bangladesh	872	819	918	−10.48	1.24	1 899	3 045	3 299	0.83	1.77	0	0	0	−55.14	0.00
China[c]	102 343	103 702	95 963	−0.73	−0.88	507	347	2 046	−4.92	17.11	2 395	2 910	1 442	18.57	−7.78
India	70 997	76 225	81 421	0.23	0.91	3 054	1 863	3 090	14.17	4.80	433	295	250	10.25	−1.84
Indonesia	0	0	0	0.00	0.00	5 006	5 329	5 534	4.80	0.68	30	32	47	5.96	4.29
Iran, Islamic Republic of	14 603	15 327	16 390	5.98	0.80	767	800	1 000	−35.11	2.55	147	403	432	50.54	0.76
Korea	6	6	9	6.85	3.93	3 561	3 935	3 741	−1.41	−0.40	11	11	11	−12.29	0.00
Malaysia	0	0	0	0.00	0.00	1 437	1 372	1 472	1.96	0.12	80	83	20	−1.83	−15.13
Pakistan	21 920	22 755	25 318	1.98	1.21	932	1 639	2 400	−0.25	6.87	733	1 500	1 500	−7.20	1.00
Saudi Arabia	2 583	2 509	564	4.83	−16.19	54	202	2 569	5.71	25.39	30	33	55	33.97	5.81
Turkey	19 603	19 879	21 581	−0.37	1.03	1 300	1 800	1 800	−3.33	2.06	1 800	1 857	2 152	−0.87	4.91
LEAST DEVELOPED COUNTRIES (LDC)	7 303	7 717	10 030	2.59	3.04	10 564	13 271	13 605	2.61	1.09	110	71	59	−19.36	−0.55
OECD	245 525	283 347	290 490	−0.99	0.56	24 013	26 484	25 127	1.41	−0.15	69 939	81 900	74 776	−2.13	−0.63
NON-OECD	362 545	375 823	398 867	1.53	0.76	86 243	94 586	101 337	0.65	1.07	38 002	39 170	51 689	7.40	3.28

For notes, see end of the table.

OECD-FAO AGRICULTURAL OUTLOOK 2008-2017 – ISBN 978-92-64-04590-3 – © OECD/FAO 2008

Table A.6. **Wheat projections** (cont.)

Crop year[a]	CONSUMPTION (kt)			Growth[b] (%)		FOOD USE (kt)			Growth[b] (%)		PER CAPITA (kg)			Growth[b] (%)	
	Average 2005-07 est.	2008	2017	1998-2007	2008-17	Average 2005-07 est.	2008	2017	1998-2007	2008-17	Average 2005-07 est.	2008	2017	1998-2007	2008-17
WORLD	620 173	635 547	689 394	0.79	0.89	451 838	465 596	494 400	1.08	0.70	68.4	68.8	66.1	−0.15	−0.41
DEVELOPED	257 900	263 304	293 353	0.61	1.12	136 232	139 295	142 892	0.34	0.27	101.8	103.4	103.6	−0.05	0.01
NORTH AMERICA	39 490	41 214	46 035	−1.53	1.07	28 402	28 993	31 607	0.18	0.93	85.6	85.7	86.2	−0.82	0.04
Canada	8 296	8 645	10 593	0.43	1.92	3 108	3 160	3 843	1.32	2.08	95.3	95.1	107.3	0.33	1.24
United States	31 194	32 569	35 442	−2.00	0.83	25 295	25 833	27 764	0.05	0.78	84.5	84.6	84.0	−0.96	−0.11
EUROPE	129 039	131 790	153 228	0.80	1.62	65 607	67 446	68 259	0.56	0.13	124.1	127.1	127.4	0.26	0.03
EU(27)	123 128	125 826	146 715	0.89	1.64	61 359	63 110	63 644	0.64	0.13	124.8	127.8	127.8	0.34	−0.02
CIS	72 793	73 464	75 318	1.13	0.16	31 980	32 206	32 606	−0.22	0.06	115.2	116.4	119.1	−0.02	0.17
Russian Federation	37 331	36 824	37 822	0.65	0.18	14 528	14 258	14 110	−0.79	−0.22	102.0	101.2	104.8	−0.35	0.28
Ukraine	11 367	11 811	11 502	−2.36	−0.43	5 767	5 885	5 327	−1.23	−1.12	123.9	128.3	124.7	−0.41	−0.33
OCEANIA DEVELOPED	7 335	7 291	9 553	5.19	2.96	2 108	2 309	2 331	2.57	0.96	85.2	91.5	85.0	1.39	0.04
Australia	6 641	6 589	8 851	5.27	3.23	1 773	1 931	1 953	3.01	1.16	86.1	91.8	85.3	1.81	0.21
New Zealand	694	702	702	4.45	0.00	335	378	378	0.44	0.00	80.8	89.6	83.5	−0.65	−0.78
OTHER DEVELOPED	9 243	9 544	9 219	0.62	−0.41	8 135	8 341	8 089	0.90	−0.36	46.2	47.2	45.9	0.52	−0.34
Japan	6 327	6 515	6 162	0.20	−0.64	5 319	5 494	5 214	0.26	−0.59	41.6	43.0	41.5	0.14	−0.41
South Africa	2 916	3 029	3 057	1.67	0.06	2 816	2 847	2 875	2.21	0.07	58.3	58.3	56.8	1.11	−0.33
DEVELOPING	362 273	372 243	396 041	0.93	0.73	315 605	326 301	351 507	1.41	0.88	59.9	60.2	57.7	−0.04	−0.44
AFRICA	48 483	50 944	59 703	3.13	1.66	44 000	46 432	53 913	3.03	1.64	49.3	49.5	47.0	0.64	−0.60
NORTH AFRICA	36 519	38 153	42 677	2.54	1.22	32 695	34 309	38 515	2.47	1.26	138.7	140.2	134.0	0.55	−0.53
Algeria	7 450	7 651	8 160	2.41	0.71	6 900	7 099	7 611	2.18	0.77	206.9	206.5	194.5	0.71	−0.68
Egypt	15 213	15 927	17 723	2.55	1.14	14 146	14 838	16 523	2.40	1.15	190.7	193.1	186.0	0.59	−0.46
SUB-SAHARAN AFRICA	11 964	12 790	16 116	6.12	2.53	11 393	12 123	15 398	4.80	2.62	17.3	17.5	17.9	2.23	0.24
LATIN AMERICA and CARIBBEAN	35 572	37 783	37 554	1.91	0.25	30 913	32 805	32 760	2.02	0.34	55.0	57.0	51.4	0.74	−0.80
Argentina	5 817	6 005	6 541	0.99	0.65	4 613	4 736	5 596	1.32	1.37	118.0	119.0	129.6	0.34	0.46
Brazil	10 674	11 603	9 439	2.16	−0.67	10 034	10 911	8 868	2.16	−0.69	53.2	56.6	41.5	0.79	−1.85
Chile	2 271	2 401	2 582	1.87	0.70	1 996	2 101	2 275	1.56	0.78	121.2	125.0	124.8	0.43	−0.12
Mexico	6 461	6 862	6 533	1.85	−0.79	4 863	5 149	4 716	1.96	−1.09	47.3	48.9	41.0	1.10	−2.06
Uruguay	475	480	550	3.40	1.38	366	380	432	1.98	1.37	109.7	113.3	125.0	1.03	1.03
ASIA and PACIFIC	278 217	283 516	299 694	0.46	0.63	240 604	247 064	264 834	1.06	0.80	63.1	63.3	61.4	−0.20	−0.31
Bangladesh	3 171	3 339	4 196	−0.39	2.23	3 051	3 299	4 152	0.47	2.24	19.6	20.4	22.4	−1.41	0.69
China[c]	100 849	100 092	96 665	−1.13	−0.36	87 036	87 566	85 065	−0.38	−0.15	66.4	65.3	60.4	−1.04	−0.81
India	73 684	76 704	83 960	1.21	1.06	66 618	69 454	76 660	1.82	1.16	57.8	58.6	57.5	0.20	−0.14
Indonesia	4 959	5 098	5 499	4.21	0.79	4 253	4 399	4 768	3.11	0.87	18.6	18.8	18.6	1.80	−0.11
Iran, Islamic Republic of	15 383	15 646	16 983	0.92	0.90	11 883	12 144	13 377	1.24	1.07	160.0	160.2	164.3	0.21	−0.26
Korea	3 580	3 756	3 755	−1.30	−0.11	2 503	2 728	2 764	1.95	0.12	51.8	56.1	55.9	1.45	−0.07
Malaysia	1 279	1 347	1 460	1.57	0.83	1 054	1 120	1 254	2.24	1.19	40.4	41.5	40.6	0.27	−0.28
Pakistan	21 662	22 764	26 286	1.22	1.61	20 562	21 645	25 058	1.73	1.65	127.7	129.6	126.7	−0.15	−0.24
Saudi Arabia	2 706	2 716	3 126	5.41	1.62	2 293	2 410	2 846	4.55	1.90	94.9	95.3	93.6	2.03	−0.14
Turkey	19 670	19 824	21 252	0.22	0.79	14 250	14 699	16 192	1.46	1.09	192.8	193.8	193.3	0.08	−0.02
LEAST DEVELOPED COUNTRIES (LDC)	18 128	19 135	23 449	3.82	2.16	16 765	17 868	22 119	3.42	2.27	23.8	24.2	24.5	1.03	0.02
OECD	207 332	212 615	241 344	0.42	1.33	119 808	123 432	127 388	0.72	0.34	98.7	100.6	99.6	0.10	−0.11
NON-OECD	412 841	422 932	448 050	0.99	0.66	332 029	342 164	367 012	1.22	0.83	61.6	61.8	59.2	−0.16	−0.43

a) Beginning crop marketing year – see Glossary of Terms for definitions.
b) Least-squares growth rate (see glossary).
c) Refers to mainland only. The economies of Chinese Taipei, Hong Kong (China) and Macau (China) are included in the Other Asia Pacific aggregate.
est.: estimate.
Source: OECD and FAO Secretariats.

StatLink http://dx.doi.org/10.1787/384007548283

Table A.7. **Coarse grain projections**

Crop year[a]	PRODUCTION (kt) Average 2005-07 est.	2008	2017	Growth[b] (%) 1998-2007	2008-17	IMPORTS (kt) Average 2005-07 est.	2008	2017	Growth[b] (%) 1998-2007	2008-17	EXPORTS (kt) Average 2005-07 est.	2008	2017	Growth[b] (%) 1998-2007	2008-17
WORLD	1 012 565	1 075 021	1 216 671	2.01	1.34	111 416	111 697	126 943	1.41	1.59	115 073	111 697	126 943	1.12	1.59
DEVELOPED	562 557	604 675	678 419	1.39	1.22	35 399	32 167	32 792	1.12	0.00	88 726	82 438	95 584	0.26	1.84
NORTH AMERICA	335 294	358 809	415 119	2.19	1.46	4 263	4 935	6 680	0.13	1.49	67 934	62 562	65 286	1.61	1.45
Canada	25 303	26 188	27 502	0.09	0.78	2 057	2 431	4 176	4.70	2.68	4 994	5 027	4 804	2.43	-0.07
United States	309 991	332 621	387 617	2.37	1.51	2 207	2 504	2 504	-2.06	0.00	62 940	57 535	60 482	1.55	1.59
EUROPE	150 104	162 541	172 404	-0.79	0.88	8 440	4 630	3 920	7.58	-1.36	8 766	8 219	11 697	-9.55	2.94
EU(27)	138 891	150 992	159 914	-0.87	0.89	7 496	3 900	3 200	7.67	-1.63	8 333	7 818	11 296	-9.88	3.06
CIS	57 474	59 872	64 334	3.84	0.67	1 326	1 674	2 039	-3.72	3.61	7 016	4 769	9 464	12.66	4.21
Russian Federation	28 925	30 117	30 239	2.98	-0.11	550	774	1 186	-10.74	4.94	1 720	1 208	1 128	28.19	-7.39
Ukraine	17 618	19 074	22 261	5.07	1.76	157	270	353	8.72	2.96	4 618	3 361	7 821	10.83	6.87
OCEANIA DEVELOPED	10 352	13 362	15 666	-1.62	1.64	123	82	169	11.13	7.40	3 826	6 232	7 671	-5.38	1.82
Australia	9 867	12 890	15 205	-1.63	1.70	0	0	0	-7.11	0.00	3 826	6 232	7 671	-5.36	1.82
New Zealand	485	472	462	-2.35	-0.24	123	82	169	12.32	7.40	0	0	0	-69.17	0.00
OTHER DEVELOPED	9 332	10 091	10 895	-0.39	0.45	21 246	20 847	19 983	-0.56	-0.48	1 184	657	1 467	-1.85	3.73
Japan	217	214	221	0.69	0.37	20 376	19 991	19 183	-0.81	-0.49	0	0	0	0.00	0.00
South Africa	9 116	9 877	10 673	-0.41	0.45	870	855	800	9.39	-0.37	1 184	657	1 467	-1.85	3.73
DEVELOPING	450 008	470 345	538 253	2.83	1.49	76 018	79 529	94 151	1.51	2.19	26 347	29 258	31 359	4.24	0.87
AFRICA	92 688	97 476	114 215	3.49	1.77	14 892	15 825	21 371	2.78	3.62	3 060	4 030	4 435	13.79	0.02
NORTH AFRICA	23 555	24 690	29 390	4.48	1.97	11 328	12 249	16 133	3.02	3.31	403	497	1 379	62.05	13.59
Algeria	1 318	1 435	1 484	15.36	0.35	2 403	2 330	2 965	3.39	2.82	0	0	0	0.00	0.00
Egypt	8 189	8 018	8 231	1.14	0.36	4 758	5 335	6 698	2.11	2.72	0	0	0	0.00	0.00
SUB-SAHARAN AFRICA	69 133	72 786	84 824	3.17	1.70	3 564	3 576	5 238	1.98	4.65	2 656	3 532	3 057	12.31	-3.14
LATIN AMERICA and CARIBBEAN	114 406	119 794	137 296	3.92	1.60	23 238	23 651	27 983	1.59	2.02	18 379	21 955	24 093	7.38	1.41
Argentina	24 274	22 891	30 277	3.59	3.13	0	0	0	0.00	0.00	13 214	12 124	16 492	4.26	3.22
Brazil	45 317	49 961	57 815	4.76	1.80	1 231	1 231	1 373	-2.26	0.56	3 893	8 054	5 357	76.74	-2.69
Chile	2 034	2 186	2 328	9.18	0.70	1 514	1 622	2 081	3.15	3.45	102	124	208	8.52	5.70
Mexico	28 459	29 386	29 365	2.23	0.01	10 477	10 362	11 361	0.43	1.05	109	169	258	10.27	1.86
Uruguay	765	965	972	7.49	0.18	61	10	12	-26.01	1.08	110	190	10	1.61	-26.59
ASIA and PACIFIC	242 914	253 076	286 742	2.09	1.33	37 888	40 053	44 796	0.98	1.68	4 908	3 274	2 830	-8.01	-1.74
Bangladesh	519	547	541	30.30	0.57	50	17	150	-0.65	17.81	0	0	0	0.00	0.00
China[c]	151 069	158 254	180 122	1.76	1.44	1 627	1 489	2 044	-6.41	3.37	3 403	1 869	1 175	-11.64	-5.47
India	33 833	35 307	40 371	1.38	1.14	93	69	80	-17.03	1.64	325	444	455	79.67	0.27
Indonesia	12 193	12 726	13 630	3.28	0.68	1 121	575	904	7.29	10.24	100	102	120	-2.19	1.80
Iran, Islamic Republic of	4 893	4 872	5 424	4.94	1.25	2 967	3 442	4 541	6.74	3.61	0	0	0	-10.65	0.00
Korea	309	315	413	-3.19	2.93	8 740	8 989	9 681	0.80	1.03	0	0	0	69.46	0.00
Malaysia	79	85	104	4.78	2.51	2 676	2 797	2 941	1.00	0.85	9	7	0	15.35	-25.06
Pakistan	3 503	3 874	4 135	6.42	0.64	26	40	22	6.89	-3.22	0	74	0	-1.26	-31.26
Saudi Arabia	418	445	518	-0.28	1.53	7 528	8 742	9 060	2.03	0.82	0	0	0	0.00	0.00
Turkey	13 294	13 155	14 930	2.32	1.33	618	705	849	-11.96	2.26	292	76	184	-12.95	9.65
LEAST DEVELOPED COUNTRIES (LDC)	42 683	45 299	51 315	3.93	1.39	2 281	2 287	4 277	1.56	6.94	2 625	3 591	3 084	13.78	-2.60
OECD	528 348	567 762	637 158	1.27	1.24	52 417	49 298	51 448	0.79	0.34	80 495	76 856	84 694	-0.49	1.67
NON-OECD	484 218	507 258	579 514	2.87	1.45	58 999	62 399	75 495	1.96	2.53	34 577	34 840	42 249	5.81	1.46

For notes, see end of the table.

OECD-FAO AGRICULTURAL OUTLOOK 2008-2017 – ISBN 978-92-64-04590-3 – © OECD/FAO 2008

Table A.7. **Coarse grain projections** (cont.)

Crop year[a]	CONSUMPTION (kt) Average 2005-07 est.	CONSUMPTION (kt) 2008	CONSUMPTION (kt) 2017	Growth[b] (%) 1998-2007	Growth[b] (%) 2008-17	FEED USE (kt) Average 2005-07 est.	FEED USE (kt) 2008	FEED USE (kt) 2017	Growth[b] (%) 1998-2007	Growth[b] (%) 2008-17	PER CAPITA (kg) Average 2005-07 est.	PER CAPITA (kg) 2008	PER CAPITA (kg) 2017	Growth[b] (%) 1998-2007	Growth[b] (%) 2008-17
WORLD	1 024 628	1 082 562	1 212 060	2.21	1.25	626 360	634 481	688 037	1.20	0.98	30.5	30.5	30.8	0.53	0.14
DEVELOPED	527 324	562 186	612 585	1.87	0.95	356 291	354 967	363 240	0.43	0.40	32.7	31.3	30.8	0.47	−0.16
NORTH AMERICA	278 889	314 601	356 868	2.62	1.29	175 745	172 824	183 351	0.07	0.75	25.2	21.3	21.4	0.76	−0.04
Canada	23 156	23 474	26 828	0.03	1.29	19 088	18 430	18 758	−0.64	0.31	51.9	36.9	46.8	−1.26	2.29
United States	255 732	291 126	330 040	2.88	1.29	156 657	154 395	164 593	0.16	0.80	22.3	19.6	18.6	1.32	−0.60
EUROPE	158 558	155 829	161 454	0.93	0.57	120 650	120 726	116 748	0.26	−0.16	46.9	45.5	45.0	1.05	−0.07
EU(27)	146 576	144 049	148 645	0.98	0.54	110 591	110 573	105 805	0.26	−0.25	49.4	48.0	47.4	1.07	−0.08
CIS	52 686	54 823	56 907	2.24	0.55	35 199	37 188	39 833	3.60	0.95	19.9	20.2	19.1	−2.16	−0.70
Russian Federation	28 232	29 265	30 273	1.05	0.52	18 617	19 466	21 385	2.19	1.24	23.3	24.2	21.1	−2.71	−1.63
Ukraine	13 511	14 635	14 814	3.11	0.30	9 271	10 448	10 405	4.68	0.17	25.8	25.5	28.9	−1.48	1.50
OCEANIA DEVELOPED	6 868	7 067	8 063	0.52	1.48	5 419	5 485	5 242	−0.15	0.24	8.5	9.4	7.4	−1.14	−1.00
Australia	6 265	6 508	7 432	0.60	1.49	4 886	4 954	4 653	−0.25	0.15	9.5	10.7	8.3	−1.00	−0.98
New Zealand	602	559	631	−0.50	1.34	533	531	589	0.55	1.06	3.6	3.4	3.0	−3.32	−1.35
OTHER DEVELOPED	30 323	29 866	29 294	−0.03	−0.25	19 277	18 744	18 066	−0.21	−0.46	28.1	28.3	29.0	0.48	0.32
Japan	20 653	20 156	19 284	−0.45	−0.54	15 268	14 733	13 947	−0.56	−0.07	1.7	1.7	1.7	1.51	0.08
South Africa	9 670	9 710	10 000	0.95	0.32	4 009	4 012	4 118	1.23	0.28	98.0	98.0	96.8	−0.27	−0.08
DEVELOPING	497 304	520 377	599 474	2.58	1.66	270 069	279 514	324 798	2.28	1.68	29.9	30.3	30.8	0.57	0.21
AFRICA	103 211	109 098	131 230	3.11	2.11	20 486	21 318	25 469	4.28	2.04	77.0	78.0	79.5	0.00	0.28
NORTH AFRICA	34 268	36 668	44 192	3.88	2.14	16 517	17 227	20 944	4.11	2.26	65.0	68.0	71.1	1.75	0.55
Algeria	3 590	3 750	4 453	5.75	1.96	2 788	2 928	3 522	7.38	2.10	20.0	20.0	20.4	0.00	0.27
Egypt	12 919	13 247	14 935	1.78	1.40	8 684	8 852	9 965	1.89	1.38	49.6	49.9	49.6	−0.03	0.00
SUB-SAHARAN AFRICA	68 040	72 400	87 038	2.73	2.10	3 969	4 091	4 525	5.06	1.09	81.4	81.6	82.3	−0.52	0.18
LATIN AMERICA and CARIBBEAN	118 155	124 701	140 951	2.64	1.44	70 257	73 350	84 211	1.72	1.70	55.0	58.4	59.1	2.66	0.07
Argentina	10 808	11 953	13 485	2.27	2.06	8 694	9 413	10 799	2.27	2.19	7.7	9.0	11.4	2.75	2.66
Brazil	42 107	45 030	53 876	2.55	1.89	30 524	31 699	37 584	2.28	1.90	33.2	40.3	45.7	1.07	0.99
Chile	3 313	3 634	4 198	5.61	1.80	2 631	2 877	3 361	5.35	1.96	18.7	19.4	20.1	2.83	0.45
Mexico	38 883	39 641	40 458	1.81	0.27	16 172	16 354	16 417	−1.58	0.10	152.7	155.3	147.3	4.12	−0.53
Uruguay	709	822	977	7.22	1.94	206	200	212	2.11	0.73	33.3	33.9	35.0	1.65	0.41
ASIA and PACIFIC	275 939	286 578	327 294	2.37	1.39	179 326	184 846	215 118	2.29	1.63	15.2	14.7	13.7	−0.54	−0.77
Bangladesh	569	565	691	18.21	2.58	283	248	330	21.73	3.78	1.8	2.0	1.9	19.96	0.03
China[c]	149 280	156 099	179 474	2.26	1.34	104 035	107 783	125 012	1.68	1.50	13.4	12.1	10.1	−1.36	−1.00
India	33 500	34 628	40 094	1.23	1.64	8 000	9 026	13 095	2.50	4.14	20.5	19.9	18.7	0.58	−0.65
Indonesia	12 934	13 241	14 432	3.28	1.01	3 933	4 020	4 674	5.57	1.72	28.0	28.3	28.0	0.71	−0.03
Iran, Islamic Republic of	7 860	8 284	9 958	5.46	2.27	7 395	7 800	9 466	5.64	2.39	1.5	1.4	1.4	−0.28	−0.31
Korea	9 107	9 269	10 092	0.92	1.10	6 895	6 781	7 021	1.39	0.59	6.9	7.5	9.1	−1.03	2.23
Malaysia	2 715	2 853	3 046	1.10	0.94	2 552	2 633	2 814	1.65	0.97	1.8	1.8	1.8	−0.68	0.18
Pakistan	3 395	3 874	4 170	5.60	0.95	1 362	1 472	1 597	10.85	0.94	8.7	10.6	9.8	−0.89	−0.59
Saudi Arabia	8 322	8 749	9 594	2.63	1.10	8 110	8 533	9 364	2.73	1.10	4.0	3.9	3.7	−1.28	−0.41
Turkey	14 003	13 132	15 545	3.15	1.62	11 333	10 466	12 319	3.44	1.48	16.5	16.2	17.1	0.07	0.62
LEAST DEVELOPED COUNTRIES (LDC)	41 226	43 011	55 509	0.22	2.00	3 435	3 583	3 941	7.51	1.17	45.0	45.7	46.6	0.06	0.26
OECD	516 841	549 777	600 809	1.89	0.97	343 108	338 903	345 779	0.13	0.35	41.6	40.3	39.7	1.89	−0.11
NON-OECD	507 787	532 785	611 251	2.55	1.52	283 251	295 578	342 258	2.60	1.67	28.0	28.4	29.0	0.15	0.26

a) Beginning crop marketing year – see Glossary of Terms for definitions.
b) Least-squares growth rate (see glossary).
c) Refers to mainland only. The economies of Chinese Taipei, Hong Kong (China) and Macau (China) are included in the Other Asia Pacific aggregate.
est.: estimate.
Source: OECD and FAO Secretariats.

StatLink http://dx.doi.org/10.1787/384058720185

Table A.8. **Rice projections**

Crop year[a]	PRODUCTION (kt)			Growth[b] (%)		IMPORTS (kt)			Growth[b] (%)		EXPORTS (kt)			Growth[b] (%)	
	Average 2005-07 est.	2008	2017	1998-2007	2008-17	Average 2005-07 est.	2008	2017	1998-2007	2008-17	Average 2005-07 est.	2008	2017	1998-2007	2008-17
WORLD	430 259	438 824	474 998	0.91	0.86	30 052	30 844	38 082	1.99	2.36	29 930	30 844	38 082	3.03	2.36
DEVELOPED	17 651	17 557	17 846	−0.37	0.05	4 562	4 830	5 641	2.41	1.82	3 816	3 677	4 930	−1.28	2.64
NORTH AMERICA	6 467	6 340	7 440	0.70	1.48	962	1 059	1 327	6.85	2.54	3 318	3 191	3 936	2.48	2.02
Canada	0	0	0	0.00	0.00	339	365	421	4.64	1.71	0	0	0	0.00	0.00
United States	6 467	6 340	7 440	0.70	1.48	623	695	906	8.25	2.96	3 318	3 191	3 936	2.48	2.02
EUROPE	1 705	1 714	1 747	−0.06	0.26	1 236	1 415	1 655	0.72	1.86	159	201	223	−1.60	1.00
EU(27)	1 693	1 703	1 736	−0.03	0.26	1 104	1 282	1 506	0.40	1.93	158	200	222	−1.43	1.00
CIS	954	947	1 096	3.18	1.28	585	724	871	−1.79	2.58	31	32	27	0.72	0.18
Russian Federation	422	410	517	4.45	2.05	255	381	302	−7.27	−1.44	19	20	10	7.25	−3.78
Ukraine	60	60	59	3.27	−0.66	107	104	140	6.84	3.29	0	0	0	−5.88	19.51
OCEANIA DEVELOPED	284	740	927	−30.10	2.54	178	100	154	10.40	4.77	142	93	585	−28.44	13.18
Australia	284	740	927	−30.10	2.54	141	63	104	12.40	5.76	142	93	585	−28.44	13.18
New Zealand	0	0	0	0.00	0.00	37	38	49	3.89	2.93	0	0	0	0.00	0.00
OTHER DEVELOPED	8 241	7 815	6 636	−0.34	−1.85	1 601	1 532	1 635	2.49	0.64	166	160	160	−13.64	0.00
Japan	8 239	7 813	6 634	−0.34	−1.85	859	799	799	0.54	0.00	166	160	160	−13.64	0.00
South Africa	2	2	2	0.00	0.00	742	733	836	5.03	1.30	0	0	0	0.00	0.00
DEVELOPING	412 608	421 266	457 152	0.97	0.89	25 491	26 014	32 440	1.92	2.46	26 114	27 167	33 152	3.76	2.33
AFRICA	13 977	14 716	18 494	3.18	2.50	8 923	8 989	12 248	6.80	3.27	1 043	1 097	857	12.35	−3.09
NORTH AFRICA	4 486	4 706	5 065	3.12	0.72	355	322	477	6.04	4.18	1 036	1 093	855	13.34	−3.08
Algeria	1	1	1	0.00	−0.04	95	95	123	7.24	2.75	0	0	0	0.00	0.00
Egypt	4 464	4 688	5 043	3.13	0.71	34	0	0	7.09	0.00	1 036	1 093	855	13.34	−3.08
SUB-SAHARAN AFRICA	9 492	10 010	13 430	3.24	3.25	8 568	8 667	11 771	6.84	3.23	7	5	2	−20.48	−6.69
LATIN AMERICA and CARIBBEAN	17 149	17 497	20 108	2.10	1.37	3 603	3 384	4 512	0.27	3.55	2 123	1 902	2 606	4.12	3.08
Argentina	973	1 012	1 606	3.81	4.20	15	15	15	−4.66	0.00	708	722	1 266	8.19	4.94
Brazil	8 220	8 397	8 284	2.45	−0.19	725	425	1 246	−8.15	13.66	275	161	185	31.88	4.18
Chile	94	88	87	4.93	−0.42	87	96	140	1.31	4.03	1	1	2	−10.05	9.04
Mexico	217	213	188	−1.86	−1.83	719	703	750	4.37	0.70	2	2	2	−2.09	−0.55
Uruguay	852	778	1 057	1.27	3.45	0	0	0	3.94	0.00	728	737	947	0.06	3.40
ASIA and PACIFIC	381 482	389 054	418 549	0.85	0.80	12 964	13 641	15 681	0.03	1.61	22 948	24 168	29 689	3.45	2.46
Bangladesh	26 466	26 746	31 455	2.36	1.73	1 094	1 880	1 536	4.73	−2.55	1	1	1	0.84	0.00
China[c]	127 146	126 683	126 855	−1.00	−0.03	650	686	761	15.54	1.26	1 410	2 244	2 221	−9.89	0.25
India	92 629	95 191	103 070	0.73	0.90	61	50	50	3.33	0.00	3 995	3 660	3 750	7.98	0.27
Indonesia	34 787	36 214	38 231	1.36	0.65	933	1 501	2 083	−19.36	3.93	0	0	0	−0.31	0.00
Iran, Islamic Republic of	2 003	2 283	2 782	4.17	2.00	1 000	833	661	0.44	−1.67	0	0	0	0.00	0.00
Korea	4 783	4 761	4 398	−1.82	−0.91	270	189	337	12.92	6.38	0	0	0	0.00	0.00
Malaysia	1 454	1 498	1 867	1.50	2.12	820	780	746	4.11	−1.05	0	0	0	0.00	0.00
Pakistan	5 491	5 482	6 003	2.06	1.17	1	0	0	−14.30	0.00	2 998	2 791	2 790	6.07	0.40
Saudi Arabia	0	0	0	0.00	0.00	1 030	1 020	1 504	3.29	4.14	0	0	0	0.00	0.00
Turkey	359	330	427	7.77	2.89	226	244	500	−2.91	7.70	1	0	0	−17.86	4.16
LEAST DEVELOPED COUNTRIES (LDC)	60 136	62 335	74 173	3.85	1.99	6 664	7 516	9 374	5.14	2.11	1 079	1 825	2 213	17.19	5.34
OECD	22 042	21 901	21 749	−0.75	−0.18	4 404	4 463	5 475	3.12	2.30	3 787	3 647	4 905	−1.30	2.66
NON-OECD	408 217	416 922	453 249	1.01	0.91	25 649	26 381	32 606	1.82	2.38	26 143	27 197	33 177	3.76	2.32

For notes, see end of the table.

OECD-FAO AGRICULTURAL OUTLOOK 2008-2017 – ISBN 978-92-64-04590-3 – © OECD/FAO 2008

Table A.8. **Rice projections** (cont.)

Crop year[a]	CONSUMPTION (kt)			Growth[b] (%)		PER CAPITA (kg)			Growth[b] (%)	
	Average 2005-07 est.	2008	2017	1998-2007	2008-17	Average 2005-07 est.	2008	2017	1998-2007	2008-17
WORLD	432 403	437 763	475 241	1.06	0.91	57.3	56.5	56.5	−0.12	0.00
DEVELOPED	18 928	18 501	18 619	0.75	0.05	14.1	13.7	13.4	0.35	−0.22
NORTH AMERICA	4 249	4 274	4 838	1.00	1.37	12.8	12.6	13.2	−0.01	0.49
Canada	339	365	421	4.64	1.71	10.4	11.0	11.8	3.64	0.88
United States	3 909	3 910	4 417	0.72	1.34	13.1	12.8	13.4	−0.29	0.45
EUROPE	2 840	2 975	3 153	0.84	0.62	5.4	5.6	5.9	0.55	0.51
EU(27)	2 700	2 831	2 994	0.71	0.59	5.5	5.7	6.0	0.41	0.49
CIS	1 537	1 609	1 940	2.44	2.01	5.5	5.7	7.0	2.60	2.14
Russian Federation	687	741	808	1.33	0.96	4.8	5.3	6.0	1.77	1.46
Ukraine	167	164	199	5.53	1.99	3.6	3.6	4.6	6.35	2.77
OCEANIA DEVELOPED	437	441	577	2.20	3.14	17.7	17.5	21.1	1.02	2.22
Australia	399	403	528	2.05	3.16	19.4	19.2	23.1	0.85	2.21
New Zealand	37	38	49	3.89	2.93	9.0	9.0	10.9	2.79	2.15
OTHER DEVELOPED	9 866	9 202	8 111	0.31	−1.44	55.8	51.9	45.7	−0.07	−1.43
Japan	9 113	8 467	7 273	0.00	−1.71	71.3	66.3	57.9	−0.12	−1.53
South Africa	752	735	838	4.67	1.29	14.6	14.1	15.7	3.94	0.97
DEVELOPING	413 474	419 262	456 622	1.08	0.95	68.2	67.1	66.2	−0.33	−0.15
AFRICA	21 993	22 579	29 870	4.29	3.07	24.8	24.4	23.9	2.07	1.15
NORTH AFRICA	3 830	3 873	4 670	1.36	2.01	13.6	13.2	14.0	0.60	0.50
Algeria	96	96	124	7.23	2.75	2.9	2.8	3.2	5.75	1.30
Egypt	3 489	3 535	4 172	1.05	1.77	38.5	37.5	39.7	0.33	0.52
SUB-SAHARAN AFRICA	18 156	18 706	25 200	5.00	3.28	24.8	24.4	27.2	2.33	1.19
LATIN AMERICA and CARIBBEAN	19 124	19 020	21 900	1.45	1.74	32.3	31.5	33.0	0.20	0.68
Argentina	280	304	360	0.47	1.88	7.1	7.6	8.3	−0.52	0.97
Brazil	9 020	8 732	9 302	0.29	1.12	47.8	45.3	43.5	−1.07	−0.04
Chile	179	185	226	2.42	2.13	10.8	10.9	12.3	1.31	1.24
Mexico	912	902	938	2.15	0.32	8.9	8.6	8.2	1.29	−0.66
Uruguay	103	102	107	5.82	0.57	10.1	10.1	11.5	−0.24	1.45
ASIA and PACIFIC	372 348	377 656	404 706	0.89	0.76	81.1	80.0	82.4	−0.34	−0.14
Bangladesh	27 992	28 944	33 014	2.86	1.50	149.0	147.9	150.6	0.98	0.24
China[c]	128 383	125 920	125 531	−0.65	−0.03	79.1	76.1	74.1	−1.22	−0.29
India	87 095	89 964	98 919	0.74	1.02	73.5	73.7	72.2	−0.58	−0.25
Indonesia	35 987	37 342	40 356	0.12	0.86	151.5	151.5	150.5	−0.11	−0.07
Iran, Islamic Republic of	2 986	3 128	3 462	2.87	1.22	36.3	36.8	36.8	2.33	0.10
Korea	5 088	5 055	4 751	0.54	−0.09	82.2	81.1	74.9	−1.04	−0.87
Malaysia	2 272	2 276	2 614	1.86	1.14	84.1	82.0	82.8	−0.17	−0.31
Pakistan	2 494	2 688	3 207	−1.04	1.90	14.0	14.5	14.9	−2.43	0.19
Saudi Arabia	1 060	1 036	1 506	3.01	4.09	40.8	39.0	47.9	0.80	2.22
Turkey	589	580	925	3.08	5.19	7.5	7.1	10.4	1.54	4.20
LEAST DEVELOPED COUNTRIES (LDC)	65 611	68 551	81 703	4.12	1.95	74.3	73.6	74.7	0.91	0.16
OECD	23 171	22 637	22 399	0.35	−0.13	18.1	17.5	16.7	−0.23	−0.57
NON-OECD	409 231	415 126	452 842	1.11	0.96	66.1	65.1	64.7	−0.22	−0.08

a) Beginning crop marketing year – see Glossary of Terms for definitions.
b) Least-squares growth rate (see glossary).
c) Refers to mainland only. The economies of Chinese Taipei, Hong Kong (China) and Macau (China) are included in the Other Asia Pacific aggregate.
est.: estimate.
Source: OECD and FAO Secretariats.

StatLink http://dx.doi.org/10.1787/384080323752

Table A.9. **Main policy assumptions for oilseed markets**

Crop year[a]		Average 02/03-06/07	07/08 est.	08/09	09/10	10/11	11/12	12/13	13/14	14/15	14/16	16/17	17/18
ARGENTINA													
Oilseed export tax	%	24.3	27.5	44.1	44.1	44.1	44.1	44.1	44.1	44.1	44.1	44.1	44.1
Oilseed meal export tax	%	20.8	24.0	41.1	41.1	41.1	41.1	41.1	41.1	41.1	41.1	41.1	41.1
Oilseed oil export tax	%	20.8	24.0	39.6	39.6	39.6	39.6	39.6	39.6	39.6	39.6	39.6	39.6
AUSTRALIA													
Tariffs													
Soybean oil	%	8.0	8.0	8.0	8.0	8.0	8.0	8.0	8.0	8.0	8.0	8.0	8.0
Rapeseed oil	%	8.0	8.0	8.0	8.0	8.0	8.0	8.0	8.0	8.0	8.0	8.0	8.0
CANADA													
Tariffs													
Rapeseed oil	%	6.4	6.4	6.4	6.4	6.4	6.4	6.4	6.4	6.4	6.4	6.4	6.4
EUROPEAN UNION[b]													
Oilseed compensation[c, d]	EUR/ha	209	31	31	31	31	31	31	31	31	31	31	31
Compulsory set-aside rate	%	10.0	10	0	10	10	10	10	10	10	10	10	10
Set-aside payment[d]	EUR/ha	208.7	31	31	31	31	31	31	31	31	31	31	31
Tariffs													
Soybean oil	%	6.0	6.0	6.0	6.0	6.0	6.0	6.0	6.0	6.0	6.0	6.0	6.0
Rapeseed oil	%	6.0	6.0	6.0	6.0	6.0	6.0	6.0	6.0	6.0	6.0	6.0	6.0
JAPAN													
New output payments													
Soybeans	bn. JPY	24.9	23.5	23.5	23.5	23.5	23.5	23.5	23.5	23.5	23.5	23.5	23.5
Tariffs													
Soybean oil	JPY/kg	10.9	10.9	10.9	10.9	10.9	10.9	10.9	10.9	10.9	10.9	10.9	10.9
Rapeseed oil	JPY/kg	10.9	10.9	10.9	10.9	10.9	10.9	10.9	10.9	10.9	10.9	10.9	10.9
KOREA													
Soybean tariff-quota	kt	1 032	1 032	1 032	1 032	1 032	1 032	1 032	1 032	1 032	1 032	1 032	1 032
in-quota tariff	%	5	5	5	5	5	5	5	5	5	5	5	5
out-of-quota tariff	%	490	487	487	487	487	487	487	487	487	487	487	487
Soybean (for food) mark up	'000 KRW/t	183	185	162	161	160	158	156	155	155	155	155	154
MEXICO													
Soybeans income payment[e]	MXN/ha	906	980	1 013	1 045	1 078	1 111	1 145	1 180	1 217	1 254	1 293	1 332
Tariffs													
Soybeans	%	33.2	33.0	33.0	33.0	33.0	33.0	33.0	33.0	33.0	33.0	33.0	33.0
Soybean meal	%	24.6	23.8	23.8	23.8	23.8	23.8	23.8	23.8	23.8	23.8	23.8	23.8
Soybean oil	%	45.3	45.0	45.0	45.0	45.0	45.0	45.0	45.0	45.0	45.0	45.0	45.0
UNITED STATES													
Soybeans loan rate	USD/t	183.7	183.7	183.7	183.7	183.7	183.7	183.7	183.7	183.7	183.7	183.7	183.7
CRP area													
Soybeans	mha	2.1	2.4	2.2	2.2	2.1	2.1	2.0	2.0	1.9	1.8	1.8	1.7
Tariffs													
Rapeseed	%	3.0	3.0	3.0	3.0	3.0	3.0	3.0	3.0	3.0	3.0	3.0	3.0
Soybean meal	%	2.2	2.2	2.2	2.2	2.2	2.2	2.2	2.2	2.2	2.2	2.2	2.2
Rapeseed meal	%	1.2	1.2	1.2	1.2	1.2	1.2	1.2	1.2	1.2	1.2	1.2	1.2
Soybean oil	%	12.7	12.7	12.7	12.7	12.7	12.7	12.7	12.7	12.7	12.7	12.7	12.7
Rapeseed oil	%	3.2	3.2	3.2	3.2	3.2	3.2	3.2	3.2	3.2	3.2	3.2	3.2
Subsidised export limits													
Oilseed oils	kt	141	141	141	141	141	141	141	141	141	141	141	141

For notes, see end of the table.

OECD-FAO AGRICULTURAL OUTLOOK 2008-2017 – ISBN 978-92-64-04590-3 – © OECD/FAO 2008

Table A.9. **Main policy assumptions for oilseed markets** (cont.)

Crop year[a]		Average 02/03-06/07	07/08 est.	08/09	09/10	10/11	11/12	12/13	13/14	14/15	14/16	16/17	17/18
CHINA													
Soybeans support price	CNY/t	1 422.4	1 610.6	1 672.9	1 725.6	1 776.0	1 832.7	1 891.0	1 950.9	2 014.5	2 080.3	2 149.9	2 219.6
Tariffs													
Soybeans	%	2.4	2.4	2.4	2.4	2.4	2.4	2.4	2.4	2.4	2.4	2.4	2.4
Soybean meal	%	6.3	6.3	6.3	6.3	6.3	6.3	6.3	6.3	6.3	6.3	6.3	6.3
Soybean oil in-quota tariff	%	9.0	9.0	9.0	9.0	9.0	9.0	9.0	9.0	9.0	9.0	9.0	9.0
Vegetable oil tariff-quota	kt	7 034.9	7 998.1	7 998.1	7 998.1	7 998.1	7 998.1	7 998.1	7 998.1	7 998.1	7 998.1	7 998.1	7 998.1
INDIA													
Input subsidy rate, oilseeds[f]	R/T	5 663	4 883	4 883	4 883	4 883	4 883	4 883	4 883	4 883	4 883	4 883	4 883
Soybean tariff	%	35	30	30	30	30	30	30	30	30	30	30	30
Rapeseed tariff	%	35	30	30	30	30	30	30	30	30	30	30	30
Sunflower tariff	%	35	30	30	30	30	30	30	30	30	30	30	30
Oilseed tariff	%	35	30	30	30	30	30	30	30	30	30	30	30
Soybean meal tariff	%	100	100	100	100	100	100	100	100	100	100	100	100
Rapeseed meal tariff	%	100	100	100	100	100	100	100	100	100	100	100	100
Sunflower meal tariff	%	100	100	100	100	100	100	100	100	100	100	100	100
Soybean oil tariff	%	45	45	45	45	45	45	45	45	45	45	45	45
Rapeseed oil tariff	%	45	45	45	45	45	45	45	45	45	45	45	45
Sunflower oil tariff	%	75	60	60	60	60	60	60	60	60	60	60	60
Palm oil tariff	%	80	50	50	50	50	50	50	50	50	50	50	50
Vegetables oil tariff	%	100	48	48	48	48	48	48	48	48	48	48	48

a) Beginning crop marketing year.
b) EU farmers also benefit from the Single Farm Payment (SFP) Scheme, which provides flat-rate payments independent from current production decisions and market developments. For the accession countries, payments are phased in with the assumption of maximum top-ups from national budgets up to 2011 through the Single Area Payment (SAP) and from 2012 through the SFP. Due to modulation, between 2.7% and 4.6% of the total SFP will go to rural development spending rather than directly to the farmers in the 15 former member states. From 2013, 4.6% of the total SFP will go to rural development spending in the accession countries.
c) Compensatory area payments, before penalties.
d) Payments made per hectare based on regional yields
e) Weighted average of autumn/winter and spring/summer.
f) Indian input subsidies consist of those for electricty, fertiliser and irrigation.
Note: The source for tariffs and Tariff Rate Quotas is AMAD (Agricultural market access database). The tariff and TRQ data are based on Most Favoured Nation rates scheduled with the WTO and exclude those under preferential or regional agreements, which may be substantially different. Tariffs are simple averages of several product lines. Specific rates are converted to ad valorem rates using world prices in the Outlook. Import quotas are based on global commitments scheduled in the WTO rather than those allocated to preferential partners under regional or other agreements. For Mexico, the NAFTA tariffs on soybeans, oil meals and soybean oil are zero after 2003.
est.: estimate.
Source: OECD and FAO Secretariats.

StatLink ⏩ http://dx.doi.org/10.1787/384084020440

Table A.10. **World oilseed projections**

		Average 02/03-06/07	07/08 est.	08/09	09/10	10/11	11/12	12/13	13/14	14/15	15/16	16/17	17/18
OILSEEDS (crop year[a])													
OECD[b]													
Production	mt	115.5	109.6	123.9	125.9	127.7	128.9	130.3	131.5	133.7	135.1	136.8	138.6
Consumption	mt	111.5	121.3	120.4	123.5	126.2	127.8	129.4	130.8	132.9	134.5	136.7	139.1
crush	mt	100.5	110.2	109.6	112.9	115.6	117.2	118.6	120.0	122.1	123.6	125.8	128.1
Closing stocks	mt	17.5	13.2	12.6	13.2	13.2	13.4	13.9	13.9	14.0	13.9	13.9	14.3
Non-OECD													
Production	mt	162.0	184.7	191.9	200.7	206.4	212.4	217.9	222.9	228.2	233.4	238.9	244.6
Consumption	mt	164.9	191.8	196.5	202.8	207.9	212.7	218.1	223.3	228.8	233.9	238.8	243.9
crush	mt	139.0	162.5	166.5	172.3	177.5	182.1	187.0	191.8	196.8	201.5	206.2	210.9
Closing stocks	mt	9.5	8.4	7.9	7.5	7.5	8.1	8.4	8.6	8.6	8.7	8.9	8.7
WORLD[c]													
Production	mt	277.5	294.3	315.8	326.5	334.2	341.3	348.2	354.4	361.8	368.5	375.7	383.2
Consumption	mt	276.4	313.1	316.9	326.3	334.1	340.6	347.4	354.1	361.8	368.4	375.5	383.0
crush	mt	239.5	272.7	276.1	285.2	293.1	299.3	305.6	311.8	318.9	325.1	331.9	339.0
Closing stocks	mt	27.0	21.6	20.5	20.7	20.7	21.5	22.3	22.5	22.6	22.7	22.8	23.0
Price[d]	USD/t	293.4	485.8	481.9	470.6	468.3	464.2	455.8	452.4	453.2	455.6	457.6	457.2
OILSEED MEALS (marketing year)													
OECD[b]													
Production	mt	73.0	79.2	78.9	81.2	83.1	84.2	85.2	86.2	87.6	88.7	90.1	91.6
Consumption	mt	96.2	103.8	105.8	107.1	108.0	108.7	109.3	110.2	111.4	112.2	113.2	114.2
Closing stocks	mt	2.2	2.2	2.1	2.1	2.1	2.1	2.1	2.1	2.1	2.1	2.1	2.1
Non-OECD													
Production	mt	101.0	116.0	120.5	124.6	128.4	131.8	135.4	138.9	142.5	146.0	149.4	152.9
Consumption	mt	73.3	89.4	94.0	98.9	103.5	107.2	111.3	115.0	118.7	122.5	126.2	130.2
Closing stocks	mt	4.1	4.9	4.5	4.3	4.3	4.3	4.4	4.4	4.4	4.4	4.4	4.5
WORLD[c]													
Production	mt	174.0	195.2	199.4	205.8	211.5	216.0	220.6	225.1	230.2	234.6	239.5	244.5
Consumption	mt	169.5	193.1	199.8	206.0	211.5	215.9	220.6	225.1	230.2	234.6	239.5	244.4
Closing stocks	mt	6.3	7.1	6.6	6.4	6.3	6.4	6.5	6.4	6.4	6.5	6.5	6.5
Price[e]	USD/t	219.5	365.7	348.2	331.5	328.4	321.6	308.4	302.6	303.4	304.0	305.8	307.0
VEGETABLE OILS (marketing year)													
OECD[b]													
Production	mt	24.8	27.3	27.6	28.4	29.1	29.6	29.9	30.3	31.0	31.5	32.1	32.8
Consumption	mt	31.4	37.0	39.4	41.5	43.3	44.2	45.2	46.2	47.2	48.3	49.2	50.2
Closing stocks	mt	2.4	2.4	2.4	2.3	2.4	2.4	2.3	2.3	2.3	2.2	2.2	2.3
Non-OECD													
Production	mt	65.8	78.8	82.9	86.1	89.3	92.3	95.4	98.5	101.6	104.7	107.7	110.7
Consumption	mt	57.7	67.7	70.7	72.9	74.9	77.6	80.1	82.6	85.3	87.7	90.5	93.2
Closing stocks	mt	5.2	5.6	6.0	6.1	6.3	6.4	6.5	6.6	6.7	6.8	6.9	7.0
WORLD[c]													
Production	mt	90.6	106.1	110.5	114.5	118.4	121.8	125.3	128.8	132.6	136.1	139.8	143.5
of which palm oil	mt	33.5	41.9	44.0	45.8	47.7	49.6	51.4	53.3	55.1	56.9	58.7	60.5
Consumption	mt	89.1	104.7	110.1	114.4	118.2	121.8	125.3	128.8	132.5	136.1	139.7	143.4
Closing stocks	mt	7.6	7.9	8.4	8.5	8.7	8.8	8.8	8.9	8.9	9.0	9.1	9.3
Oil price[f]	USD/t	587.5	1 015.1	986.9	1 017.9	1 026.3	1 031.2	1 043.8	1 048.0	1 050.9	1 055.9	1 060.3	1 055.1

a) Beginning crop marketing year.
b) Excludes Iceland but includes the 8 EU members that are not members of the OECD.
c) Source of historic data is USDA.
d) Weighted average oilseed price, European port.
e) Weighted average meal price, European port.
f) Weighted average price of oilseed oils and palm oil, European port.
est: estimate.
Source: OECD and FAO Secretariats.

StatLink 🔗 http://dx.doi.org/10.1787/384102346200

OECD-FAO AGRICULTURAL OUTLOOK 2008-2017 – ISBN 978-92-64-04590-3 – © OECD/FAO 2008

Table A.11. Oilseed projections

Crop year[a]	PRODUCTION (kt)			Growth[b] (%)		IMPORTS (kt)			Growth[b] (%)		EXPORTS (kt)			Growth[b] (%)	
	Average 2005-07 est.	2008	2017	1998-2007	2008-17	Average 2005-07 est.	2008	2017	1998-2007	2008-17	Average 2005-07 est.	2008	2017	1998-2007	2008-17
WORLD	299 791	315 785	383 185	3.95	2.06	80 131	80 052	97 488	5.35	2.10	76 732	80 052	97 488	5.00	2.10
DEVELOPED	135 444	140 543	162 627	1.72	1.54	26 953	23 451	22 489	−0.06	−0.88	37 999	37 311	35 806	0.90	−0.45
NORTH AMERICA	94 505	94 834	99 507	0.88	0.55	1 405	1 409	1 227	5.00	−0.76	35 099	33 423	28 220	2.09	−1.67
Canada	12 306	12 613	14 735	2.59	1.55	575	562	662	−0.41	0.89	6 996	7 651	6 449	5.15	−1.64
United States	82 199	82 220	84 772	0.67	0.38	830	847	565	11.28	−2.21	28 103	25 773	21 770	1.48	−1.67
EUROPE	23 889	26 749	35 830	2.24	3.02	18 869	15 316	14 866	0.13	−1.06	690	795	795	−18.19	0.00
EU(27)	23 215	26 046	35 085	2.25	3.08	18 295	14 731	14 217	0.16	−1.16	672	777	777	−18.73	0.00
CIS	14 973	16 322	23 271	10.06	3.58	212	194	101	−4.95	−7.34	1 664	2 263	5 024	−0.25	6.60
Russian Federation	7 467	7 720	10 807	8.99	3.28	33	33	37	−15.06	0.56	430	476	1 716	−7.78	9.11
Ukraine	6 136	7 073	10 409	10.43	3.97	10	8	15	15.84	7.32	1 032	1 514	2 915	4.95	5.96
OCEANIA DEVELOPED	1 059	1 571	2 305	−10.78	4.11	27	8	8	1.78	0.00	514	820	1 481	−16.94	6.44
Australia	1 055	1 567	2 301	−10.81	4.12	26	6	6	2.43	0.00	513	819	1 480	−16.95	6.44
New Zealand	4	4	4	0.00	0.00	2	2	2	5.71	0.00	0	0	0	−4.73	−0.22
OTHER DEVELOPED	1 018	1 066	1 714	−2.31	4.85	6 440	6 524	6 287	−1.37	−0.36	32	10	286	−13.46	24.40
Japan	228	230	228	1.70	−0.08	6 408	6 506	6 234	1.35	−0.42	0	0	0	9.87	0.00
South Africa	790	837	1 486	3.22	5.84	32	18	53	−6.11	10.45	32	10	286	−13.54	24.42
DEVELOPING	164 346	175 242	220 558	6.06	2.46	53 178	56 601	74 999	9.22	3.13	38 733	42 741	61 682	10.70	3.88
AFRICA	1 328	1 378	1 654	2.42	1.96	1 823	2 028	2 271	16.32	1.27	59	86	88	5.42	−0.17
NORTH AFRICA	329	342	470	2.78	3.46	1 761	1 981	2 206	16.55	1.20	3	3	8	0.10	10.87
Algeria	100	101	101	0.00	−0.05	47	49	72	70.95	4.50	0	0	0	0.00	0.00
Egypt	116	124	202	7.11	5.23	1 072	1 257	1 373	21.83	1.00	3	3	3	0.00	0.00
SUB-SAHARAN AFRICA	998	1 037	1 184	2.31	1.42	61	48	65	11.06	3.98	55	83	80	5.98	−0.86
LATIN AMERICA and CARIBBEAN	113 603	124 159	159 104	8.01	2.68	7 287	7 378	8 718	0.69	1.46	38 054	42 134	61 094	10.81	3.93
Argentina	49 407	53 618	61 744	8.02	1.57	633	874	1 000	8.47	1.01	9 800	12 409	12 586	9.11	0.54
Brazil	55 001	59 041	82 594	7.92	3.48	157	26	340	−25.91	14.04	23 750	23 673	40 005	12.04	5.36
Chile	77	84	93	0.00	1.00	237	265	369	12.17	3.72	7	7	7	−3.38	0.00
Mexico	135	134	128	−0.54	−0.49	4 818	4 830	5 404	0.10	1.23	1	1	1	−3.69	0.36
Uruguay	796	960	1 500	29.71	4.84	4	3	9	24.37	11.69	658	781	1 194	42.32	4.58
ASIA and PACIFIC	49 335	49 705	59 799	2.43	1.93	44 060	47 195	64 011	11.05	3.44	620	520	500	6.03	0.43
Bangladesh	229	239	245	−0.96	0.20	157	169	266	−5.70	5.10	0	0	0	0.00	0.00
China[d]	29 981	29 277	34 594	1.78	1.65	30 878	33 052	48 418	15.94	4.11	480	416	394	9.86	−0.59
India	15 607	16 479	20 217	5.42	2.27	26	5	5	−2.49	0.00	35	5	5	8.23	0.00
Indonesia	739	651	690	−7.58	0.73	1 365	1 552	1 731	1.17	1.31	0	0	0	0.00	0.00
Iran, Islamic Republic of	157	169	273	−0.72	5.15	855	990	1 354	9.98	3.48	2	2	5	14.07	6.86
Korea	112	118	118	−1.61	0.00	1 294	1 250	1 446	−1.02	1.51	0	0	0	−1.84	0.00
Malaysia	0	0	0	0.00	0.45	580	533	521	−0.03	−0.25	27	28	13	−9.18	−8.24
Pakistan	437	454	624	−1.27	3.40	1 061	1 235	1 824	19.80	4.40	3	0	0	9.77	0.00
Saudi Arabia	0	0	0	0.00	0.00	2	2	2	−13.08	2.56	0	0	0	46.58	0.00
Turkey	764	892	1 172	−1.56	2.83	1 762	1 738	2 089	10.75	2.15	2	2	0	−10.80	−12.82
LEAST DEVELOPED COUNTRIES (LDC)	1 048	1 070	1 122	2.96	0.41	274	261	383	−2.01	4.50	18	34	18	−3.17	−6.82
OECD	120 091	123 904	138 623	0.97	1.21	34 531	30 982	31 280	0.36	−0.21	36 288	35 024	30 479	0.99	−1.34
NON-OECD	179 700	191 881	244 561	6.32	2.58	45 600	49 070	66 208	10.94	3.34	40 444	45 028	67 009	9.94	4.08

For notes, see end of the table.

Table A.11. **Oilseed projections** (cont.)

Crop year[a]	CONSUMPTION (kt)			Growth[b] (%)		DOMESTIC CRUSH (kt)			Growth[b] (%)	
	Average 2005-07 est.	2008	2017	1998-2007	2008-17	Average 2005-07 est.	2008	2017	1998-2007	2008-17
WORLD	305 338	316 885	382 983	4.22	2.05	266 725	276 104	338 958	4.47	2.20
DEVELOPED	125 445	127 253	148 955	1.96	1.66	113 195	115 920	137 305	2.07	1.76
NORTH AMERICA	61 625	63 095	72 418	1.05	1.49	55 376	57 566	66 960	1.32	1.61
Canada	5 976	6 021	8 939	0.58	4.34	4 978	5 167	7 866	0.93	4.69
United States	55 649	57 074	63 479	1.11	1.14	50 398	52 399	59 094	1.37	1.25
EUROPE	42 169	41 562	49 644	1.77	1.73	39 566	39 127	47 143	1.89	1.81
EU(27)	40 941	40 292	48 268	1.80	1.76	38 451	37 970	45 886	1.93	1.84
CIS	13 521	14 250	18 348	11.88	2.82	11 190	11 950	15 657	11.71	3.02
Russian Federation	7 083	7 273	9 128	11.16	2.57	6 551	6 707	8 508	11.37	2.69
Ukraine	5 094	5 567	7 509	12.30	3.32	3 731	4 302	6 009	11.96	3.70
OCEANIA DEVELOPED	582	759	832	−0.97	0.83	569	750	822	−0.87	0.84
Australia	577	754	827	−0.99	0.83	565	745	818	−0.88	0.84
New Zealand	5	5	5	2.20	0.02	4	4	4	1.49	0.00
OTHER DEVELOPED	7 548	7 587	7 714	−1.02	0.23	6 494	6 528	6 724	−1.24	0.38
Japan	6 754	6 742	6 461	−0.81	−0.42	5 780	5 759	5 522	−1.05	−0.41
South Africa	794	845	1 253	−2.76	4.37	714	769	1 202	−2.76	4.94
DEVELOPING	179 893	189 632	234 028	6.04	2.30	153 529	160 184	201 653	6.55	2.51
AFRICA	3 071	3 320	3 837	8.76	1.60	2 288	2 508	2 860	9.67	1.45
NORTH AFRICA	2 067	2 319	2 668	13.14	1.55	1 756	1 974	2 206	13.08	1.23
Algeria	147	149	172	5.73	1.62	115	115	126	3.60	0.95
Egypt	1 161	1 378	1 572	19.19	1.46	1 045	1 239	1 402	19.19	1.37
SUB-SAHARAN AFRICA	1 004	1 001	1 169	2.58	1.72	532	534	654	2.12	2.23
LATIN AMERICA and CARIBBEAN	83 400	89 647	106 800	6.18	1.90	77 486	81 063	96 988	6.10	1.95
Argentina	40 047	42 022	50 189	7.83	1.84	39 557	41 350	49 114	8.25	1.82
Brazil	32 568	36 309	42 978	5.28	1.95	29 260	30 694	37 060	4.33	2.14
Chile	307	342	455	8.50	3.17	276	308	406	8.50	3.08
Mexico	4 982	4 969	5 620	0.14	1.19	4 371	4 274	4 812	0.69	1.17
Uruguay	130	175	308	15.16	6.23	112	152	281	16.91	6.75
ASIA and PACIFIC	93 423	96 665	123 391	5.84	2.68	73 755	76 612	101 806	6.96	3.11
Bangladesh	386	409	511	−2.97	2.49	347	367	451	−2.97	2.28
China[c]	61 016	62 847	82 709	7.14	3.01	49 679	51 481	70 769	8.45	3.46
India	15 557	16 479	20 218	5.29	2.28	14 325	15 171	18 654	5.27	2.31
Indonesia	2 104	2 171	2 420	−2.50	1.20	5	5	5	−0.81	−0.07
Iran, Islamic Republic of	1 007	1 157	1 622	7.58	3.74	906	1 045	1 502	7.58	4.01
Korea	1 406	1 368	1 564	−1.08	1.39	992	936	1 117	−1.70	1.82
Malaysia	553	505	507	0.63	0.07	498	447	443	0.63	−0.08
Pakistan	1 501	1 679	2 446	8.44	4.16	1 351	1 518	2 265	8.44	4.43
Saudi Arabia	2	2	2	−13.72	2.71	2	2	2	−10.93	2.86
Turkey	2 552	2 621	3 254	6.11	2.40	1 826	1 804	2 304	4.28	2.71
LEAST DEVELOPED COUNTRIES (LDC)	1 303	1 305	1 487	1.91	1.46	949	955	1 080	1.02	1.38
OECD	119 405	120 425	139 060	1.19	1.49	107 914	109 630	128 055	1.35	1.59
NON-OECD	185 933	196 460	243 923	6.59	2.38	158 810	166 474	210 903	7.07	2.59

a) Beginning crop marketing year – see Glossary of Terms for definitions.
b) Least-squares growth rate (see glossary).
c) Refers to mainland only. The economies of Chinese Taipei, Hong Kong (China) and Macau (China) are included in the Other Asia Pacific aggregate.

est.: estimate.
Source: OECD and FAO Secretariats.

StatLink 🖳 http://dx.doi.org/10.1787/384128100717

OECD-FAO AGRICULTURAL OUTLOOK 2008-2017 – ISBN 978-92-64-04590-3 – © OECD/FAO 2008

Table A.12. Oilseed meal projections

Marketing year	PRODUCTION (kt)			Growth[a] (%)		IMPORTS (kt)			Growth[a] (%)		EXPORTS (kt)			Growth[a] (%)	
	Average 2005-07 est.	2008	2017	1998-2007	2008-17	Average 2005-07 est.	2008	2017	1998-2007	2008-17	Average 2005-07 est.	2008	2017	1998-2007	2008-17
WORLD	192 837	199 364	244 505	4.66	2.20	57 468	64 787	75 329	5.37	1.61	63 564	64 787	75 329	7.05	1.61
DEVELOPED	78 321	80 044	93 733	1.75	1.64	32 632	35 696	33 774	4.18	-0.59	12 681	12 372	15 495	5.17	2.02
NORTH AMERICA	42 671	44 006	50 772	1.25	1.52	3 112	3 093	2 872	6.27	-0.78	9 352	8 595	11 138	2.27	2.24
Canada	3 107	2 900	4 415	-0.66	4.69	1 452	1 672	1 576	7.13	-0.66	1 661	1 492	2 616	5.09	6.27
United States	39 564	41 106	46 357	1.41	1.25	1 661	1 421	1 296	5.61	-0.93	7 692	7 103	8 522	1.70	1.27
EUROPE	26 039	25 709	30 994	1.90	1.83	24 825	27 446	24 541	2.80	-1.23	1 046	1 191	1 191	10.36	0.00
EU(27)	25 384	25 031	30 255	1.95	1.85	24 290	26 900	23 921	2.71	-1.29	855	1 000	1 000	12.35	0.00
CIS	4 850	5 447	6 972	11.91	2.88	1 378	1 449	1 778	12.92	2.44	2 274	2 580	3 160	21.84	2.06
Russian Federation	2 798	3 080	3 760	11.10	2.49	737	737	871	12.56	2.52	832	880	869	39.48	-0.69
Ukraine	1 565	1 853	2 588	12.53	3.70	90	104	135	34.38	2.95	1 290	1 546	2 137	16.58	3.58
OCEANIA DEVELOPED	334	438	468	-1.16	0.53	670	858	1 024	13.02	2.21	2	0	0	-0.75	0.00
Australia	332	435	465	-1.19	0.53	538	713	878	13.79	2.62	2	0	0	-0.72	0.00
New Zealand	2	2	2	3.30	0.00	132	145	145	10.25	0.00	0	0	0	-5.42	0.00
OTHER DEVELOPED	4 427	4 445	4 527	-1.29	0.25	2 647	2 849	3 559	8.92	2.47	6	6	6	15.37	0.00
Japan	4 019	4 007	3 842	-1.31	-0.41	1 724	1 799	2 224	8.71	2.35	0	0	0	6.39	0.00
South Africa	408	438	685	-1.21	4.94	923	1 050	1 334	9.63	2.66	6	6	6	17.24	0.00
DEVELOPING	114 516	119 320	150 772	7.06	2.56	24 836	29 091	41 555	6.54	3.81	50 884	52 415	59 833	7.24	1.50
AFRICA	1 678	1 850	2 108	10.70	1.46	2 613	3 021	4 797	6.26	5.03	34	35	27	-0.79	-2.75
NORTH AFRICA	1 303	1 473	1 648	14.58	1.24	2 405	2 758	4 452	6.14	5.24	4	6	4	0.00	-2.58
Algeria	73	73	79	4.40	0.95	665	676	1 016	11.66	4.43	0	0	0	0.00	0.00
Egypt	804	958	1 083	20.03	1.37	951	1 197	1 940	1.03	5.35	2	2	2	0.00	0.00
SUB-SAHARAN AFRICA	376	377	461	2.17	2.22	209	263	345	7.76	2.54	30	29	23	-0.89	-2.77
LATIN AMERICA and CARIBBEAN	59 029	61 392	73 420	6.68	1.95	5 463	6 070	8 694	6.04	4.14	44 589	46 234	53 328	7.42	1.59
Argentina	30 055	31 012	36 835	9.15	1.82	0	0	0	0.00	0.00	29 012	29 709	34 771	9.34	1.60
Brazil	22 455	23 585	28 462	4.77	2.13	147	111	230	-4.30	7.94	13 628	14 563	16 454	4.11	1.68
Chile	199	223	295	9.69	3.08	755	848	1 052	7.37	2.81	2	2	5	6.72	9.04
Mexico	3 261	3 192	3 584	0.65	1.14	189	428	626	23.67	5.77	0	0	0	-54.00	18.22
Uruguay	62	86	150	10.21	6.75	94	90	114	5.88	2.60	6	5	0	-11.97	-16.49
ASIA and PACIFIC	53 809	56 078	75 243	7.38	3.22	16 759	20 000	28 064	6.74	3.52	6 261	6 146	6 478	6.03	0.82
Bangladesh	208	220	270	-2.97	2.28	227	324	522	19.10	5.27	0	0	0	0.00	0.00
China[b]	37 022	38 419	53 464	9.00	3.60	849	1 790	3 861	6.42	6.60	673	0	0	3.48	0.00
India	10 114	10 770	13 244	5.21	2.31	2	0	0	9.82	0.00	4 758	5 221	4 961	6.76	-0.28
Indonesia	1	2	2	-3.04	-0.07	2 403	2 655	3 458	8.95	2.82	10	10	10	-6.49	0.00
Iran, Islamic Republic of	701	810	1 164	7.82	4.01	776	984	926	8.94	-0.69	65	105	145	53.96	3.63
Korea	774	730	871	1.67	1.02	2 013	2 202	2 286	4.87	0.74	0	0	0	0.00	0.00
Malaysia	393	352	360	0.66	-0.08	908	1 070	1 627	6.57	4.50	47	42	145	5.14	13.41
Pakistan	844	964	1 438	8.80	4.43	317	397	487	19.67	2.28	65	62	82	20.05	3.03
Saudi Arabia	1	1	1	-13.82	0.00	710	808	1 110	3.45	3.55	0	0	0	0.00	0.00
Turkey	1 035	1 062	1 356	6.29	2.71	1 022	1 049	1 799	6.32	5.76	76	91	273	30.56	11.85
LEAST DEVELOPED COUNTRIES (LDC)	553	555	632	1.08	1.46	334	444	678	9.03	4.55	19	19	21	1.68	1.06
OECD	77 891	78 894	91 625	1.30	1.53	33 365	36 685	35 181	3.91	-0.42	10 442	9 842	12 567	3.59	2.15
NON-OECD	114 946	120 471	152 880	7.51	2.62	24 103	28 102	40 148	6.98	3.78	53 122	54 945	62 762	7.58	1.50

For notes, see end of the table.

Table A.12. **Oilseed meal projections** (cont.)

Marketing year	CONSUMPTION (kt)			Growth[b] (%)	
	Average 2005-07 est.	2008	2017	1998-2007	2008-17
WORLD	**186 623**	**199 830**	**244 445**	**4.21**	**2.18**
DEVELOPED	**98 239**	**103 447**	**112 010**	**2.30**	**0.86**
NORTH AMERICA	**36 384**	**38 574**	**42 506**	**1.38**	**1.16**
Canada	2 890	3 094	3 375	−0.33	0.98
United States	33 494	35 480	39 131	1.53	1.17
EUROPE	**49 808**	**51 973**	**54 344**	**2.46**	**0.36**
EU(27)	48 809	50 940	53 176	2.46	0.34
CIS	**3 956**	**4 316**	**5 590**	**9.11**	**3.23**
Russian Federation	2 703	2 937	3 762	8.48	3.37
Ukraine	375	410	586	7.05	3.95
OCEANIA DEVELOPED	**1 002**	**1 296**	**1 491**	**6.72**	**1.65**
Australia	867	1 148	1 343	6.28	1.85
New Zealand	134	148	148	10.10	0.00
OTHER DEVELOPED	**7 090**	**7 288**	**8 079**	**1.93**	**1.18**
Japan	5 767	5 806	6 066	1.25	0.53
South Africa	1 322	1 482	2 013	5.42	3.40
DEVELOPING	**88 384**	**96 383**	**132 435**	**6.85**	**3.43**
AFRICA	**4 238**	**4 836**	**6 879**	**7.92**	**3.85**
NORTH AFRICA	**3 691**	**4 225**	**6 096**	**8.58**	**4.02**
Algeria	738	749	1 095	10.75	4.14
Egypt	1 740	2 153	3 021	6.78	3.76
SUB-SAHARAN AFRICA	**547**	**611**	**783**	**4.13**	**2.55**
LATIN AMERICA and CARIBBEAN	**19 796**	**21 619**	**28 728**	**5.18**	**3.14**
Argentina	959	1 152	2 006	5.30	6.01
Brazil	9 002	9 670	12 238	6.27	2.56
Chile	946	1 069	1 342	7.72	2.85
Mexico	3 449	3 625	4 210	1.18	1.70
Uruguay	151	171	273	12.61	5.11
ASIA and PACIFIC	**64 350**	**69 928**	**96 829**	**7.33**	**3.49**
Bangladesh	435	544	793	3.11	4.17
China[b]	37 198	40 209	57 326	8.81	3.76
India	5 558	5 549	8 283	4.33	4.23
Indonesia	2 328	2 647	3 450	8.72	2.82
Iran, Islamic Republic of	1 388	1 690	1 945	7.48	1.56
Korea	2 772	2 934	3 157	2.43	1.02
Malaysia	1 254	1 381	1 832	4.37	3.02
Pakistan	1 096	1 293	1 842	10.73	3.90
Saudi Arabia	711	808	1 111	3.38	3.55
Turkey	1 974	2 019	2 882	5.61	3.84
LEAST DEVELOPED COUNTRIES (LDC)	**869**	**980**	**1 289**	**3.26**	**3.00**
OECD	**100 758**	**105 822**	**114 239**	**2.04**	**0.82**
NON-OECD	**85 865**	**94 008**	**130 207**	**7.38**	**3.53**

a) Least-squares growth rate (see glossary).
b) Refers to mainland only. The economies of Chinese Taipei, Hong Kong (China) and Macau (China) are included in the Other Asia Pacific aggregate.
est.: estimate.
Source: OECD and FAO Secretariats.

StatLink ⬛🔗 http://dx.doi.org/10.1787/384208071684

OECD-FAO AGRICULTURAL OUTLOOK 2008-2017 – ISBN 978-92-64-04590-3 – © OECD/FAO 2008

Table A.13. **Vegetable oil projections**

Marketing year	PRODUCTION (kt) Average 2005-07 est.	2008	2017	Growth[a] (%) 1998-2007	2008-17	IMPORTS (kt) Average 2005-07 est.	2008	2017	Growth[a] (%) 1998-2007	2008-17	EXPORTS (kt) Average 2005-07 est.	2008	2017	Growth[a] (%) 1998-2007	2008-17
WORLD	102 453	110 506	143 499	5.63	2.86	44 169	48 889	63 175	7.34	2.93	45 740	48 889	63 176	7.47	2.93
DEVELOPED	30 026	31 212	37 566	2.61	1.96	11 445	14 265	21 885	8.56	4.51	4 788	4 804	7 434	1.50	5.13
NORTH AMERICA	11 632	12 179	14 559	1.30	1.94	1 734	1 843	2 232	10.32	2.17	2 114	1 756	3 055	0.27	6.66
Canada	1 634	1 833	2 799	0.51	4.86	261	307	323	14.38	0.56	1 062	1 036	1 575	4.90	5.32
United States	9 998	10 346	11 760	1.43	1.34	1 473	1 536	1 909	9.98	2.47	1 052	720	1 479	-3.21	8.23
EUROPE	11 986	12 009	14 466	2.19	1.80	6 717	9 091	15 420	9.71	5.44	170	99	99	-30.79	0.00
EU(27)	11 711	11 723	14 156	2.22	1.82	6 344	8 694	15 007	9.67	5.61	71	0	0	-76.51	0.00
CIS	4 458	4 951	6 333	11.64	2.88	1 348	1 441	2 137	3.12	4.44	2 136	2 505	3 765	19.85	4.64
Russian Federation	2 523	2 787	3 367	11.72	2.37	649	649	635	-2.26	-0.09	614	859	1 155	25.22	3.90
Ukraine	1 613	1 837	2 569	11.58	3.72	284	352	727	24.68	7.97	1 462	1 586	2 518	18.74	5.01
OCEANIA DEVELOPED	222	292	322	-0.39	0.93	386	542	589	11.33	1.06	55	55	55	1.79	0.00
Australia	221	292	322	-0.37	0.93	224	380	427	7.60	1.49	55	55	55	1.78	0.00
New Zealand	1	0	0	0.64	0.00	162	162	162	18.30	0.00	0	0	0	-4.39	0.00
OTHER DEVELOPED	1 728	1 780	1 887	-0.77	0.68	1 260	1 349	1 507	7.05	1.26	311	388	461	5.82	1.90
Japan	1 530	1 567	1 553	-0.36	-0.06	583	611	713	6.19	1.72	251	333	358	5.09	0.79
South Africa	198	213	333	-3.72	4.04	677	738	793	7.85	0.86	60	55	103	9.79	6.88
DEVELOPING	72 427	79 294	105 933	7.10	3.20	32 723	34 623	41 290	6.06	2.17	40 952	44 085	55 741	8.32	2.66
AFRICA	2 317	2 556	3 218	2.57	2.57	5 155	5 541	7 653	6.78	3.64	362	385	549	4.55	3.96
NORTH AFRICA	367	413	460	10.43	1.20	2 578	2 824	3 929	4.26	3.72	108	137	238	6.78	6.06
Algeria	39	39	43	1.96	0.95	598	645	900	7.38	3.70	54	69	144	49.71	8.05
Egypt	197	236	267	17.88	1.36	1 270	1 420	2 018	3.34	3.89	50	66	90	-7.34	3.44
SUB-SAHARAN AFRICA	1 949	2 143	2 750	1.49	2.81	2 577	2 717	3 724	9.84	3.56	254	247	312	4.29	2.59
LATIN AMERICA and CARIBBEAN	17 616	18 904	23 438	5.74	2.35	2 970	3 204	4 370	4.84	3.86	11 046	11 451	12 885	7.33	1.47
Argentina	8 200	8 651	10 698	6.30	2.27	0	0	0	0.00	0.00	7 408	7 755	9 372	6.81	1.96
Brazil	5 749	6 053	7 324	5.09	2.14	95	74	31	-12.18	-7.52	2 383	2 296	1 367	7.76	-4.16
Chile	65	72	95	5.92	3.08	301	309	372	10.02	2.05	3	1	4	2.54	12.49
Mexico	926	922	1 114	1.19	1.96	590	616	618	2.28	0.70	40	43	43	-3.09	0.00
Uruguay	32	42	77	16.02	6.75	40	40	45	17.12	1.04	2	2	2	5.00	1.80
ASIA and PACIFIC	52 495	57 835	79 277	7.84	3.49	24 599	25 878	29 267	7.27	1.59	29 544	32 249	42 307	8.78	3.03
Bangladesh	132	139	171	-2.97	2.28	1 194	1 311	1 823	8.19	3.65	0	0	0	0.00	0.00
China[b]	11 315	11 954	16 826	7.77	3.71	7 616	8 601	8 414	10.70	0.03	181	90	78	3.93	-1.75
India	3 825	4 011	4 970	5.37	2.41	5 235	5 243	6 276	0.36	1.80	147	0	0	44.94	0.00
Indonesia	17 302	20 043	27 940	12.67	3.70	55	67	113	14.07	5.83	13 018	15 151	20 315	16.39	3.32
Iran, Islamic Republic of	169	194	279	7.18	4.01	1 120	1 136	1 312	0.85	1.55	113	90	0	-10.07	-66.19
Korea	170	188	200	-1.61	1.81	521	540	561	7.28	0.57	4	6	28	-1.94	16.47
Malaysia	16 107	17 599	23 835	8.40	3.38	570	554	533	5.87	-0.43	14 275	15 100	19 903	5.17	3.05
Pakistan	412	454	677	8.57	4.43	1 778	1 828	2 067	2.68	1.35	117	90	0	72.27	-38.56
Saudi Arabia	0	0	0	-5.94	0.00	411	417	631	8.12	4.56	9	9	9	3.34	-0.12
Turkey	621	602	775	2.40	2.80	957	959	1 135	8.23	2.06	87	35	101	2.52	11.41
LEAST DEVELOPED COUNTRIES (LDC)	802	852	1 065	1.22	2.49	3 780	4 001	5 390	9.38	3.34	86	89	99	4.73	1.21
OECD	26 942	27 579	32 818	1.56	1.79	11 362	14 075	21 141	9.11	4.31	2 703	2 308	3 718	-4.50	5.73
NON-OECD	75 511	82 927	110 681	7.44	3.20	32 806	34 813	42 033	6.79	2.29	43 037	46 581	59 457	8.70	2.77

For notes, see end of the table.

Table A.13. **Vegetable oil projections** (cont.)

Marketing year	CONSUMPTION (kt)			Growth[a] (%)		PER CAPITA (kg)			Growth[a] (%)	
	Average 2005-07 est.	2008	2017	1998-2007	2008-17	Average 2005-07 est.	2008	2017	1998-2007	2008-17
WORLD	**100 916**	**110 074**	**143 356**	**5.70**	**2.88**	**15.3**	**16.3**	**19.2**	**4.46**	**1.77**
DEVELOPED	**36 723**	**40 694**	**51 986**	**4.46**	**2.54**	**27.4**	**30.2**	**37.7**	**4.07**	**2.28**
NORTH AMERICA	**11 207**	**12 332**	**13 704**	**2.79**	**1.09**	**33.7**	**36.4**	**37.4**	**1.79**	**0.20**
Canada	864	1 097	1 546	−1.23	3.43	26.5	33.0	43.2	−2.23	2.59
United States	10 343	11 234	12 158	3.18	0.83	34.5	36.8	36.8	2.17	−0.06
EUROPE	**18 541**	**20 977**	**29 783**	**5.71**	**3.57**	**35.1**	**39.5**	**55.6**	**5.41**	**3.47**
EU(27)	17 993	20 393	29 159	5.74	3.64	36.6	41.3	58.5	5.44	3.54
CIS	**3 743**	**3 860**	**4 705**	**5.75**	**2.27**	**13.5**	**14.0**	**17.2**	**5.95**	**2.38**
Russian Federation	2 562	2 576	2 847	5.40	1.23	18.0	18.3	21.1	5.85	1.73
Ukraine	508	577	779	5.13	3.27	10.9	12.6	18.2	5.95	4.05
OCEANIA DEVELOPED	**555**	**779**	**856**	**6.60**	**1.08**	**22.4**	**30.9**	**31.2**	**5.42**	**0.16**
Australia	392	617	694	3.62	1.34	19.0	29.4	30.3	2.42	0.40
New Zealand	163	162	162	18.00	0.00	39.3	38.4	35.8	16.90	−0.78
OTHER DEVELOPED	**2 678**	**2 746**	**2 938**	**1.82**	**0.78**	**15.2**	**15.6**	**16.7**	**1.44**	**0.80**
Japan	1 869	1 851	1 915	0.88	0.40	14.6	14.5	15.2	0.76	0.58
South Africa	809	896	1 023	4.25	1.53	16.8	18.3	20.2	3.16	1.13
DEVELOPING	**64 193**	**69 380**	**91 371**	**6.45**	**3.08**	**12.2**	**12.8**	**15.0**	**5.00**	**1.77**
AFRICA	**7 094**	**7 666**	**10 316**	**5.32**	**3.30**	**7.9**	**8.2**	**9.0**	**2.93**	**1.07**
NORTH AFRICA	**2 826**	**3 072**	**4 149**	**4.79**	**3.33**	**12.0**	**12.6**	**14.4**	**2.88**	**1.54**
Algeria	585	615	799	5.83	2.90	17.5	17.9	20.4	4.35	1.46
Egypt	1 414	1 591	2 195	5.10	3.56	19.0	20.7	24.7	3.29	1.95
SUB-SAHARAN AFRICA	**4 268**	**4 594**	**6 166**	**5.68**	**3.29**	**6.5**	**6.6**	**7.2**	**3.11**	**0.90**
LATIN AMERICA and CARIBBEAN	**9 611**	**10 453**	**14 890**	**3.98**	**3.75**	**17.1**	**18.2**	**23.4**	**2.70**	**2.60**
Argentina	796	893	1 330	1.97	4.80	20.4	22.4	30.8	0.98	3.89
Brazil	3 563	3 720	5 980	3.20	4.63	18.9	19.3	28.0	1.83	3.47
Chile	363	380	462	9.53	2.19	22.0	22.6	25.3	8.40	1.29
Mexico	1 476	1 495	1 689	2.15	1.56	14.3	14.2	14.7	1.29	0.58
Uruguay	70	80	120	18.34	4.49	20.9	23.8	34.6	18.22	4.14
ASIA and PACIFIC	**47 488**	**51 260**	**66 165**	**7.19**	**2.91**	**12.5**	**13.1**	**15.3**	**5.92**	**1.80**
Bangladesh	1 355	1 451	1 994	6.89	3.53	8.7	9.0	10.8	5.02	1.98
China[b]	18 794	20 402	25 164	11.16	2.58	14.2	15.2	17.7	10.49	1.92
India	8 922	9 254	11 246	2.34	2.07	7.7	7.8	8.4	0.72	0.76
Indonesia	4 255	4 972	7 717	5.82	4.84	18.6	21.2	30.2	4.51	3.87
Iran, Islamic Republic of	1 179	1 241	1 592	3.33	2.78	16.8	17.2	19.6	2.30	1.45
Korea	695	702	733	4.40	0.58	14.4	14.4	14.8	3.89	0.39
Malaysia	2 555	2 913	4 440	8.42	4.65	97.8	107.8	143.9	6.45	3.18
Pakistan	2 059	2 190	2 732	2.72	2.48	12.8	13.1	13.8	0.84	0.59
Saudi Arabia	401	408	622	8.11	4.64	16.6	16.1	20.5	5.59	2.60
Turkey	1 501	1 508	1 802	5.39	2.02	20.3	19.9	21.5	4.01	0.92
LEAST DEVELOPED COUNTRIES (LDC)	**4 471**	**4 756**	**6 354**	**7.57**	**3.24**	**6.4**	**6.5**	**7.0**	**5.18**	**0.99**
OECD	**35 584**	**39 377**	**50 203**	**4.30**	**2.52**	**29.3**	**32.1**	**39.3**	**3.68**	**2.06**
NON-OECD	**65 332**	**70 697**	**93 154**	**6.52**	**3.09**	**12.1**	**12.8**	**15.0**	**5.14**	**1.83**

a) Least-squares growth rate (see glossary).
b) Refers to mainland only. The economies of Chinese Taipei, Hong Kong (China) and Macau (China) are included in the Other Asia Pacific aggregate.
est.: estimate.
Source: OECD and FAO Secretariats.

StatLink ⟨≡⟩ http://dx.doi.org/10.1787/384215854413

OECD-FAO AGRICULTURAL OUTLOOK 2008-2017 – ISBN 978-92-64-04590-3 – © OECD/FAO 2008

Table A.14. **Main policy assumptions for sugar markets**

Crop year[a]		06/07	07/08 est.	08/09	09/10	10/11	11/12	12/13	13/14	14/15	15/16	16/17	17/18
MAIN ASSUMPTIONS FOR SUGAR MARKETS													
ARGENTINA													
Tariff, sugar	ARS/t	35.0	35.0	35.0	35.0	35.0	35.0	35.0	35.0	35.0	35.0	35.0	35.0
BRAZIL													
Cane allocation to sugar	%	49.5	49.0	48.5	48.0	47.5	47.0	46.5	46.0	45.5	45.0	44.5	44.5
Tariff, raw sugar	%	35.0	35.0	35.0	35.0	35.0	35.0	35.0	35.0	35.0	35.0	35.0	35.0
Tariff, white sugar	%	35.0	35.0	35.0	35.0	35.0	35.0	35.0	35.0	35.0	35.0	35.0	35.0
Ethanol blending ratio with gazoline	%	25.0	25.0	25.0	25.0	25.0	25.0	25.0	25.0	25.0	25.0	25.0	25.0
CANADA													
Tariff, raw sugar	CAD/t	24.7	24.7	24.7	24.7	24.7	24.7	24.7	24.7	24.7	24.7	24.7	24.7
Tariff, white sugar	CAD/t	30.9	30.9	30.9	30.9	30.9	30.9	30.9	30.9	30.9	30.9	30.9	30.9
CHINA[b]													
TRQ sugar	kt	1 954	1 954	1 954	1 954	1 954	1 954	1 954	1 954	1 954	1 954	1 954	1 954
Tariff, in-quota, raw sugar	%	15.0	15.0	15.0	15.0	15.0	15.0	15.0	15.0	15.0	15.0	15.0	15.0
Tariff, In-quota, white sugar	%	50.0	50.0	50.0	50.0	50.0	50.0	50.0	50.0	50.0	50.0	50.0	50.0
Tariff, over-quota	%	50.0	50.0	50.0	50.0	50.0	50.0	50.0	50.0	50.0	50.0	50.0	50.0
EU[c]													
Roforonce price, white sugar[d]	EUR/t	632	632	542	404	404	404	404	404	404	404	404	405
Effective quota[e]	kt rse	19 459	16 848	16 510	16 470	15 806	15 807	15 808	15 809	15 810	15 811	15 812	15 813
Subsidised export limits													
Quantity Limit	kt rse	1 431	1 431	1 431	1 431	1 431	1 431	1 431	1 431	1 431	1 431	1 431	1 431
Value Limit	000 EUR	534 426	534 426	534 426	534 426	534 426	534 426	534 426	534 426	534 426	534 426	534 426	534 426
Tariff, raw sugar	EUR/t	339	339	339	339	339	339	339	339	339	339	339	339
Tariff, white sugar	EUR/t	419	419	419	419	419	419	419	419	419	419	419	419
INDIA													
Intervention price, sugar cane	INR/t	750	750	750	750	750	750	750	750	750	750	750	750
Applied tariff, raw sugar	%	60.0	60.0	60.0	60.0	60.0	60.0	60.0	60.0	60.0	60.0	60.0	60.0
INDONESIA													
Tariff, white sugar	%	25.0	25.0	25.0	25.0	25.0	25.0	25.0	25.0	25.0	25.0	25.0	25.0
JAMAICA													
Applied tariff, white sugar	%	40.0	40.0	40.0	40.0	40.0	40.0	40.0	40.0	40.0	40.0	40.0	40.0
JAPAN													
Minimum stabilisation price, raw sugar	JPY/kg	152	152	152	152	152	152	152	152	152	152	152	152
Tariff, raw sugar	JPY/kg	71.8	71.8	71.8	71.8	71.8	71.8	71.8	71.8	71.8	71.8	71.8	71.8
Tariff, white sugar	JPY/kg	103.1	103.1	103.1	103.1	103.1	103.1	103.1	103.1	103.1	103.1	103.1	103.1
KOREA													
Tariff, raw sugar	%	18.0	18.0	18.0	18.0	18.0	18.0	18.0	18.0	18.0	18.0	18.0	18.0
MEXICO													
Mexico common external tariff, raw sugar	MXN/t	4 305	4 325	4 403	4 462	4 521	4 572	4 621	4 669	4 718	4 767	4 816	4 867
Mexico common external tariff, white sugar	MXN/t	4 305	4 325	4 403	4 462	4 521	4 572	4 621	4 669	4 718	4 767	4 816	4 867
RUSSIA													
Tariff, raw sugar[f]	%	66.6	84.8	95.0	85.8	66.3	53.9	42.6	45.5	41.5	40.5	41.0	43.9
Tariff, white sugar[f]	USD/t	48.5	67.1	79.1	71.7	53.2	39.3	31.4	32.5	28.1	28.0	28.5	29.9

For notes, see end of the table.

Table A.14. **Main policy assumptions for sugar markets** (cont.)

Crop year[a]		06/07	07/08 est.	08/09	09/10	10/11	11/12	12/13	13/14	14/15	15/16	16/17	17/18
UNITED STATES[c]													
Loan rate, cane sugar	USD/t	397	397	397	397	397	397	397	397	397	397	397	397
Loan rate, beet sugar	USD/t	504.9	504.9	504.9	504.9	504.9	504.9	504.9	504.9	504.9	504.9	504.9	504.9
TRQ, raw sugar	kt rse	1 701	1 650	1 201	1 203	1 205	1 207	1 212	1 214	1 216	1 219	1 223	1 226
TRQ, refined sugar	kt rse	49	49	49	49	49	49	49	49	49	49	49	49
Raw sugar 2nd tier WTO tariff	USD/t	339	339	339	339	339	339	339	339	339	339	339	339
White sugar 2nd tier WTO tariff	USD/t	357	357	357	357	357	357	357	357	357	357	357	357
Raw sugar 2nd tier NAFTA tariff	USD/t	67	33	0	0	0	0	0	0	0	0	0	0
SOUTH AFRICA													
Tariff, raw sugar	%	105.0	105.0	105.0	105.0	105.0	105.0	105.0	105.0	105.0	105.0	105.0	105.0
TANZANIA													
Applied tariff, white sugar	%	25.0	25.0	25.0	25.0	25.0	25.0	25.0	25.0	25.0	25.0	25.0	25.0
VIETNAM													
Applied tariff, white sugar	%	40.0	40.0	40.0	40.0	40.0	40.0	40.0	40.0	40.0	40.0	40.0	40.0

a) Beginning crop marketing year.
b) Refers to mainland only.
c) In addition, price based special safeguard actions may apply.
d) Reference price for consumers.
e) Production that receives official support. Includes the 10 new member countries from May 2004, Bulgaria and Romania.
f) Assumes a wholesale price target of USD 470 per tonne as the basis for setting the floating tariff duty.
The source for tariffs (except United States and Russia) is AMAD. The source for Russia and United States tariffs is ERS, USDA.
est: estimate. rse : raw sugar equivalent.
Source: OECD and FAO Secretariats.

StatLink http://dx.doi.org/10.1787/384227810354

Table A.15. **World sugar projections (in raw sugar equivalent)**

Crop year[a]		Average 02/03-06/07	07/08 est.	08/09	09/10	10/11	11/12	12/13	13/14	14/15	15/16	16/17	17/18
OECD													
Production	kt rse	39,783	36 558	35 876	35 765	35 533	35 601	35 306	36 022	36 366	36 653	36 871	37 047
Consumption	kt rse	40,280	40 911	41 072	41 202	41 022	41 175	41 249	41 539	41 824	42 139	42 464	42 728
Closing stocks	kt rse	17,373	16 887	16 789	16 776	16 768	16 669	16 197	15 991	15 872	15 873	15 921	16 164
NON-OECD													
Production	kt rse	110,890	129 481	130 610	133 043	134 872	136 321	138 209	141 017	142 735	145 772	148 742	151 997
Consumption	kt rse	105,108	117 474	123 657	126 728	129 105	130 709	132 746	135 997	138 647	141 218	143 504	146 055
Closing stocks	kt rse	50,127	66 667	68 490	69 351	69 611	69 746	69 770	69 524	68 324	67 464	67 153	67 281
WORLD													
Production	kt rse	150,674	166 039	166 487	168 808	170 405	171 922	173 515	177 039	179 101	182 425	185 613	189 044
Consumption	kt rse	145,389	158 385	164 729	167 930	170 126	171 884	173 995	177 535	180 472	183 357	185 968	188 782
Closing stocks	kt rse	67,710	83 554	85 279	86 127	86 379	86 415	85 967	85 515	84 197	83 337	83 074	83 445
Price, raw sugar[b]	USD/t	237.1	229.3	216.0	228.0	257.6	280.4	304.5	298.0	307.1	309.6	308.2	301.7
Price, white sugar[c]	USD/t	291.2	289.1	268.1	280.8	317.8	351.8	374.5	371.3	384.9	385.0	383.4	379.1

a) Beginning crop marketing year.
b) Raw sugar world price, ICE Inc. No. 11, f.o.b. stowed Caribbean port (including Brazil), bulk spot price, October/September.
c) Refined sugar price, London No. 5, f.o.b. Europe, spot, October/September.
est: estimate.
Source: OECD and FAO Secretariats.

StatLink http://dx.doi.org/10.1787/384250803044

Table A.16. **World sugar projections (in raw sugar equivalent)**

Crop year[a]	PRODUCTION (kt)			Growth[b] (%)		IMPORTS (kt)			Growth[b] (%)		EXPORTS (kt)			Growth[b] (%)	
	Average 2005-07 est.	2008	2017	1998-2007	2008-17	Average 2005-07 est.	2008	2017	1998-2007	2008-17	Average 2005-07 est.	2008	2017	1998-2007	2008-17
WORLD	161 564	166 487	189 044	2.45	1.39	45 333	48 656	59 657	1.29	2.05	49 123	48 656	59 657	2.60	2.05
DEVELOPED	41 526	39 211	42 052	−0.34	0.87	14 428	14 697	15 251	−1.86	0.11	10 181	7 463	8 784	−3.93	1.84
NORTH AMERICA	7 456	7 865	8 052	−0.72	0.48	3 671	3 659	4 871	3.82	2.78	334	257	257	11.60	0.00
Canada	113	94	141	1.19	4.73	1 324	1 310	1 569	1.76	1.84	65	30	30	17.26	0.00
United States	7 344	7 771	7 912	−0.75	0.42	2 348	2 348	3 302	5.18	3.25	269	227	227	10.86	0.00
EUROPE	19 527	17 500	16 923	−1.79	−0.49	4 272	4 258	5 560	−2.37	2.62	4 116	1 876	1 981	−10.37	0.28
EU(27)	18 554	16 510	15 813	−2.16	−0.58	3 164	3 231	4 692	−4.12	3.64	3 590	1 349	1 435	−13.55	0.34
CIS	6 283	5 999	8 348	6.71	3.87	4 630	5 034	2 965	−4.99	−6.02	1 074	1 128	1 505	7.69	3.89
Russian Federation	3 229	3 111	4 026	9.86	2.87	3 287	3 455	2 351	−6.40	−4.15	238	201	294	−3.26	4.10
Ukraine	2 332	2 202	3 066	3.09	3.81	53	361	49	−24.68	−22.94	97	198	601	−6.76	15.49
OCEANIA DEVELOPED	4 899	4 358	5 098	−1.03	2.33	237	259	276	0.14	0.70	3 598	3 096	4 014	−0.98	3.22
Australia	4 899	4 358	5 098	−1.03	2.33	7	5	5	9.89	0.00	3 577	3 077	3 995	−0.99	3.24
New Zealand	0	0	0	0.00	0.00	230	254	271	−0.05	0.71	21	19	19	1.01	0.00
OTHER DEVELOPED	3 361	3 489	3 631	−0.22	0.35	1 618	1 488	1 580	−1.36	0.30	1 060	1 106	1 026	−3.44	−1.87
Japan	903	940	939	0.72	0.00	1 433	1 287	1 321	−1.29	−0.13	4	2	2	−2.99	0.00
South Africa	2 457	2 549	2 692	−0.55	0.48	184	201	258	−1.39	2.80	1 055	1 104	1 024	−3.46	−1.87
DEVELOPING	120 039	127 276	146 992	3.56	1.54	30 906	33 960	44 405	2.98	2.82	38 942	41 193	50 873	4.62	2.09
AFRICA	7 669	8 244	9 460	2.60	1.58	7 700	8 049	10 904	3.60	3.16	2 685	2 986	3 558	4.98	1.81
NORTH AFRICA	2 321	2 320	2 835	2.39	2.21	3 564	3 833	4 723	1.55	2.24	281	292	333	7.30	1.36
Algeria	0	0	0	0.00	0.00	1 138	1 186	1 382	2.05	1.83	21	10	10	40.12	0.00
Egypt	1 849	1 840	2 243	3.68	2.04	973	1 067	1 489	−1.66	3.60	165	184	224	0.72	2.04
SUB-SAHARAN AFRICA	5 041	5 534	6 213	2.59	1.38	4 135	4 225	6 150	5.70	3.87	2 256	2 479	2 977	4.08	1.93
LATIN AMERICA and CARIBBEAN	51 647	51 646	65 346	3.73	2.56	1 963	1 868	1 870	3.93	−0.25	25 571	25 393	36 059	5.04	3.74
Argentina	2 488	2 678	3 278	5.34	2.55	0	1	0	−12.10	−17.32	643	775	1 205	18.06	4.79
Brazil	32 226	31 475	41 467	6.69	2.91	0	0	0	0.00	0.00	19 076	18 831	27 323	9.29	4.00
Chile	402	412	540	−2.76	3.34	286	292	261	3.05	−1.59	1	0	0	−39.74	0.00
Mexico	5 566	5 948	6 889	1.56	1.69	262	210	18	31.68	−28.51	450	711	1 640	−3.91	7.60
Uruguay	7	10	10	−13.13	0.00	107	116	118	−0.15	0.06	5	6	6	1.59	0.00
ASIA and PACIFIC	59 874	66 400	71 374	3.49	0.72	21 023	23 915	31 213	2.75	2.83	10 612	12 745	11 199	3.51	−2.03
Bangladesh	158	152	164	0.22	0.95	980	1 091	1 396	3.73	2.57	0	0	0	0.00	0.00
China[c]	12 198	14 123	15 694	5.52	1.20	1 233	2 811	3 800	7.86	3.22	189	128	133	−8.84	0.41
India	26 759	28 547	28 970	3.93	0.12	13	65	1 257	−48.68	33.90	2 092	2 200	33	37.80	−38.27
Indonesia	2 567	2 791	3 659	6.34	3.16	1 515	1 862	2 143	−2.66	1.41	3	1	1	−20.00	0.00
Iran, Islamic Republic of	1 290	1 448	1 857	5.21	2.87	805	877	776	−4.57	−1.37	0	0	0	0.00	0.00
Korea	0	0	0	0.00	0.00	1 647	1 841	2 142	1.98	1.59	341	309	407	0.38	3.36
Malaysia	63	67	79	−7.42	2.26	1 440	1 554	1 932	2.38	2.37	400	424	530	5.28	2.43
Pakistan	3 722	4 343	5 163	1.80	1.97	794	412	574	25.30	3.53	38	43	52	−25.92	1.97
Saudi Arabia	0	0	0	0.00	0.00	1 229	1 263	1 538	7.33	2.27	412	417	492	17.10	1.83
Turkey	2 129	2 206	2 493	−2.61	1.51	26	27	70	16.99	7.60	66	22	25	−32.47	1.51
LEAST DEVELOPED COUNTRIES (LDC)	2 951	3 239	3 949	4.38	2.29	3 512	3 821	5 283	2.41	3.26	615	708	1 011	10.97	3.13
OECD	37 609	35 876	37 047	−1.11	0.45	10 882	10 911	13 768	0.47	2.21	8 405	5 813	7 845	−5.75	3.21
NON-OECD	123 955	130 610	151 997	3.73	1.63	34 426	37 718	45 819	1.54	2.00	40 652	42 821	51 787	4.91	1.88

For notes, see end of the table.

OECD-FAO AGRICULTURAL OUTLOOK 2008-2017 – ISBN 978-92-64-04590-3 – © OECD/FAO 2008

Table A.16. **World sugar projections (in raw sugar equivalent)** *(cont.)*

Crop year[a]	CONSUMPTION (kt)			Growth[b] (%)		PER CAPITA (kg)			Growth[b] (%)	
	Average 2005-07 est.	2008	2017	1998-2007	2008-17	Average 2005-07 est.	2008	2017	1998-2007	2008-17
WORLD	**153 272**	**164 729**	**188 782**	**2.25**	**1.50**	**23.2**	**24.4**	**25.3**	**1.02**	**0.39**
DEVELOPED	**45 967**	**46 555**	**48 298**	**0.33**	**0.41**	**34.3**	**34.5**	**35.0**	**−0.06**	**0.15**
NORTH AMERICA	**10 742**	**11 152**	**12 509**	**0.46**	**1.30**	**32.4**	**32.9**	**34.1**	**−0.54**	**0.41**
Canada	1 365	1 384	1 680	1.34	2.09	41.9	41.7	46.9	0.35	1.25
United States	9 377	9 768	10 829	0.34	1.18	31.3	32.0	32.7	−0.67	0.29
EUROPE	**20 087**	**20 024**	**20 323**	**0.36**	**0.16**	**38.0**	**37.7**	**37.9**	**0.06**	**0.06**
EU(27)	18 647	18 569	18 784	0.31	0.13	37.9	37.6	37.7	0.00	0.03
CIS	**9 839**	**9 944**	**9 761**	**0.12**	**−0.20**	**35.5**	**35.9**	**35.6**	**0.32**	**−0.10**
Russian Federation	6 350	6 353	6 077	0.09	−0.46	44.6	45.1	45.1	0.54	0.04
Ukraine	2 241	2 337	2 474	0.43	0.57	48.1	51.0	57.9	1.25	1.36
OCEANIA DEVELOPED	**1 423**	**1 460**	**1 551**	**2.56**	**0.70**	**57.6**	**57.9**	**56.6**	**1.38**	**−0.22**
Australia	1 192	1 225	1 299	2.65	0.68	57.9	58.3	56.8	1.46	−0.26
New Zealand	231	235	252	2.08	0.76	55.8	55.7	55.7	0.98	−0.02
OTHER DEVELOPED	**3 875**	**3 975**	**4 154**	**−0.36**	**0.50**	**22.0**	**22.5**	**23.6**	**−0.74**	**0.52**
Japan	2 284	2 331	2 259	−0.79	−0.33	17.9	18.2	18.0	−0.91	−0.16
South Africa	1 591	1 644	1 895	0.32	1.58	33.0	33.7	37.4	−0.78	1.17
DEVELOPING	**107 306**	**118 174**	**140 484**	**3.15**	**1.90**	**20.4**	**21.8**	**23.0**	**1.70**	**0.59**
AFRICA	**12 568**	**13 241**	**16 587**	**2.99**	**2.39**	**14.0**	**14.1**	**14.5**	**0.60**	**0.16**
NORTH AFRICA	**5 563**	**5 788**	**7 074**	**2.11**	**2.13**	**23.6**	**23.6**	**24.6**	**0.19**	**0.34**
Algeria	1 100	1 153	1 348	1.90	1.68	33.1	33.6	34.4	0.42	0.24
Egypt	2 599	2 678	3 384	2.33	2.49	35.0	34.9	38.1	0.51	0.88
SUB-SAHARAN AFRICA	**6 842**	**7 282**	**9 318**	**3.92**	**2.60**	**10.4**	**10.5**	**10.9**	**1.35**	**0.22**
LATIN AMERICA and CARIBBEAN	**26 367**	**27 868**	**30 954**	**2.51**	**1.18**	**46.9**	**48.4**	**48.5**	**1.23**	**0.03**
Argentina	1 737	1 815	2 036	2.05	1.24	44.4	45.6	47.2	1.07	0.34
Brazil	11 481	12 546	14 116	3.19	1.32	60.9	65.1	66.0	1.82	0.16
Chile	695	723	803	0.58	1.13	42.2	43.0	44.0	−0.55	0.23
Mexico	5 536	5 476	5 297	2.58	−0.22	53.8	52.0	46.1	1.71	−1.20
Uruguay	116	120	122	0.23	0.06	34.0	35.9	35.3	0.10	−0.29
ASIA and PACIFIC	67 397	76 013	91 769	3.47	2.08	17.7	19.5	21.3	2.21	0.97
Bangladesh	1 130	1 216	1 526	2.78	2.39	7.2	7.5	8.2	0.91	0.83
China[c]	13 366	16 003	19 252	6.10	1.50	10.1	12.5	13.5	5.43	0.84
India	22 175	25 494	31 532	3.15	2.41	19.2	21.5	23.6	1.52	1.11
Indonesia	4 349	4 559	5 726	3.06	2.48	19.0	19.5	22.4	1.75	1.51
Iran, Islamic Republic of	2 165	2 257	2 620	1.69	1.57	30.8	31.3	32.2	0.66	0.24
Korea	1 366	1 494	1 715	4.54	1.33	28.3	30.7	34.7	4.04	1.15
Malaysia	1 129	1 207	1 476	1.60	2.16	43.2	44.7	47.8	−0.37	0.69
Pakistan	4 325	4 607	5 501	3.41	1.91	26.9	27.6	27.8	1.53	0.02
Saudi Arabia	767	837	1 038	3.66	2.46	31.7	33.1	34.1	1.14	0.41
Turkey	2 090	2 184	2 495	1.50	1.53	28.3	28.8	29.8	0.11	0.42
LEAST DEVELOPED COUNTRIES (LDC)	**5 916**	**6 312**	**8 089**	**3.37**	**2.62**	**8.4**	**8.6**	**9.0**	**0.98**	**0.38**
OECD	**40 586**	**41 072**	**42 728**	**0.78**	**0.46**	**33.4**	**33.5**	**33.4**	**0.17**	**0.00**
NON-OECD	**112 686**	**123 657**	**146 055**	**2.81**	**1.83**	**20.9**	**22.3**	**23.6**	**1.44**	**0.57**

a) Beginning crop marketing year – see the Glossary of Terms for definitions.
b) Least-squares growth rate (see glossary).
c) Refers to mainland only. The economies of Chinese Taipei, Hong Kong (China) and Macau (China) are included in the Other Asia Pacific aggregate.
est.: estimate.
Source: OECD and FAO Secretariats.

StatLink ᵃⁱˢᴾ http://dx.doi.org/10.1787/384374482442

Table A.17. **Main policy assumptions for meat markets**

		Average 2002-06	2007 est.	2008	2009	2010	2011	2012	2013	2014	2015	2016	2017
ARGENTINA													
Beef export tax	%	7	15	15	15	15	15	15	15	15	15	15	15
CANADA													
Beef tariff-quota	kt pw	76	76	76	76	76	76	76	76	76	76	76	76
in-quota tariff	%	0	0	0	0	0	0	0	0	0	0	0	0
out-of-quota tariff	%	27	27	27	27	27	27	27	27	27	27	27	27
Poultry meat tariff-quota	kt pw	45	45	45	45	45	45	45	45	45	45	45	45
in-quota tariff	%	2	2	2	2	2	2	2	2	2	2	2	2
out-of-quota tariff	%	197	197	197	197	197	197	197	197	197	197	197	197
EUROPEAN UNION[a]													
Beef basic price[b, c, d]	EUR/kg dw	2.22	2.22	2.22	2.22	2.22	2.22	2.22	2.22	2.22	2.22	2.22	2.23
Beef buy-in price[d, e]	EUR/kg dw	1.56	1.56	1.56	1.56	1.56	1.56	1.56	1.56	1.56	1.56	1.56	1.56
Pig meat basic price[c]	EUR/kg dw	1.51	1.51	1.51	1.51	1.51	1.51	1.51	1.51	1.51	1.51	1.51	1.51
Sheep meat basic price	EUR/kg dw	5.04	5.04	5.04	5.04	5.04	5.04	5.04	5.04	5.04	5.04	5.04	5.04
Sheep basic rate[f]	EUR/head	21.00	21.00	21.0	21.0	21.0	21.0	21.0	21.0	21.0	21.0	21.0	21.0
Male bovine premium[g]	EUR/head	137	0	0	0	0	0	0	0	0	0	0	0
Adult bovine slaughter premium[h]	EUR/head	61	0	0	0	0	0	0	0	0	0	0	0
Calf slaughter premium	EUR/head	30	0	0	0	0	0	0	0	0	0	0	0
Suckler cow premium	EUR/head	120	0	0	0	0	0	0	0	0	0	0	0
Beef tariff-quota	kt pw	216	216	216	216	216	216	216	216	216	216	216	216
Pig meat tariff-quota	kt pw	167	167	167	167	167	167	167	167	167	167	167	167
Poultry meat tariff-quota	kt pw	623	623	623	623	623	623	623	623	623	623	623	623
Sheep meat tariff-quota	kt cwe	285	285	285	285	285	285	285	285	285	285	285	285
Subsidised export limits[c]													
Beef[i]	kt cwe	990	990	990	990	990	990	990	990	990	990	990	990
Pig meat[i]	kt cwe	588	588	588	588	588	588	588	588	588	588	588	589
Poultry meat	kt cwe	431	431	431	431	431	431	431	431	431	431	431	431
JAPAN[j]													
Beef stabilisation prices													
Upper price	JPY/kg dw	1 010	1 010	1 010	1 010	1 010	1 010	1 010	1 010	1 010	1 010	1 010	1 010
Lower price	JPY/kg dw	780	780	780	780	780	780	780	780	780	780	780	780
Beef tariff	%	39	39	39	39	39	39	39	39	39	39	39	39
Pig meat stabilisation prices													
Upper price	JPY/kg dw	480	480	480	480	480	480	480	480	480	480	480	480
Lower price	JPY/kg dw	365	365	365	365	365	365	365	365	365	365	365	365
Pig meat import system[k]													
Tariff	%	4	4	4	4	4	4	4	4	4	4	4	4
Standard import price	JPY/kg dw	410	410	410	410	410	410	410	410	410	410	410	410
Poultry meat tariff	%	7	7	7	7	7	7	7	7	7	7	7	7
KOREA													
Beef tariff	%	40	40	40	40	40	40	40	40	40	40	40	40
Beef mark-up	%	0	0	0	0	0	0	0	0	0	0	0	0
Pig meat tariff	%	22	22	22	22	22	22	22	22	22	22	22	22
Poultry meat tariff	%	21	21	21	21	21	21	21	21	21	21	21	21
MEXICO													
Pig meat tariff	%	45	45	45	45	45	45	45	45	45	45	45	45
Pig meat NAFTA tariff	%	0	0	0	0	0	0	0	0	0	0	0	0
Poultry meat tariff-quota	kt pw	41	41	41	41	41	41	41	41	41	41	41	41
in-quota tariff	%	50	50	50	50	50	50	50	50	50	50	50	50
out-of-quota tariff	%	229	228	228	228	228	228	228	228	228	228	228	228

For notes, see end of the table.

OECD-FAO AGRICULTURAL OUTLOOK 2008-2017 – ISBN 978-92-64-04590-3 – © OECD/FAO 2008

Table A.17. **Main policy assumptions for meat markets** (cont.)

		Average 2002-06	2007 est.	2008	2009	2010	2011	2012	2013	2014	2015	2016	2017
RUSSIA													
Beef tariff-quota	kt pw	459	468	474	480	480	480	480	480	480	480	480	480
in-quota tariff	%	15	15	15	15	15	15	15	15	15	15	15	15
out-of-quota tariff	%	54	52	50	40	40	40	40	40	40	40	40	40
Pigmeat tariff-quota	kt pw	467	485	494	502	502	502	502	502	502	502	502	502
in-quota tariff	%	15	15	15	15	15	15	15	15	15	15	15	15
out-of-quota tariff	%	76	55	60	60	60	60	60	60	60	60	60	60
Poultry meat tariff-quota	kt pw	844	1 171	1 212	1 252	1 252	1 252	1 252	1 252	1 252	1 252	1 252	1 252
in-quota tariff	%	25	25	25	25	25	25	25	25	25	25	25	25
UNITED STATES													
Beef tariff-quota	kt pw	697	697	697	697	697	697	697	697	697	697	697	697
in-quota tariff	%	5	5	5	5	5	5	5	5	5	5	5	5
out-of-quota tariff	%	26	26	26	26	26	26	26	26	26	26	26	26
CHINA													
Beef tariff	%	18	16	16	16	16	16	16	16	16	16	16	16
Pig meat tariff	%	16	16	16	16	16	16	16	16	16	16	16	16
Sheep meat tariff	%	16	15	15	15	15	15	15	15	15	15	15	15
Poultry meat tariff	%	19	19	19	19	19	19	19	19	19	19	19	19
INDIA													
Beef tariff	%	102	100	100	100	100	100	100	100	100	100	100	100
Pig meat tariff	%	102	100	100	100	100	100	100	100	100	100	100	100
Sheep meat tariff	%	94	92	92	92	92	92	92	92	92	92	92	92
Poultry meat tariff	%	00	07	07	87	87	87	87	87	87	87	87	87
Eggs tariff	%	150	150	150	150	150	150	150	150	150	150	150	150
SOUTH AFRICA													
Sheepmeat tariff-quota	kt pw	6	6	6	6	6	6	6	6	6	6	6	6
in-quota tariff	%	20	20	20	20	20	20	20	20	20	20	20	20
out-of-quota tariff	%	103	96	96	96	96	96	96	96	96	96	96	96

a) EU farmers also benefit from the Single Farm Payment (SFP) Scheme, which provides flat-rate payments independent from current production decisions and market developments. For the accession countries, payments are phased in with the assumption of maximum top-ups from national budgets up to 2011 through the Single Area Payment (SAP) and from 2012 through the SFP. Due to modulation, between 2.7% and 4.6% of the total SFP will go to rural development spending rather than directly to the farmers in the 15 former member states. From 2013, 4.6% of the total SFP will go to rural development spending in the accession countries.

b) Price for R3 grade male cattle.

c) Year beginning 1 July, except for E10 which is calendar year. Poland has a commitment on export subsidies on unspecified meat.

d) Ending 1 July 2002, replaced by basic price for storage.

e) Starting 1 July 2002.

f) A supplementary payment of 7 euro per head is provided for Less Favoured Areas.

g) Weighted average of all bull and steers payments.

h) Includes national envelopes for beef.

i) Includes live trade.

j) Year beginning 1 April.

k) Pig carcass imports. Emergency import procedures triggered from November 1995 to March 1996, from July 1996 to June 1997, from August 2001 to March 2002, from August 2002 to March 2003 and from August 2003 to March 2004.

Note: The source for tariffs and Tariff Rate Quotas (excluding Russia) is AMAD (Agricultural market access database). The tariff and TRQ data are based on Most Favoured Nation rates scheduled with the WTO and exclude those under preferential or regional agreements, which may be substantially different. Tariffs are simple averages of several product lines. Specific rates are converted to ad valorem rates using world prices in the Outlook. Import quotas are based on global commitments scheduled in the WTO rather than those allocated to preferential partners under regional or other agreements. For Mexico, the NAFTA in-quota tariff on poultry meat is zero and the tariff-rate quota is unlimited from 2003.

est.: estimate.

Source: OECD and FAO Secretariats.

StatLink ᗺᖴ◼ http://dx.doi.org/10.1787/384415613442

Table A.18. **World meat projections**

Calendar year[a]		Average 2002-06	2007 est.	2008	2009	2010	2011	2012	2013	2014	2015	2016	2017
OECD[b]													
BEEF AND VEAL[c]													
Production	kt cwe	26 465	26 872	26 576	26 287	26 280	26 448	26 500	26 585	26 759	26 900	27 075	27 200
Consumption	kt cwe	26 771	27 081	26 967	26 910	26 986	27 198	27 268	27 389	27 551	27 691	27 860	28 028
Ending stocks	kt cwe	1 014	1 010	1 008	1 023	1 029	1 031	1 041	1 043	1 048	1 068	1 077	1 051
Per capita consumption	kg rwt	15.6	15.5	15.4	15.3	15.2	15.3	15.2	15.2	15.3	15.3	15.3	15.3
Price, Australia[d]	AUD/100 kg dw	295	282	312	302	296	289	276	288	300	308	319	333
Price, EU[e]	EUR/100 kg dw	257	276	275	279	281	283	286	289	295	300	303	306
Price, USA[f]	USD/100 kg dw	291	327	327	323	325	323	311	317	321	323	323	329
Price, Argentina[g]	USD/100 kg dw	121	152	143	142	139	138	136	138	143	144	148	147
PIG MEAT[h]													
Production	kt cwe	37 113	38 140	37 939	37 890	37 958	38 130	38 037	38 166	38 709	38 979	39 455	39 797
Consumption	kt cwe	35 842	36 661	36 396	36 253	36 381	36 590	36 523	36 693	37 170	37 434	37 876	38 194
Ending stocks	kt cwe	801	811	809	827	817	834	862	827	838	843	840	840
Per capita consumption	kg rwt	23.3	23.4	23.1	22.9	22.9	22.9	22.8	22.8	22.9	23.0	23.2	23.3
Price, EU[i]	EUR/100 kg dw	131	131	149	150	150	148	151	150	148	151	148	152
Price, USA[j]	USD/100 kg dw	137	143	143	156	172	177	165	170	167	163	161	159
POULTRY MEAT													
Production	kt rtc	36 287	37 785	38 632	39 055	39 403	39 682	39 980	40 532	40 865	41 283	41 781	42 380
Consumption	kt rtc	34 590	36 081	36 945	37 299	37 696	37 848	38 088	38 622	38 984	39 370	39 833	40 404
Ending stocks	kt rtc	1 128	1 081	1 125	1 124	1 124	1 122	1 120	1 118	1 116	1 115	1 113	1 111
Per capita consumption	kg rwt	25.4	26.0	26.5	26.6	26.8	26.7	26.8	27.0	27.2	27.3	27.5	27.8
Price, EU[k]	EUR/100 kg rtc	102	112	116	119	121	118	116	120	121	123	124	125
Price, USA[l]	USD/100 kg rtc	144	168	167	161	166	169	164	168	170	172	174	177
SHEEP MEAT													
Production	kt cwe	2 762	2 904	2 802	2 762	2 748	2 751	2 749	2 749	2 751	2 750	2 750	2 748
Consumption	kt cwe	2 417	2 482	2 465	2 404	2 392	2 381	2 366	2 360	2 356	2 349	2 345	2 340
Ending stocks	kt cwe	522	533	514	514	514	514	514	514	514	514	514	518
Per capita consumption	kg rwt	1.8	1.8	1.8	1.7	1.7	1.7	1.7	1.7	1.6	1.6	1.6	1.6
Price, Australia[m]	AUD/100 kg dw	346	323	327	328	332	337	341	345	349	353	357	361
Price, Australia[n]	AUD/100 kg dw	172	130	132	140	141	142	143	144	146	147	148	150
Price, New Zealand[o]	NZD/100 kg dw	379	319	313	345	366	380	386	392	399	405	420	436
TOTAL MEAT													
Per capita consumption	kg rwt	66.1	66.8	66.8	66.5	66.6	66.6	66.4	66.7	67.0	67.2	67.6	68.1
Non-OECD													
BEEF AND VEAL													
Production	kt cwe	36 955	40 534	41 342	42 663	44 160	45 481	46 430	47 439	48 704	49 972	51 096	52 201
Consumption	kt cwe	36 452	40 042	41 150	42 184	43 580	44 867	45 762	46 733	47 996	49 255	50 388	51 489
Per capita consumption	kg rwt	4.9	5.1	5.2	5.3	5.4	5.5	5.5	5.5	5.6	5.7	5.8	5.8
Ending stocks	kt cwe	66	60	60	58	58	58	58	58	58	58	58	58
PIG MEAT													
Production	kt cwe	63 172	64 936	66 541	69 180	71 326	72 774	74 903	77 234	79 132	81 016	83 129	85 452
Consumption	kt cwe	63 946	65 916	67 826	70 503	72 593	73 969	76 054	78 400	80 307	82 193	84 341	86 681
Per capita consumption	kg rwt	9.5	9.4	9.6	9.8	10.0	10.0	10.2	10.4	10.5	10.6	10.7	10.9
Ending stocks	kt cwe	48	51	51	51	51	51	51	51	51	51	51	51
POULTRY MEAT													
Production	kt rtc	43 596	47 908	49 715	51 650	52 940	53 937	55 625	57 314	58 959	60 403	61 938	63 327
Consumption	kt rtc	45 117	49 419	51 352	53 401	54 648	55 772	57 519	59 223	60 839	62 316	63 888	65 306
Per capita consumption	kg rwt	7.6	8.0	8.2	8.4	8.5	8.5	8.7	8.8	9.0	9.1	9.2	9.3
Ending stocks	kt rtc	222	158	157	162	161	161	163	166	169	169	169	169

For notes, see end of the table.

OECD-FAO AGRICULTURAL OUTLOOK 2008-2017 – ISBN 978-92-64-04590-3 – © OECD/FAO 2008

Table A.18. **World meat projections** (cont.)

Calendar year[a]		Average 2002-06	2007 est.	2008	2009	2010	2011	2012	2013	2014	2015	2016	2017
SHEEP MEAT													
Production	*kt cwe*	10 935	10 828	11 022	11 319	11 575	11 831	12 084	12 329	12 583	12 839	13 100	13 358
Consumption	*kt cwe*	11 259	11 230	11 484	11 793	12 052	12 326	12 614	12 898	13 197	13 503	13 792	14 080
Per capita consumption	*kg rwt*	1.9	1.8	1.8	1.9	1.9	1.9	1.9	1.9	1.9	2.0	2.0	2.0
Ending stocks	*kt cwe*	5	5	5	5	5	5	5	5	5	5	5	5
TOTAL MEAT													
Per capita consumption	*kg rwt*	23.8	24.3	24.7	25.3	25.7	25.9	26.3	26.6	27.0	27.3	27.7	28.0

a) Year ending 30 September fo New Zealand
b) Excludes Iceland but includes the 8 EU members that are not members of the OECD. Carcass weight to retail weight conversion factors of 0.7 for beef and veal, 0.78 for pig meat and 0.88 for sheep meat. Rtc to retail weight conversion factor 0.88 for poultry meat.
c) Do not balance due to statistical differences in New Zealand.
d) Weighted average price of cows 201-260 kg, steers 301-400 kg, yearling < 200 kg dw.
e) Producer price.
f) Choice steers, 1100-1300 lb lw, Nebraska - lw to dw conversion factor 0.63.
g) Buenos Aires wholesale price linier, young bulls.
h) Do not balance due to consumption in Canada which excludes non-food parts.
i) Pig producer price.
j) Barrows and gilts, No. 1-3, 230-250 lb lw, Iowa/South Minnesota lw to dw conversion factor 0.74.
k) Weighted average farmgate live fowls, top quality, (lw to rtc conversion of 0.75), EU15 starting in 1995.
l) Wholesale weighted average broiler price 12 cities.
m) Saleyard price, lamb, 16-20 kg dw.
n) Saleyard price, wethers, < 22 kg dw.
o) Lamb schedule price, all grade average
est.: estimate.
Source: OECD and FAO Secretariats.

StatLink 🔗 http://dx.doi.org/10.1787/384434060610

Table A.19. **Beef and veal projections**[a]

Calendar year[b]	PRODUCTION[c] (kt)			Growth[d] (%)		IMPORTS[f] (kt)			Growth[d] (%)		EXPORTS[f] (kt)			Growth[d] (%)	
	Average 2005-07 est.	2008	2017	1998-2007	2008-17	Average 2005-07 est.	2008	2017	1998-2007	2008-17	Average 2005-07 est.	2008	2017	1998-2007	2008-17
WORLD	66 361	68 107	79 475	1.57	1.73	6 790	7 675	9 787	3.14	3.03	7 365	7 643	10 218	3.46	3.45
DEVELOPED	29 380	29 303	30 235	−0.40	0.44	4 042	4 363	5 290	1.23	2.41	3 229	3 359	3 835	−3.94	1.86
NORTH AMERICA	12 922	12 964	13 903	−0.25	0.95	1 650	1 752	1 959	0.86	1.50	1 001	1 299	1 858	0.58	4.91
Canada	1 694	1 685	1 414	1.06	−1.39	159	227	337	−7.56	3.96	505	447	502	0.58	3.14
United States	11 228	11 279	12 490	−0.43	1.26	1 491	1 525	1 623	2.06	1.06	496	851	1 356	−12.13	5.68
EUROPE	8 548	8 504	8 126	−1.04	−0.46	710	713	955	6.94	3.22	177	84	50	−21.14	−6.01
EU(27)	8 106	8 040	7 543	−1.02	−0.66	607	605	829	6.47	3.47	171	77	43	−21.56	−6.77
CIS	3 780	3 751	4 080	−1.00	0.91	978	1 149	1 660	5.27	4.75	88	76	133	−9.62	6.17
Russian Federation	1 760	1 688	1 959	−1.84	1.79	834	836	871	5.94	0.24	4	4	4	−2.17	0.00
Ukraine	523	518	515	−5.26	−0.47	54	80	317	45.24	15.44	22	1	1	−49.95	0.00
OCEANIA DEVELOPED	2 962	2 888	2 876	0.94	−0.05	13	9	9	10.08	0.00	1 958	1 893	1 787	1.42	−0.65
Australia	2 322	2 266	2 278	0.84	0.15	8	3	3	16.34	0.00	1 429	1 374	1 278	1.27	−0.66
New Zealand	640	622	598	1.30	−0.77	5	6	6	4.93	0.00	529	519	509	1.80	−0.62
OTHER DEVELOPED	1 168	1 196	1 248	1.69	0.50	692	739	706	−5.41	−0.55	6	7	7	0.33	0.00
Japan	507	499	526	−0.44	0.56	668	718	682	−5.47	−0.61	0	0	0	−20.78	0.00
South Africa	661	697	723	3.62	0.45	24	21	24	−2.46	1.38	6	7	7	1.32	0.00
DEVELOPING	36 981	38 804	49 241	3.36	2.60	2 747	3 313	4 497	6.55	3.83	4 135	4 284	6 384	14.45	4.52
AFRICA	4 416	4 403	5 380	2.09	2.22	558	797	903	11.10	2.50	50	44	41	−6.75	−3.52
NORTH AFRICA	1 239	1 173	1 446	3.56	2.28	377	486	583	10.40	3.01	1	1	3	7.98	−3.97
Algeria	99	101	115	−1.67	1.43	107	103	143	27.15	3.41	0	0	0	−5.51	29.92
Egypt	592	502	551	2.85	1.06	222	272	383	4.83	3.56	1	1	2	12.95	7.68
SUB-SAHARAN AFRICA	3 177	3 230	3 934	1.57	2.20	181	311	320	13.05	1.61	49	43	38	−6.99	−2.57
LATIN AMERICA and CARIBBEAN	17 173	17 956	22 045	3.42	2.30	699	769	1 116	3.21	4.17	3 517	3 578	5 605	16.32	5.19
Argentina	3 099	3 107	3 458	2.57	1.16	4	4	3	−13.94	−3.66	617	507	818	10.18	6.32
Brazil	8 967	9 527	12 400	5.02	2.95	62	74	26	−6.21	−7.91	2 150	2 384	3 947	20.74	5.63
Chile	234	258	339	−0.23	3.01	170	177	241	7.51	3.57	15	14	27	65.68	6.92
Mexico	1 528	1 574	1 565	1.69	−0.16	252	286	458	−0.97	4.63	22	23	24	28.46	−0.04
Uruguay	527	517	585	2.26	1.39	10	12	27	51.09	9.01	431	382	470	10.66	2.34
ASIA and PACIFIC	15 393	16 445	21 815	3.68	3.01	1 490	1 747	2 478	6.90	4.21	568	662	737	9.08	0.92
Bangladesh	184	182	231	1.03	2.54	1	14	11	82.75	20.30	0	0	0	81.60	−6.32
China[g]	7 486	8 044	11 660	5.66	3.89	3	6	23	−10.38	15.59	87	102	137	4.55	3.03
India	3 352	3 744	4 687	2.43	2.47	0	0	0	26.09	0.00	429	494	522	11.56	0.45
Indonesia	474	486	546	4.79	1.45	45	52	70	9.79	2.65	0	0	0	29.07	−1.36
Iran, Islamic Republic of	355	363	400	2.23	1.08	112	125	214	15.81	5.70	0	0	0	22.69	16.60
Korea	210	217	226	−6.77	0.34	245	293	543	3.68	6.26	0	0	0	−1.59	0.00
Malaysia	11	18	18	−0.61	−0.22	180	183	244	8.67	3.15	3	3	5	6.38	5.14
Pakistan	1 057	1 068	1 409	2.84	2.98	3	94	37	78.37	5.33	3	4	7	34.42	−4.77
Saudi Arabia	20	21	25	0.15	1.98	137	155	229	13.06	4.39	2	2	0	−10.69	−13.85
Turkey	356	360	411	−0.06	1.50	0	0	0	16.57	−8.38	0	7	1	1.55	5.27
LEAST DEVELOPED COUNTRIES (LDC)	3 296	3 351	3 829	1.88	1.50	124	219	305	18.59	5.08	2	3	3	−18.38	−4.39
OECD	26 814	26 766	27 274	−0.33	0.30	3 461	3 692	4 509	0.22	2.23	3 152	3 300	3 714	−3.70	1.72
NON-OECD	39 547	41 342	52 201	3.02	2.55	3 329	3 984	5 278	7.07	3.78	4 212	4 343	6 505	13.13	4.57

For notes, see end of the table.

OECD-FAO AGRICULTURAL OUTLOOK 2008-2017 – ISBN 978-92-64-04590-3 – © OECD/FAO 2008

Table A.19. **Beef and veal projections**[a] (cont.)

Calendar year[b]	CONSUMPTION (kt)			Growth[d] (%)		PER CAPITA (kg)			Growth[d] (%)	
	Average 2005-07 est.	2008	2017	1998-2007	2008-17	Average 2005-07 est.	2008	2017	1998-2007	2008-17
WORLD	65 798	68 117	79 516	1.52	1.73	7.0	7.0	7.4	0.29	0.61
DEVELOPED	30 317	30 427	32 030	0.31	0.63	15.9	15.8	16.2	−0.08	0.37
NORTH AMERICA	13 849	13 684	14 325	0.60	0.59	29.2	28.3	27.4	−0.40	−0.30
Canada	1 056	1 061	1 069	0.58	0.04	22.7	22.4	20.9	−0.41	−0.79
United States	12 793	12 623	13 256	0.60	0.63	29.9	28.9	28.1	−0.40	−0.26
EUROPE	9 081	9 155	9 192	0.34	0.05	12.0	12.1	12.0	0.03	−0.05
EU(27)	8 485	8 530	8 354	0.30	−0.22	12.1	12.1	11.7	−0.01	−0.31
CIS	4 683	4 837	5 622	0.19	1.81	11.8	12.2	14.4	0.39	1.91
Russian Federation	2 596	2 529	2 835	−0.01	1.29	12.8	12.6	14.7	0.44	1.79
Ukraine	564	600	834	−1.87	3.49	8.5	9.2	13.7	−1.04	4.28
OCEANIA DEVELOPED	838	805	925	0.23	1.46	23.7	22.3	23.6	−0.95	0.54
Australia	724	700	825	0.30	1.82	24.6	23.3	25.2	−0.89	0.88
New Zealand	114	106	100	−0.38	−1.06	19.3	17.5	15.5	−1.47	−1.84
OTHER DEVELOPED	1 866	1 946	1 965	−1.32	0.11	7.4	7.7	7.8	−1.70	0.13
Japan	1 172	1 217	1 207	−3.40	−0.11	6.4	6.7	6.7	−3.52	0.07
South Africa	694	729	758	3.13	0.48	10.1	10.5	10.5	2.04	0.07
DEVELOPING	35 481	37 689	47 487	2.85	2.54	4.7	4.9	5.5	1.19	1.22
AFRICA	4 060	5 216	6 333	2.01	2.00	3.9	3.9	3.9	0.52	0.15
NORTH AFRICA	1 632	1 687	2 063	4.34	2.56	4.9	4.8	5.0	2.43	0.77
Algeria	208	209	265	6.84	2.51	4.4	4.3	4.7	5.36	1.06
Egypt	826	790	955	2.89	2.05	7.8	7.2	7.5	1.08	0.44
SUB-SAHARAN AFRICA	3 326	3 528	4 270	2.28	2.30	3.5	3.6	3.5	−0.29	−0.08
LATIN AMERICA and CARIBBEAN	14 030	14 710	17 271	1.37	1.70	17.5	17.9	19.0	0.09	0.55
Argentina	2 406	2 604	2 643	1.18	−0.09	44.5	45.8	42.9	0.30	1.00
Brazil	6 773	7 032	8 447	1.90	1.95	25.1	25.5	27.7	0.61	0.79
Chile	389	419	547	2.05	3.06	16.6	17.5	21.0	0.92	2.15
Mexico	1 553	1 605	1 792	0.86	1.17	10.6	10.7	10.9	−0.01	0.20
Uruguay	103	141	136	−10.73	−0.43	21.6	29.4	27.5	−10.85	−0.78
ASIA and PACIFIC	16 492	17 750	23 883	3.76	3.00	3.8	3.2	3.9	2.48	2.12
Bangladesh	185	196	242	1.10	2.87	0.8	0.8	0.9	−0.77	1.32
China[e]	7 402	7 948	11 545	5.66	3.92	3.9	4.1	5.7	5.00	3.26
India	2 924	3 250	4 165	1.60	2.74	1.8	1.9	2.2	0.13	1.40
Indonesia	568	597	694	4.96	1.69	1.7	1.8	1.9	3.66	0.72
Iran, Islamic Republic of	467	489	615	4.43	2.48	4.7	4.7	5.3	3.40	1.15
Korea	457	521	704	−2.38	4.09	6.6	7.5	10.8	−2.89	3.91
Malaysia	203	218	284	7.91	2.87	5.4	5.7	6.4	5.03	1.40
Pakistan	1 050	1 150	1 425	2.77	2.97	4.6	4.8	5.0	0.89	1.08
Saudi Arabia	158	179	261	11.20	4.25	4.6	4.9	6.0	8.68	2.21
Turkey	360	355	409	0.15	1.48	3.4	3.3	3.4	−1.23	0.38
LEAST DEVELOPED COUNTRIES (LDC)	3 335	3 505	4 118	2.32	1.95	3.3	3.3	3.2	−0.07	−0.29
OECD	26 962	26 967	28 028	0.24	0.46	15.6	15.4	15.3	−0.37	0.01
NON-OECD	38 836	41 150	51 489	2.48	2.48	5.0	5.2	5.8	1.11	1.23

a) Imports of meat do not equal exports because world market clearing is achieved on total trade, i.e including trade of live animals (in carcass weight equivalent).
b) Year ending 30 June for Australia and 31 May for New Zealand.
c) Gross indigenous production.
d) Least-squares growth rate (see glossary).
e) Refers to mainland only. The economies of Chinese Taipei, Hong Kong (China) and Macau (China) are included in the Other Asia Pacific aggregate.
f) Excludes trade of live animals.
est.: estimate.
Source: OECD and FAO Secretariats.

StatLink 🔗 http://dx.doi.org/10.1787/384445431007

Table A.20. **Pig meat projections**[a]

Calendar year[b]	PRODUCTION[c] (kt)			Growth[d] (%)		IMPORTS[f] (kt)			Growth[d] (%)		EXPORTS[f] (kt)			Growth[d] (%)	
	Average 2005-07 est.	2008	2017	1998-2007	2008-17	Average 2005-07 est.	2008	2017	1998-2007	2008-17	Average 2005-07 est.	2008	2017	1998-2007	2008-17
WORLD	104 168	104 481	125 239	2.24	1.97	4 649	5 184	6 601	6.54	2.56	5 279	5 483	7 051	7.44	2.61
DEVELOPED	39 247	40 228	42 925	0.65	0.71	2 980	3 124	3 718	5.58	2.08	3 905	4 021	4 897	5.75	1.96
NORTH AMERICA	11 512	11 887	12 950	1.75	1.00	599	608	743	4.59	2.26	2 394	2 635	3 614	10.66	2.99
Canada	2 247	2 180	2 383	3.56	1.30	143	156	183	10.52	1.76	1 064	956	1 002	9.60	0.61
United States	9 265	9 707	10 567	1.34	0.93	456	452	561	3.17	2.43	1 330	1 680	2 612	11.59	4.07
EUROPE	22 891	22 903	23 780	0.05	0.42	220	179	179	10.63	0.00	1 350	1 216	1 052	−0.23	−1.30
EU(27)	21 883	21 856	22 791	0.08	0.46	76	44	44	10.24	0.00	1 333	1 198	1 034	−0.30	−1.32
CIS	3 017	3 649	4 622	1.45	2.39	819	914	1 123	6.11	2.36	94	96	162	10.91	5.83
Russian Federation	1 672	2 147	2 894	1.49	2.88	634	645	656	3.32	0.29	14	13	15	11.83	0.99
Ukraine	629	730	897	−0.50	2.31	70	33	119	30.50	14.19	9	4	0	0.86	−10.26
OCEANIA DEVELOPED	426	417	394	0.43	−0.43	211	245	288	19.14	2.49	66	73	68	7.06	1.56
Australia	387	377	356	0.81	−0.41	176	205	232	21.66	2.32	65	73	68	7.07	1.56
New Zealand	39	40	38	−2.87	−0.58	35	40	56	11.30	3.27	0	0	0	2.60	2.96
OTHER DEVELOPED	1 400	1 373	1 179	0.16	−1.77	1 131	1 178	1 384	4.19	1.97	1	1	1	−5.25	−1.78
Japan	1 249	1 220	1 003	−0.24	−2.24	1 101	1 136	1 306	3.96	1.73	0	0	0	9.81	4.75
South Africa	151	153	175	3.96	1.38	30	43	78	16.91	6.80	1	1	1	−6.56	−4.62
DEVELOPING	64 922	64 253	82 314	3.30	2.68	1 669	2 060	2 883	8.61	3.23	1 374	1 461	2 154	13.87	4.22
AFRICA	709	753	987	2.68	2.67	81	100	226	8.33	9.05	8	72	46	8.50	−4.29
NORTH AFRICA	5	6	7	−1.05	2.53	0	0	1	−7.16	10.09	0	0	0	16.03	20.32
Algeria	0	0	0	0.15	0.00	0	0	0	25.20	0.00	0	0	0	12.23	0.00
Egypt	2	3	4	−4.77	1.80	0	0	0	−29.14	9.71	0	0	0	−50.13	20.32
SUB-SAHARAN AFRICA	704	747	980	2.71	2.68	81	100	225	8.91	9.05	8	72	46	8.48	−4.30
LATIN AMERICA and CARIBBEAN	5 908	6 389	8 772	4.23	3.41	486	479	622	7.33	2.44	765	808	1 360	23.90	5.45
Argentina	255	295	632	2.54	8.85	23	12	5	−14.97	−8.12	2	3	109	−1.45	38.24
Brazil	2 868	3 161	4 630	5.47	4.00	6	2	2	21.27	−0.03	598	619	1 050	26.54	5.87
Chile	476	555	622	9.16	1.30	2	3	2	0.41	−4.78	125	136	95	29.92	−4.91
Mexico	1 073	1 069	1 148	1.47	0.71	302	338	444	11.41	2.68	31	30	30	1.88	−0.06
Uruguay	20	22	37	−4.20	5.47	10	10	14	6.29	4.26	0	0	0	13.17	20.88
ASIA and PACIFIC	58 304	57 111	72 555	3.23	2.60	1 102	1 481	2 035	9.31	2.97	601	581	748	7.21	2.99
Bangladesh	0	0	0	0.00	0.00	0	0	0	1.03	0.00	0	0	0	0.00	0.00
China[e]	49 693	48 146	61 859	3.04	2.70	106	137	287	1.25	6.90	512	464	559	15.81	2.13
India	509	520	629	1.12	2.13	0	−1	1	46.50	−5.09	1	0	0	33.09	1.56
Indonesia	617	595	616	1.60	0.34	5	74	127	25.61	7.97	4	8	8	32.24	1.26
Iran, Islamic Republic of	0	0	0	0.00	0.00	0	0	0	−1.40	0.00	0	0	0	34.69	0.00
Korea	1 092	1 139	1 148	2.17	0.34	262	223	528	11.17	7.40	18	34	34	−19.29	0.00
Malaysia	210	189	226	−0.34	1.63	35	104	139	15.98	4.78	1	1	1	−2.94	3.25
Pakistan	0	0	0	0.00	0.00	0	0	0	79.36	0.00	0	0	0	0.00	0.00
Saudi Arabia	0	0	0	0.00	0.00	5	5	5	18.60	0.03	0	0	0	−52.69	2.11
Turkey	0	0	0	3.65	1.43	0	0	0	−13.71	37.42	0	0	0	−3.37	1.37
LEAST DEVELOPED COUNTRIES (LDC)	731	771	978	1.90	2.33	52	70	153	13.76	9.04	0	4	2	0.39	−5.21
OECD	37 591	37 940	39 788	0.67	0.54	2 566	2 608	3 368	6.39	2.71	3 849	3 979	4 789	5.21	1.82
NON-OECD	66 577	66 541	85 452	3.22	2.70	2 083	2 576	3 233	6.82	2.41	1 430	1 504	2 262	16.23	4.45

For notes, see end of the table.

OECD-FAO AGRICULTURAL OUTLOOK 2008-2017 – ISBN 978-92-64-04590-3 – © OECD/FAO 2008

Table A.20. **Pig meat projections**[a] (cont.)

Calendar year[b]	CONSUMPTION (kt)			Growth[d] (%)		PER CAPITA (kg)			Growth[d] (%)	
	Average 2005-07 est.	2008	2017	1998-2007	2008-17	Average 2005-07 est.	2008	2017	1998-2007	2008-17
WORLD	103 491	104 222	124 875	2.18	1.97	12.2	12.0	13.0	0.95	0.85
DEVELOPED	38 124	39 154	41 559	0.54	0.69	22.2	22.7	23.5	0.15	0.43
NORTH AMERICA	9 519	9 702	9 887	0.37	0.44	22.4	22.4	21.0	−0.63	−0.44
Canada	761	778	829	−2.10	0.93	18.2	18.3	18.1	−3.10	0.10
United States	8 757	8 923	9 058	0.61	0.40	22.8	22.8	21.4	−0.40	−0.49
EUROPE	21 746	21 850	22 892	0.14	0.50	32.1	32.1	33.3	−0.16	0.40
EU(27)	20 595	20 670	21 770	0.13	0.55	32.7	32.7	34.1	−0.18	0.45
CIS	3 759	4 488	5 605	2.11	2.29	10.6	12.7	16.0	2.31	2.40
Russian Federation	2 309	2 800	3 557	1.83	2.34	12.7	15.5	20.6	2.28	2.84
Ukraine	690	759	1 016	0.88	3.24	11.6	12.9	18.5	1.70	4.02
OCEANIA DEVELOPED	572	589	614	4.03	0.63	18.0	18.2	17.5	2.85	−0.28
Australia	498	510	521	4.34	0.48	18.9	18.9	17.7	3.15	−0.46
New Zealand	74	79	93	2.09	1.54	14.0	14.7	16.1	0.99	0.76
OTHER DEVELOPED	2 529	2 525	2 562	1.69	0.15	11.2	11.2	11.3	1.31	0.17
Japan	2 349	2 330	2 309	1.43	−0.11	14.3	14.2	14.3	1.32	0.07
South Africa	180	195	253	5.51	2.83	2.9	3.1	3.9	4.42	2.43
DEVELOPING	65 366	65 068	83 316	3.24	2.66	9.7	9.4	10.7	1.79	1.34
AFRICA	773	757	1 164	2.96	4.25	0.7	0.6	0.8	0.56	2.02
NORTH AFRICA	5	6	8	−1.31	3.08	0.0	0.0	0.0	−6.22	1.29
Algeria	0	0	0	7.36	0.00	0.0	0.0	0.0	5.89	−1.44
Egypt	2	3	4	−10.10	2.17	0.0	0.0	0.0	−11.92	0.56
SUB-SAHARAN AFRICA	768	751	1 156	3.03	4.26	0.9	0.8	1.1	0.46	1.88
LATIN AMERICA and CARIBBEAN	5 555	6 000	8 084	3.08	3.03	7.9	8.3	9.9	1.80	1.88
Argentina	276	305	528	−0.23	6.45	5.5	6.0	9.5	−1.21	5.54
Brazil	2 276	2 544	3 582	2.90	3.51	9.4	10.3	13.1	1.54	2.35
Chile	353	422	529	5.75	2.93	16.7	19.6	22.7	4.63	2.03
Mexico	1 381	1 417	1 612	3.13	1.28	10.5	10.5	10.9	2.27	0.30
Uruguay	30	32	51	−1.39	5.10	7.0	7.4	11.4	−1.51	4.76
ASIA and PACIFIC	58 928	58 212	74 068	3.27	2.60	12.1	11.6	13.4	2.00	1.49
Bangladesh	0	0	0	1.03	0.00	0.0	0.0	0.0	30.47	−1.55
China[e]	49 287	47 819	61 587	2.95	2.72	29.0	27.8	33.8	2.28	2.06
India	508	520	631	1.08	2.14	0.3	0.3	0.4	−0.54	0.04
Indonesia	601	647	721	1.67	1.34	2.0	2.2	2.2	0.36	0.36
Iran, Islamic Republic of	0	0	0	0.00	0.00	0.0	0.0	0.0	0.00	0.00
Korea	1 325	1 328	1 642	4.45	2.12	21.4	21.3	25.9	3.94	1.93
Malaysia	244	292	364	2.41	2.66	7.3	8.4	9.2	0.44	1.19
Pakistan	0	0	0	79.36	0.00	0.0	0.0	0.0	139.03	0.00
Saudi Arabia	5	5	5	18.52	0.00	0.1	0.2	0.1	−15.44	−2.05
Turkey	0	0	0	7.77	0.00	0.0	0.0	0.0	17.35	−1.10
LEAST DEVELOPED COUNTRIES (LDC)	784	778	1 126	2.47	3.66	0.9	0.8	1.0	0.08	1.42
OECD	36 104	36 396	38 194	0.38	0.57	23.2	23.1	23.3	−0.04	0.11
NON-OECD	67 387	67 826	86 681	3.13	2.64	9.7	9.6	10.9	1.75	1.39

a) Imports of meat do not equal exports because world market clearing is achieved on total trade, i.e including trade of live animals (in carcass weight equivalent).
b) Year ending 30 June for Australia and 31 May for New Zealand.
c) Gross indigenous production.
d) Least-squares growth rate (see glossary).
e) Refers to mainland only. The economies of Chinese Taipei, Hong Kong (China) and Macau (China) are included in the Other Asia Pacific aggregate.
f) Excludes trade of live animals.
est.: estimate.
Source: OECD and FAO Secretariats.

StatLink 🔢 http://dx.doi.org/10.1787/384463431521

Table A.21. **Poultry meat projections**

Calendar year[a]	PRODUCTION (kt)			Growth[b] (%)		IMPORTS (kt)			Growth[b] (%)		EXPORTS (kt)			Growth[b] (%)	
	Average 2005-07 est.	2008	2017	1998-2007	2008-17	Average 2005-07 est.	2008	2017	1998-2007	2008-17	Average 2005-07 est.	2008	2017	1998-2007	2008-17
WORLD	83 794	88 346	105 707	3.33	1.97	8 139	8 827	11 102	3.01	2.30	8 355	8 828	11 102	3.78	2.30
DEVELOPED	37 048	38 731	43 593	2.37	1.29	3 605	3 697	3 864	4.06	0.48	3 811	4 006	4 407	0.33	1.15
NORTH AMERICA	19 805	20 849	22 974	2.31	1.02	236	261	256	6.82	−0.07	2 863	3 153	3 616	1.03	1.68
Canada	1 172	1 220	1 423	2.09	1.60	211	228	225	5.56	−0.14	154	180	210	3.34	1.70
United States	18 632	19 629	21 552	2.32	0.99	26	33	30	28.09	0.50	2 709	2 973	3 406	0.90	1.68
EUROPE	11 657	11 724	12 640	1.18	0.83	897	948	1 053	9.03	1.10	866	771	652	−2.01	−2.05
EU(27)	11 413	11 468	12 345	1.18	0.81	745	785	863	10.18	0.97	853	755	624	−2.11	−2.29
CIS	2 319	2 874	4 047	10.39	3.92	1 835	1 728	2 141	3.28	2.09	41	49	90	10.21	6.82
Russian Federation	1 528	1 973	2 776	10.34	3.79	1 332	1 212	1 252	0.89	0.18	5	7	7	4.51	0.00
Ukraine	535	621	856	13.83	3.90	156	134	358	15.54	9.97	14	15	36	43.03	9.18
OCEANIA DEVELOPED	1 000	1 053	1 134	4.51	0.91	0	0	0	0.00	0.00	28	20	36	1.90	6.39
Australia	833	882	953	4.08	0.96	0	0	0	0.00	0.00	28	20	36	1.90	6.39
New Zealand	168	170	181	6.82	0.60	0	0	0	0.00	0.00	0	0	0	0.00	0.00
OTHER DEVELOPED	2 267	2 231	2 798	2.14	2.38	637	760	414	0.32	−5.81	13	13	13	−2.94	0.00
Japan	1 320	1 220	1 337	1.23	0.74	397	544	317	−4.59	−4.83	2	2	2	−14.10	0.00
South Africa	947	1 011	1 461	3.56	4.10	239	216	98	16.01	−8.24	11	11	11	−0.93	0.00
DEVELOPING	46 745	49 615	62 114	4.14	2.47	4 533	5 131	7 238	2.23	3.42	4 543	4 822	6 695	7.57	3.14
AFRICA	2 670	2 784	3 683	2.67	3.17	534	620	1 030	10.57	5.13	46	57	125	7.98	9.79
NORTH AFRICA	1 566	1 641	2 149	2.87	3.03	47	63	239	5.82	14.06	22	32	99	41.05	14.21
Algeria	262	272	343	1.41	2.68	8	5	11	5.68	13.40	0	0	32	−0.67	48.82
Egypt	753	789	1 006	3.97	2.75	25	39	157	16.54	13.89	21	27	55	51.23	7.67
SUB-SAHARAN AFRICA	1 104	1 143	1 534	2.38	3.38	487	557	791	11.01	3.33	24	25	26	−1.60	0.19
LATIN AMERICA and CARIBBEAN	18 072	18 951	23 970	5.89	2.57	1 182	1 199	2 060	9.20	4.27	3 212	3 332	4 753	18.47	2.82
Argentina	1 140	1 248	1 888	2.80	4.56	16	0	0	−14.89	0.00	102	71	131	26.68	4.38
Brazil	9 246	9 591	11 930	7.46	2.08	0	0	0	−24.59	0.52	2 971	3 080	4 409	18.89	2.77
Chile	593	656	741	5.23	1.58	23	26	54	49.06	8.27	89	121	85	15.74	−0.89
Mexico	2 485	2 496	2 711	5.22	0.93	512	503	647	12.29	3.49	1	1	1	−19.10	2.17
Uruguay	54	60	85	−0.75	4.01	1	2	1	8.05	2.12	0	0	7	−68.90	26.01
ASIA and PACIFIC	26 004	27 881	34 461	3.20	2.34	2 817	3 312	4 148	−0.90	2.69	1 285	1 432	1 816	−4.76	3.76
Bangladesh	125	128	183	1.97	4.02	3	6	4	7.67	−7.25	0	0	0	−13.00	0.00
China[c]	14 103	15 218	18 181	2.59	1.79	583	913	1 141	−5.46	4.44	501	595	770	−0.93	2.73
India	2 086	2 318	3 690	11.66	5.15	0	0	0	54.32	0.00	4	10	129	−2.13	24.35
Indonesia	1 079	1 240	1 450	5.97	1.88	3	1	52	−9.05	30.76	0	13	0	−62.03	−14.04
Iran, Islamic Republic of	841	903	1 003	1.34	1.34	23	26	64	7.69	6.11	21	22	43	15.64	7.11
Korea	435	473	560	0.97	1.92	91	114	130	6.90	1.25	2	2	3	3.29	2.76
Malaysia	1 046	1 077	1 223	3.83	1.56	28	23	0	−6.21	−42.86	95	94	17	−0.43	−18.29
Pakistan	390	401	596	3.31	4.53	1	23	30	1.44	1.63	4	5	8	20.21	6.62
Saudi Arabia	547	583	731	2.66	2.79	467	483	790	4.14	4.71	6	4	0	−15.71	−7.16
Turkey	937	976	1 221	7.04	2.58	78	77	122	30.45	4.16	37	28	72	16.19	10.30
LEAST DEVELOPED COUNTRIES (LDC)	1 114	1 182	1 593	2.33	3.52	444	479	652	10.79	2.59	9	10	13	−6.40	3.28
OECD	37 489	38 632	42 380	2.22	0.99	2 099	2 326	2 377	5.82	0.57	3 787	3 961	4 355	0.32	1.14
NON-OECD	46 305	49 715	63 327	4.29	2.67	6 040	6 501	8 725	2.16	2.83	4 568	4 867	6 747	7.52	3.13

For notes, see end of the table.

OECD-FAO AGRICULTURAL OUTLOOK 2008-2017 – ISBN 978-92-64-04590-3 – © OECD/FAO 2008

Table A.21. **Poultry meat projections** (cont.)

Calendar year[a]	CONSUMPTION (kt)			Growth[b] (%)		PER CAPITA (kg)			Growth[b] (%)	
	Average 2005-07 est.	2008	2017	1998-2007	2008-17	Average 2005-07 est.	2008	2017	1998-2007	2008-17
WORLD	83 663	88 297	105 709	3.28	1.97	11.1	11.5	12.4	2.05	0.86
DEVELOPED	36 854	38 373	43 052	2.77	1.23	24.2	25.1	27.5	2.38	0.97
NORTH AMERICA	17 192	17 903	19 614	2.61	0.91	45.6	46.5	47.1	1.60	0.02
Canada	1 229	1 266	1 438	2.49	1.31	33.2	33.5	35.3	1.49	0.47
United States	15 963	16 637	18 176	2.62	0.88	46.9	48.0	48.4	1.61	−0.01
EUROPE	11 690	11 905	13 044	1.91	1.02	19.5	19.7	21.4	1.61	0.92
EU(27)	11 307	11 500	12 586	1.90	1.01	20.2	20.5	22.2	1.59	0.91
CIS	4 121	4 554	6 098	6.91	3.21	13.1	14.5	19.6	7.12	3.32
Russian Federation	2 863	3 179	4 020	5.35	2.55	17.7	19.8	26.3	5.80	3.05
Ukraine	677	740	1 178	14.05	5.28	12.8	14.2	24.3	14.88	6.06
OCEANIA DEVELOPED	972	1 033	1 098	4.59	0.74	34.6	36.0	35.2	3.41	−0.18
Australia	805	862	917	4.17	0.77	34.4	36.1	35.3	2.97	−0.18
New Zealand	168	170	181	6.82	0.60	35.6	35.6	35.2	5.72	−0.18
OTHER DEVELOPED	2 879	2 978	3 199	1.72	0.86	14.4	14.8	16.0	1.35	0.87
Japan	1 704	1 761	1 651	−0.33	−0.62	11.7	12.1	11.6	−0.45	−0.44
South Africa	1 175	1 217	1 548	5.39	2.67	21.4	21.9	20.9	4.30	2.27
DEVELOPING	46 809	49 924	62 657	3.69	2.51	7.8	8.1	9.0	2.24	1.19
AFRICA	3 160	3 346	4 599	3.70	3.44	3.1	3.1	3.5	1.30	1.21
NORTH AFRICA	1 590	1 671	2 299	2.77	3.47	5.9	6.0	7.0	0.85	1.68
Algeria	270	277	321	1.51	1.65	7.1	7.1	7.2	0.04	0.20
Egypt	757	801	1 108	3.86	3.61	9.0	9.2	11.0	2.04	2.00
SUB-SAHARAN AFRICA	1 570	1 675	2 299	4.71	3.40	2.1	2.1	2.4	2.14	1.02
LATIN AMERICA and CARIBBEAN	16 041	16 817	21 277	4.51	2.66	25.1	25.7	29.4	3.23	1.51
Argentina	1 054	1 176	1 757	1.10	4.61	23.7	26.0	35.8	0.12	3.71
Brazil	6 276	6 511	7 522	4.13	1.72	29.3	29.7	31.0	2.77	0.56
Chile	526	560	710	4.56	2.39	28.1	29.4	34.3	3.43	1.49
Mexico	2 996	2 997	3 357	6.22	1.39	25.6	25.1	25.7	5.36	0.41
Uruguay	55	62	79	−0.39	2.83	14.5	16.2	20.1	−0.51	2.48
ASIA and PACIFIC	27 608	29 761	36 793	3.24	2.31	6.4	6.7	7.5	1.97	1.20
Bangladesh	129	134	186	2.07	3.62	0.7	0.7	0.9	0.20	2.07
China[c]	14 186	15 535	18 552	2.38	1.90	9.4	10.2	11.5	1.71	1.24
India	2 083	2 308	3 561	11.70	4.83	1.6	1.7	2.3	10.08	3.52
Indonesia	1 082	1 227	1 503	5.92	2.25	4.2	4.6	5.2	4.61	1.27
Iran, Islamic Republic of	844	906	1 024	1.06	1.37	10.6	11.0	11.1	0.04	0.04
Korea	524	585	688	1.48	1.79	9.5	10.6	12.2	0.98	1.61
Malaysia	870	1 000	1 207	3.86	2.05	33.0	32.8	34.4	1.89	0.58
Pakistan	387	419	618	3.22	4.34	2.1	2.2	2.8	1.33	2.45
Saudi Arabia	1 008	1 062	1 521	3.60	3.75	36.7	37.0	44.0	1.08	1.71
Turkey	979	1 025	1 270	7.72	2.40	11.7	11.9	13.3	6.34	1.29
LEAST DEVELOPED COUNTRIES (LDC)	1 549	1 651	2 231	4.33	3.24	1.9	2.0	2.2	1.94	1.00
OECD	35 805	36 945	40 404	2.63	0.96	26.0	26.5	27.8	2.02	0.50
NON-OECD	47 858	51 352	65 306	3.78	2.65	7.8	8.2	9.3	2.41	1.39

a) Year ending 30 June for Australia and 31 May for New Zealand.
b) Least-squares growth rate (see glossary).
c) Refers to mainland only. The economies of Chinese Taipei, Hong Kong (China) and Macau (China) are included in the Other Asia Pacific aggregate.
est.: estimate.
Source: OECD and FAO Secretariats.

StatLink 🔗 http://dx.doi.org/10.1787/384481282702

Table A.22. **Sheep meat projections**[a]

Calendar year[b]	PRODUCTION[c] (kt)			Growth[d] (%)		IMPORTS[f] (kt)			Growth[d] (%)		EXPORTS[f] (kt)			Growth[d] (%)	
	Average 2005-07 est.	2008	2017	1998-2007	2008-17	Average 2005-07 est.	2008	2017	1998-2007	2008-17	Average 2005-07 est.	2008	2017	1998-2007	2008-17
WORLD	13 644	13 911	16 164	-0.67	1.66	821	873	1 024	3.36	1.92	931	923	979	1.78	0.81
DEVELOPED	3 397	3 350	3 442	0.28	0.38	477	482	499	3.75	0.48	870	858	902	1.78	0.71
NORTH AMERICA	111	112	131	-2.26	1.70	107	112	115	6.21	0.31	6	5	5	9.73	0.18
Canada	18	21	30	5.57	3.54	21	23	31	4.62	3.31	0	0	0	-0.66	2.63
United States	92	90	101	-3.41	1.22	85	89	84	6.63	-0.61	6	5	5	10.46	0.00
EUROPE	1 210	1 185	1 116	-0.44	-0.60	283	286	297	5.06	0.43	11	10	9	23.64	-1.40
EU(27)	1 113	1 084	1 014	-0.59	-0.66	271	273	283	5.01	0.46	5	4	4	27.45	0.00
CIS	625	612	771	2.32	2.56	9	19	27	4.70	5.87	1	1	1	-4.99	-0.64
Russian Federation	196	159	250	3.36	5.00	9	12	12	5.73	0.00	0	0	0	-63.77	0.00
Ukraine	16	18	21	-1.82	1.58	0	1	1	86.10	7.99	0	0	0	-1.68	37.42
OCEANIA DEVELOPED	1 307	1 294	1 272	0.04	-0.06	7	9	9	4.70	0.00	852	842	888	1.63	0.74
Australia	755	774	802	-0.21	0.59	0	0	0	0.00	0.00	381	394	481	1.80	2.41
New Zealand	553	520	470	0.39	-1.07	7	9	9	4.70	0.00	471	448	407	1.51	-0.94
OTHER DEVELOPED	145	146	153	2.01	0.52	72	57	51	-4.04	-1.00	0	0	0	-12.45	0.00
Japan	0	0	0	0.00	0.00	52	47	32	-0.60	-4.23	0	0	0	0.00	0.00
South Africa	145	146	153	2.01	0.52	20	10	20	-10.07	7.71	0	0	0	-12.45	0.00
DEVELOPING	10 247	10 561	12 722	-0.62	2.04	343	391	525	2.26	3.48	62	65	77	0.67	2.00
AFRICA	3 360	3 332	3 839	-5.25	1.56	48	68	139	17.40	8.42	8	8	6	-7.08	-5.87
NORTH AFRICA	624	641	740	2.85	1.55	33	44	79	25.29	7.04	3	4	3	11.49	-1.51
Algeria	225	221	240	3.44	0.82	10	20	35	17.51	7.08	0	0	0	-0.98	0.00
Egypt	60	64	70	-4.63	1.04	1	1	2	-9.90	11.06	0	0	0	3.72	4.38
SUB-SAHARAN AFRICA	2 735	2 691	3 099	-6.58	1.56	15	23	60	8.04	10.47	5	4	3	-13.01	-9.32
LATIN AMERICA and CARIBBEAN	449	472	579	3.36	2.21	54	63	69	1.77	1.66	22	19	24	0.77	2.43
Argentina	0	0	0	0.00	0.00	0	0	0	0.00	0.00	0	0	0	0.00	0.00
Brazil	166	181	262	6.63	3.98	1	1	1	-18.97	0.00	0	0	0	33.20	0.00
Chile	16	17	18	-0.89	0.72	0	0	0	23.86	0.00	7	7	8	6.44	1.56
Mexico	47	47	48	5.81	0.04	40	43	42	3.60	-0.06	0	0	0	6.07	0.00
Uruguay	42	45	55	-3.80	2.23	0	0	0	0.00	0.00	15	11	15	0.47	3.05
ASIA and PACIFIC	6 438	6 757	8 304	2.62	2.26	241	260	317	0.61	2.23	32	38	47	3.38	3.40
Bangladesh	140	142	152	1.09	0.75	0	0	0	-39.34	49.45	0	0	1	-10.04	-3.84
China[e]	3 265	3 514	4 731	3.86	3.25	10	9	9	-0.74	-0.15	9	10	8	4.15	-2.05
India	727	719	793	0.71	1.06	0	0	0	-29.70	0.00	11	12	13	3.18	0.35
Indonesia	130	138	150	6.95	0.93	1	5	9	6.26	8.85	0	0	0	22.50	0.00
Iran, Islamic Republic of	524	545	576	3.03	0.58	0	0	0	-15.70	0.00	0	1	0	71.27	-19.65
Korea	2	2	2	-5.35	0.00	6	6	6	1.13	0.00	0	0	0	-96.80	0.00
Malaysia	0	0	0	3.42	0.85	20	22	26	5.51	1.95	0	0	0	-14.74	2.24
Pakistan	563	625	769	3.02	2.30	0	0	0	-13.49	0.00	8	12	19	39.70	10.51
Saudi Arabia	42	33	36	14.35	1.06	45	53	61	-2.08	1.63	1	1	1	0.53	3.60
Turkey	317	318	309	-2.33	-0.31	0	0	0	23.83	0.00	0	0	0	-43.33	-24.27
LEAST DEVELOPED COUNTRIES (LDC)	2 669	2 614	3 019	-6.99	1.59	5	7	15	-1.00	7.06	4	2	1	-9.62	-28.52
OECD	2 929	2 889	2 806	-0.51	-0.23	489	496	494	4.28	-0.01	864	852	897	1.71	0.74
NON-OECD	10 715	11 022	13 358	-0.39	2.11	332	376	530	1.23	4.06	67	71	82	1.68	1.63

For notes, see end of the table.

Table A.22. **Sheep meat projections** (cont.)

Calendar year[b]	CONSUMPTION (kt)			Growth[d] (%)		PER CAPITA (kg)			Growth[d] (%)	
	Average 2005-07 est.	2008	2017	1998-2007	2008-17	Average 2005-07 est.	2008	2017	1998-2007	2008-17
WORLD	**13 540**	**13 948**	**16 420**	**−0.56**	**1.83**	**1.8**	**1.8**	**1.9**	**−1.78**	**0.71**
DEVELOPED	**2 922**	**2 909**	**2 992**	**0.70**	**0.43**	**1.9**	**1.9**	**1.9**	**0.31**	**0.17**
NORTH AMERICA	**203**	**211**	**233**	**1.07**	**1.10**	**0.5**	**0.5**	**0.6**	**0.07**	**0.21**
Canada	39	43	59	5.47	3.55	1.1	1.1	1.5	4.48	2.72
United States	164	168	174	0.20	0.37	0.5	0.5	0.5	−0.80	−0.52
EUROPE	**1 483**	**1 464**	**1 406**	**0.38**	**−0.39**	**2.5**	**2.4**	**2.3**	**0.07**	**−0.49**
EU(27)	1 378	1 353	1 294	0.30	−0.43	2.5	2.4	2.3	−0.01	−0.53
CIS	**620**	**615**	**784**	**2.05**	**2.74**	**2.0**	**2.0**	**2.5**	**2.25**	**2.85**
Russian Federation	191	156	247	2.35	5.07	1.2	1.0	1.6	2.79	5.57
Ukraine	16	19	22	−1.78	1.89	0.3	0.4	0.5	−0.95	2.68
OCEANIA DEVELOPED	**380**	**400**	**336**	**−1.18**	**−1.47**	**13.5**	**13.9**	**10.8**	**−2.36**	**−2.39**
Australia	291	319	269	−1.30	−1.34	12.4	13.3	10.3	−2.50	−2.29
New Zealand	89	81	68	−0.82	−1.97	19.0	16.9	13.2	−1.91	−2.75
OTHER DEVELOPED	**236**	**210**	**233**	**0.15**	**0.83**	**1.2**	**1.1**	**1.2**	**−0.23**	**0.85**
Japan	62	47	32	−0.60	−4.23	0.4	0.3	0.2	−0.72	−4.05
South Africa	183	171	201	0.41	1.89	3.3	3.1	3.5	−0.68	1.48
DEVELOPING	**10 618**	**11 040**	**13 428**	**−0.54**	**2.16**	**1.8**	**1.8**	**1.9**	**−1.99**	**0.85**
AFRICA	**3 382**	**3 395**	**4 064**	**−5.03**	**2.00**	**3.3**	**3.2**	**3.1**	**−7.42**	**−0.23**
NORTH AFRICA	**658**	**684**	**824**	**3.41**	**2.06**	**2.5**	**2.5**	**2.5**	**1.50**	**0.27**
Algeria	235	241	275	3.79	1.46	6.2	6.2	6.2	2.31	0.01
Egypt	64	67	80	−4.30	1.92	0.8	0.8	0.8	−6.11	0.31
SUB-SAHARAN AFRICA	**2 724**	**2 710**	**3 241**	**−6.48**	**1.99**	**3.6**	**3.4**	**3.3**	**−9.05**	**−0.39**
LATIN AMERICA and CARIBBEAN	**477**	**512**	**620**	**3.12**	**2.14**	**0.7**	**0.8**	**0.9**	**1.85**	**1.00**
Argentina	0	0	0	0.00	0.00	0.0	0.0	0.0	0.00	0.00
Brazil	168	182	263	5.99	3.96	0.8	0.8	1.1	4.62	2.80
Chile	9	10	10	−4.45	0.07	0.5	0.5	0.5	−5.57	−0.83
Mexico	87	91	92	4.45	0.12	0.7	0.8	0.7	3.59	−0.85
Uruguay	23	29	34	−7.70	1.75	6.1	7.6	8.6	−7.82	1.40
ASIA and PACIFIC	**6 760**	**7 133**	**8 743**	**2.43**	**2.24**	**1.6**	**1.6**	**1.8**	**1.16**	**1.13**
Bangladesh	140	142	151	1.01	0.71	0.8	0.8	0.7	−0.87	−0.84
China[e]	3 265	3 514	4 732	3.85	3.25	2.2	2.3	2.9	3.18	2.59
India	714	704	777	0.63	1.08	0.5	0.5	0.5	−0.99	−0.23
Indonesia	131	143	159	6.95	1.29	0.5	0.5	0.5	5.64	0.32
Iran, Islamic Republic of	521	537	574	2.77	0.74	6.5	6.5	6.2	1.74	−0.60
Korea	8	8	8	2.41	0.00	0.1	0.1	0.1	1.91	−0.18
Malaysia	21	23	28	5.50	1.93	0.7	0.8	0.8	3.53	0.46
Pakistan	554	626	776	2.82	2.52	3.0	3.3	3.5	0.94	0.63
Saudi Arabia	144	148	169	−0.07	1.48	5.3	5.2	4.9	−2.60	−0.57
Turkey	317	317	308	−2.21	−0.33	3.8	3.7	3.2	−3.59	−1.43
LEAST DEVELOPED COUNTRIES (LDC)	**2 647**	**2 622**	**3 120**	**−6.95**	**1.93**	**3.3**	**3.1**	**3.0**	**−9.34**	**−0.31**
OECD	**2 462**	**2 465**	**2 340**	**−0.08**	**−0.46**	**1.8**	**1.8**	**1.6**	**−0.69**	**−0.92**
NON-OECD	**11 078**	**11 484**	**14 080**	**−0.37**	**2.26**	**1.8**	**1.8**	**2.0**	**−1.74**	**1.00**

a) Imports of meat do not equal exports because of an incomplete coverage of international trade.
b) Year ending 30 June for Australia and 31 May for New Zealand.
c) Gross indigenous production.
d) Least-squares growth rate (see glossary).
e) Refers to mainland only. The economies of Chinese Taipei, Hong Kong (China) and Macau (China) are included in the Other Asia Pacific aggregate.
f) Excludes trade of live animals.
est.: estimate.
Source: OECD and FAO Secretariats.

StatLink ᴍᴤ http://dx.doi.org/10.1787/384485440666

Table A.23. **Main policy assumptions for dairy markets**

Calendar year[a]		Average 2002-06	2007 est.	2008	2009	2010	2011	2012	2013	2014	2015	2016	2017
ARGENTINA													
Dairy export tax	%	7	5	5	5	5	5	5	5	5	5	5	5
CANADA													
Milk target price[b]	CADc/litre	65	72	72	73	74	75	76	76	77	78	79	80
Butter support price	CAD/t	6 393	6 870	6 932	7 135	7 278	7 424	7 572	7 723	7 878	8 036	8 196	8 360
SMP support price	CAD/t	5 427	5 921	5 933	6 123	6 113	6 170	6 212	6 230	6 265	6 333	6 378	6 421
Dairy subsidy	CAD/hl	0.07	0.00	0.00	0.00	0.00	0.00	0.00	0.00	0.00	0.00	0.00	0.00
Cheese tariff-quota	kt pw	20	20	20	20	20	20	20	20	20	20	20	20
in-quota tariff	%	1	1	1	1	1	1	1	1	1	1	1	1
out-of-quota tariff	%	246	246	246	246	246	246	246	246	246	246	246	246
Subsidised export limits[c]													
Cheese	kt pw	9	9	9	9	9	9	9	9	9	9	9	9
SMP	kt pw	45	45	45	45	45	45	45	45	45	45	45	45
EUROPEAN UNION[d]													
Milk quota[e]	mt pw	143	143	146	146	146	146	146	146	146	146	146	146
Butter intervention price	EUR/t	3 075	2 528	2 462	2 462	2 462	2 464	2 464	2 464	2 464	2 464	2 464	2 464
SMP intervention price	EUR/t	1 963	1 747	1 747	1 747	1 747	1 747	1 747	1 747	1 747	1 747	1 747	1 747
Butter tariff-quotas	kt pw	90	90	90	90	90	90	90	90	90	90	90	90
Cheese tariff-quota	kt pw	103	103	103	103	103	103	103	103	103	103	103	103
SMP tariff-quota	kt pw	71	71	71	71	71	71	71	71	71	71	71	71
Subsidised export limits[a]													
Butter	kt pw	412	412	412	412	412	412	412	412	412	412	412	412
Cheese	kt pw	332	332	332	332	332	332	332	332	332	332	332	332
SMP	kt pw	323	323	323	323	323	323	323	323	323	323	323	323
JAPAN													
Direct payments	JPY/kg	11	11	11	11	11	11	11	11	11	11	11	11
Cheese tariff[f]	%	31	31	31	31	31	31	31	31	31	31	31	31
Tariff-quotas													
Butter	kt pw	2	2	2	2	2	2	2	2	2	2	2	2
in-quota tariff	%	35	35	35	35	35	35	35	35	35	35	35	35
out-of-quota tariff	%	733	733	733	733	733	733	733	733	733	733	733	733
SMP	kt pw	116	116	116	116	116	116	116	116	116	116	116	116
in-quota tariff	%	16	16	16	16	16	16	16	16	16	16	16	16
out-of-quota tariff	%	210	210	210	210	210	210	210	210	210	210	210	210
WMP	t pw	0.3	0.3	0.3	0.3	0.3	0.3	0.3	0.3	0.3	0.3	0.3	0.3
in-quota tariff	%	24	24	24	24	24	24	24	24	24	24	24	24
out-of-quota tariff	%	316	316	316	316	316	316	316	316	316	316	316	316
KOREA													
Tariff-quotas													
Butter	kt pw	0.4	0.4	0.4	0.4	0.4	0.4	0.4	0.4	0.4	0.4	0.4	0.4
in-quota tariff	%	40	40	40	40	40	40	40	40	40	40	40	40
out-of-quota tariff	%	89	89	89	89	89	89	89	89	89	89	89	89
SMP	kt pw	1.0	1.0	1.0	1.0	1.0	1.0	1.0	1.0	1.0	1.0	1.0	1.0
in-quota tariff	%	20	20	20	20	20	20	20	20	20	20	20	20
out-of-quota tariff	%	176	176	176	176	176	176	176	176	176	176	176	176
WMP	kt pw	0.6	0.6	0.6	0.6	0.6	0.6	0.6	0.6	0.6	0.6	0.6	0.6
in-quota tariff	%	40	40	40	40	40	40	40	40	40	40	40	40
out-of-quota tariff	%	176	176	176	176	176	176	176	176	176	176	176	176

For notes, see end of the table.

Table A.23. **Main policy assumptions for dairy markets** (cont.)

Calendar year[a]		Average 2002-06	2007 est.	2008	2009	2010	2011	2012	2013	2014	2015	2016	2017
MEXICO													
Butter tariff	%	0	0	0	0	0	0	0	0	0	0	0	0
Tariff-quotas													
Cheese	kt pw	9	9	9	9	9	9	9	9	9	9	9	9
in-quota tariff	%	50	50	50	50	50	50	50	50	50	50	50	50
out-of-quota tariff	%	126	125	125	125	125	125	125	125	125	125	125	125
SMP	kt pw	90	90	90	90	90	90	90	90	90	90	90	90
in-quota tariff	%	0	0	0	0	0	0	0	0	0	0	0	0
out-of-quota tariff	%	126	125	125	125	125	125	125	125	125	125	125	125
Liconsa social program	MXN mn	484	1 000	1 000	1 000	1 000	1 000	1 000	1 000	1 000	1 000	1 000	1 000
RUSSIA													
Butter tariff	%	20	20	5	5	5	5	5	5	5	5	5	5
Cheese tariff	%	15	15	5	5	5	5	5	5	5	5	5	5
UNITED STATES[g]													
Milk support price[b]	USDc/litre	22	22	22	22	22	22	22	22	22	22	22	22
Target price[h]	USDc/litre	NA	37.3	0.0	0.0	0.0	0.0	0.0	0.0	0.0	0.0	0.0	0.0
Butter support price	USD/t	2 243	2 315	2 315	2 315	2 315	2 315	2 315	2 315	2 316	2 316	2 316	2 317
SMP support price	USD/t	1 801	1 764	1 764	1 764	1 764	1 764	1 764	1 764	1 764	1 764	1 764	1 765
Butter tariff-quota	kt pw	13	13	13	13	13	13	13	13	13	13	13	13
in-quota tariff	%	10	10	10	10	10	10	10	10	10	10	10	10
out-of-quota tariff	%	112	112	112	112	112	112	112	112	112	112	112	112
Cheese tariff-quota	kt pw	135	135	135	135	135	135	135	135	135	135	135	135
in-quota tariff	%	12	12	12	12	12	12	12	12	12	12	12	12
out-of-quota tariff	%	87	87	87	87	87	87	87	87	87	87	87	87
Subsidised export limits[a]													
Butter	kt pw	21	21	21	21	21	21	21	21	21	21	21	21
SMP	kt pw	68	68	68	68	68	68	68	68	68	68	68	68
INDIA													
Milk tariff	%	80	80	80	80	80	80	80	80	80	80	80	80
Butter tariff	%	44	40	40	40	40	40	40	40	40	40	40	40
Cheese tariff	%	41	40	40	40	40	40	40	40	40	40	40	40
Whole milk powder tariff	%	20	20	20	20	20	20	20	20	20	20	20	20
SOUTH AFRICA													
Milk powder tariff-quota	kt pw	4	4	4	4	4	4	4	4	4	4	4	4
in-quota tariff	%	20	20	20	20	20	20	20	20	20	20	20	20
out-of-quota tariff	%	85	81	81	81	81	81	81	81	81	81	81	81

a) Year ending 30 June for Australia and 31 May for New Zealand.
b) For manufacturing milk.
c) The effective volume of cheese and SMP subsidized exports will be lower reflecting the binding nature of subsidized export limits in value terms.
d) EU farmers also benefit from the Single Farm Payment (SFP) Scheme, which provides flat-rate payments independent from current production decisions and market developments. For the accession countries, payments are phased in with the assumption of maximum top-ups from national budgets up to 2011 through the Single Area Payment (SAP) and from 2012 through the SFP. Due to modulation, between 2.7% and 4.6% of the total SFP will go to rural development spending rather than directly to the farmers in the 15 former member states. From 2013, 4.6% of the total SFP will go to rural development spending in the accession countries.
e) Total quota, EU27 starting in 1999.
f) Excludes processed cheese.
g) Year beginning 1 January.
h) The counter-cyclical payment is determined as a 45% difference in 2005 and a 34% difference in 2006 and 2007, between the target price and the Boston class I price.
Note: The source for tariffs and Tariff Rate Quotas (except Russia) is AMAD (Agricultural market access database). The tariff and TRQ data are based on Most Favoured Nation rates scheduled with the WTO and exclude those under preferential or regional agreements, which may be substantially different. Tariffs are simple averages of several product lines. Specific rates are converted to ad valorem rates using world prices in the Outlook. Import quotas are based on global commitments scheduled in the WTO rather than those allocated to preferential partners under regional or other agreements.
est.: estimate.
Source: OECD and FAO Secretariats.

StatLink ᴍᴀᴇ http://dx.doi.org/10.1787/384501087786

Table A.24. **World dairy projections (butter and cheese)**

Calendar year[a]		Average 2002-06	2007 est.	2008	2009	2010	2011	2012	2013	2014	2015	2016	2017
BUTTER													
OECD[b]													
Production	kt pw	3 679	3 618	3 580	3 581	3 586	3 601	3 612	3 612	3 619	3 623	3 626	3 628
Consumption	kt pw	3 076	3 184	3 189	3 177	3 168	3 170	3 171	3 165	3 159	3 153	3 146	3 138
Stock changes	kt pw	4	−37	−8	−4	−3	−3	−2	−3	−3	−3	−4	−4
Non-OECD													
Production	kt pw	4 666	5 597	5 976	6 213	6 415	6 606	6 815	7 028	7 218	7 417	7 631	7 824
Consumption	kt pw	5 131	6 018	6 386	6 626	6 842	7 046	7 264	7 483	7 686	7 896	8 120	8 323
WORLD													
Production	kt pw	8 345	9 215	9 556	9 793	10 002	10 208	10 427	10 640	10 837	11 040	11 256	11 452
Consumption	kt pw	8 207	9 202	9 575	9 803	10 010	10 216	10 435	10 648	10 845	11 049	11 266	11 462
Stock changes	kt pw	−2	−43	−18	−9	−8	−7	−7	−7	−7	−8	−8	−9
Price[c]	USD/100 kg	162	294	301	290	266	256	257	260	264	268	270	272
CHEESE													
OECD[b]													
Production	kt pw	14 163	14 974	15 332	15 642	15 867	16 041	16 228	16 389	16 542	16 688	16 846	16 980
Consumption	kt pw	13 729	14 555	14 919	15 201	15 423	15 606	15 801	15 973	16 150	16 315	16 493	16 649
Stock changes	kt pw	−6	−34	−7	5	11	5	6	8	9	9	11	5
Non-OECD													
Production	kt pw	3 966	4 314	4 420	4 503	4 623	4 734	4 841	4 947	5 055	5 155	5 254	5 345
Consumption	kt pw	4 340	4 750	4 848	4 946	5 064	5 172	5 270	5 362	5 445	5 525	5 602	5 678
WORLD													
Production	kt pw	18 129	19 289	19 752	20 145	20 491	20 776	21 070	21 336	21 597	21 842	22 099	22 325
Consumption	kt pw	18 069	19 305	19 767	20 147	20 487	20 777	21 071	21 335	21 595	21 840	22 095	22 326
Stock changes	kt pw	−14	−53	−14	−2	4	−2	−1	1	2	2	4	−2
Price[d]	USD/100 kg	235	402	419	394	360	350	350	352	354	356	357	358

a) Year ending 30 June for Australia and 31 May for New Zealand in OECD aggregate.
b) Excludes Iceland but includes the 8 EU members that are not members of the OECD.
c) f.o.b. export price, butter, 82% butterfat, Oceania.
d) f.o.b. export price, cheddar cheese, 39% moisture, Oceania.
est.: estimate.
Source: OECD and FAO Secretariats.

StatLink ▆▅▊▙ http://dx.doi.org/10.1787/384510536625

Table A.25. **World dairy projections (powders and casein)**

Calendar year[a]		Average 2002-06	2007 est.	2008	2009	2010	2011	2012	2013	2014	2015	2016	2017
SKIM MILK POWDER													
OECD[b]													
Production	kt pw	2 695	2 524	2 581	2 566	2 576	2 598	2 625	2 644	2 679	2 718	2 767	2 808
Consumption	kt pw	1 970	1 789	1 850	1 874	1 892	1 903	1 921	1 930	1 941	1 950	1 962	1 970
Stock changes	kt pw	−70	−2	4	3	2	1	1	1	−1	0	0	0
Non-OECD													
Production	kt pw	729	678	781	834	863	893	931	972	998	1 012	1 019	1 025
Consumption	kt pw	1 478	1 450	1 447	1 468	1 500	1 540	1 593	1 650	1 707	1 755	1 805	1 846
WORLD													
Production	kt pw	3 424	3 201	3 362	3 400	3 440	3 491	3 556	3 617	3 677	3 730	3 786	3 833
Consumption	kt pw	3 376	3 238	3 297	3 342	3 392	3 443	3 514	3 580	3 648	3 705	3 766	3 817
Stock changes	kt pw	−70	−1	6	4	4	3	3	3	1	2	2	1
Price[c]	USD/100 kg	191	432	355	331	314	308	306	305	303	304	304	305
WHOLE MILK POWDER													
OECD[b]													
Production	kt pw	1 887	1 802	1 690	1 700	1 737	1 750	1 773	1 791	1 804	1 820	1 835	1 854
Consumption	kt pw	741	730	724	722	721	720	717	715	715	714	713	713
Non-OECD													
Production	kt pw	1 834	2 219	2 379	2 440	2 514	2 595	2 667	2 740	2 819	2 899	2 969	3 043
Consumption	kt pw	2 665	3 073	3 347	3 421	3 533	3 628	3 726	3 818	3 910	4 007	4 093	4 186
WORLD													
Production	kt pw	3 721	4 021	4 069	4 140	4 251	4 346	4 440	4 531	4 623	4 719	4 805	4 897
Consumption	kt pw	3 406	3 810	4 071	4 142	4 253	4 348	4 442	4 533	4 624	4 721	4 807	4 899
Price[d]	USD/100 kg	192	417	366	333	311	304	303	305	307	308	310	311
WHEY POWDER													
Non-OECD													
Wholesale price, USA[e]	USD/100 kg	54	134	92	88	93	96	101	102	104	109	111	114
CASEIN													
Price[f]	USD/100 kg	577	1 030	957	805	807	753	784	755	777	757	772	759

a) Year ending 30 June for Australia and 31 May for New Zealand in OECD aggregate.
b) Excludes Iceland but includes the 8 EU members that are not members of the OECD.
c) f.o.b. export price, non-fat dry milk, 1.25% butterfat, Oceania.
d) f.o.b. export price, WMP 26% butterfat, Oceania.
e) Edible dry whey, Wisconsin, plant.
f) Export price, New Zealand.
est.: estimate.
Source: OECD and FAO Secretariats.

StatLink 📊 http://dx.doi.org/10.1787/384511341810

Table A.26. **Butter projections**

Calendar year[a]	PRODUCTION (kt)			Growth[b] (%)		IMPORTS (kt)			Growth[b] (%)		EXPORTS (kt)			Growth[b] (%)	
	Average 2005-07 est.	2008	2017	1998-2007	2008-17	Average 2005-07 est.	2008	2017	1998-2007	2008-17	Average 2005-07 est.	2008	2017	1998-2007	2008-17
WORLD	8 798	9 556	11 452	2.69	2.00	731	745	916	2.67	2.32	840	745	916	2.06	2.32
DEVELOPED	4 017	3 980	4 139	−0.15	0.44	285	302	373	2.61	2.49	745	632	736	1.24	1.71
NORTH AMERICA	727	747	811	1.68	0.96	25	23	24	−0.96	0.35	17	38	17	13.88	−5.86
Canada	78	83	87	−1.12	0.21	10	8	8	10.80	0.00	3	3	2	−11.27	−3.83
United States	648	664	724	2.05	1.06	16	15	16	−4.70	0.52	14	35	15	23.44	−5.98
EUROPE	2 202	2 145	1 956	−0.66	−0.99	96	91	91	−1.45	0.05	260	108	60	2.76	−6.76
EU(27)	2 133	2 078	1 889	−0.66	−1.02	86	80	80	−1.62	0.00	257	104	57	2.91	−7.02
CIS	503	526	643	1.01	2.16	144	164	243	2.94	4.66	68	87	107	7.59	2.75
Russian Federation	273	278	326	0.55	1.61	108	131	199	3.29	4.95	3	3	3	−1.07	0.00
Ukraine	108	110	129	−1.37	1.86	0	0	0	−30.66	0.00	21	27	30	5.63	2.40
OCEANIA DEVELOPED	492	470	634	−1.02	3.22	9	10	10	0.26	0.00	400	394	553	−0.39	3.58
Australia	142	117	176	−3.16	4.47	9	10	10	1.56	0.00	78	73	125	−5.15	5.78
New Zealand	350	353	458	−0.03	2.77	0	0	0	7.66	0.00	323	322	427	1.06	3.00
OTHER DEVELOPED	93	92	95	−1.04	0.23	10	15	4	20.27	−12.65	0	5	0	−33.30	−25.52
Japan	80	75	80	−1.39	0.69	8	14	3	39.96	−15.97	0	0	0	−68.37	0.00
South Africa	13	17	16	1.85	−1.80	2	1	1	−0.10	11.46	0	5	0	−33.92	−25.52
DEVELOPING	4 781	5 576	7 313	5.66	2.99	445	443	544	2.89	2.21	95	113	180	10.14	5.23
AFRICA	240	255	308	2.81	2.19	113	110	125	1.38	1.25	1	1	1	−4.37	−0.51
NORTH AFRICA	166	179	224	3.47	2.57	94	90	96	0.90	0.56	0	0	0	1.31	−1.64
Algeria	2	2	2	2.49	0.58	13	12	14	6.43	0.95	0	0	0	−75.51	9.04
Egypt	121	131	166	3.70	2.65	48	44	32	−1.22	−3.22	0	0	0	8.75	3.31
SUB-SAHARAN AFRICA	74	76	84	1.43	1.23	19	20	29	4.09	3.92	1	1	1	−5.06	−0.31
LATIN AMERICA and CARIBBEAN	219	231	288	1.52	2.13	26	21	32	−6.13	5.14	25	35	64	4.48	6.45
Argentina	44	41	44	−1.40	0.13	0	0	0	−77.77	0.00	10	13	23	8.14	6.28
Brazil	78	81	106	1.27	2.47	1	1	8	−38.87	33.02	2	2	2	20.10	−0.87
Chile	17	20	26	6.13	3.19	2	1	0	5.89	5.45	1	2	2	22.03	−0.03
Mexico	15	15	15	0.72	−0.23	4	4	5	32.77	2.34	0	0	0	−35.79	23.20
Uruguay	15	18	31	−0.19	6.29	0	0	0	−46.95	0.00	9	12	24	−1.46	7.81
ASIA and PACIFIC	4 322	5 090	6 717	6.09	3.06	307	312	387	4.64	2.32	68	76	115	13.79	4.68
Bangladesh	20	23	20	1.99	−0.48	1	1	1	−8.48	−4.50	0	2	0	−84.50	−23.47
China[c]	120	142	207	5.69	4.12	33	34	39	9.73	1.66	0	0	0	−7.17	0.00
India	3 191	3 894	5 235	7.60	3.24	2	0	0	−13.54	0.00	13	10	10	30.09	0.00
Indonesia	0	0	0	0.00	−3.09	12	13	17	4.15	3.45	0	0	0	−7.95	5.17
Iran, Islamic Republic of	154	163	204	1.63	2.64	37	31	27	11.12	−2.21	0	0	1	4.37	8.35
Korea	5	4	4	8.07	1.26	1	1	1	8.76	1.07	0	0	0	17.99	0.00
Malaysia	0	0	0	0.00	0.96	12	12	13	4.39	0.65	1	1	0	4.33	−9.29
Pakistan	590	598	756	3.02	2.67	0	11	22	−19.85	13.75	0	0	0	−43.76	9.04
Saudi Arabia	5	5	5	0.33	0.67	44	55	99	10.07	6.56	31	40	85	71.07	8.24
Turkey	123	141	145	0.78	0.28	7	3	6	5.63	6.97	0	0	0	−2.65	−4.77
LEAST DEVELOPED COUNTRIES (LDC)	158	156	155	1.22	0.23	12	14	35	2.60	8.83	1	3	1	−2.02	−4.19
OECD	3 627	3 580	3 628	−0.28	0.17	142	138	133	0.10	−0.47	675	537	627	0.84	1.70
NON-OECD	5 171	5 976	7 824	5.25	2.96	588	607	784	2.65	2.87	165	208	289	8.51	3.79

For notes, see end of the table.

OECD-FAO AGRICULTURAL OUTLOOK 2008-2017 – ISBN 978-92-64-04590-3 – © OECD/FAO 2008

Table A.26. **Butter projections** (cont.)

Calendar year[a]	CONSUMPTION (kt)			Growth[b] (%)		PER CAPITA (kg)			Growth[b] (%)	
	Average 2005-07 est.	2008	2017	1998-2007	2008-17	Average 2005-07 est.	2008	2017	1998-2007	2008-17
WORLD	**8 731**	**9 575**	**11 462**	**2.95**	**1.99**	**1.3**	**1.4**	**1.5**	**1.73**	**0.88**
DEVELOPED	**3 597**	**3 659**	**3 781**	**0.23**	**0.38**	**2.7**	**2.7**	**2.7**	**−0.16**	**0.12**
NORTH AMERICA	**722**	**741**	**819**	**1.30**	**1.06**	**2.2**	**2.2**	**2.2**	**0.30**	**0.18**
Canada	87	86	92	0.29	0.41	2.7	2.6	2.6	−0.70	−0.43
United States	635	655	727	1.44	1.15	2.1	2.1	2.2	0.44	0.26
EUROPE	**2 091**	**2 129**	**1 988**	**−0.42**	**−0.71**	**4.0**	**4.0**	**3.7**	**−0.73**	**−0.81**
EU(27)	2 014	2 054	1 912	−0.43	−0.74	4.1	4.2	3.8	−0.75	−0.84
CIS	**579**	**603**	**779**	**0.60**	**2.80**	**2.1**	**2.2**	**2.8**	**0.80**	**2.91**
Russian Federation	377	406	521	0.80	2.78	2.6	2.9	3.9	1.25	3.28
Ukraine	87	83	99	−2.50	1.78	1.9	1.8	2.3	−1.68	2.56
OCEANIA DEVELOPED	**102**	**85**	**92**	**−0.80**	**0.90**	**4.1**	**3.4**	**3.3**	**−1.98**	**−0.02**
Australia	71	54	60	−1.23	1.43	3.4	2.6	2.6	−2.43	0.48
New Zealand	31	31	31	0.00	−0.07	7.6	7.5	6.9	−1.10	−0.85
OTHER DEVELOPED	**102**	**99**	**103**	**1.06**	**0.52**	**0.6**	**0.6**	**0.6**	**0.68**	**0.54**
Japan	88	87	86	0.65	−0.14	0.7	0.7	0.7	0.53	0.04
South Africa	14	12	17	4.63	4.39	0.3	0.3	0.3	3.53	3.98
DEVELOPING	**5 134**	**5 916**	**7 681**	**5.34**	**2.88**	**1.0**	**1.1**	**1.3**	**3.89**	**1.56**
AFRICA	**352**	**364**	**432**	**2.35**	**1.92**	**0.4**	**0.4**	**0.4**	**−0.05**	**−0.31**
NORTH AFRICA	**260**	**269**	**320**	**2.46**	**1.93**	**1.1**	**1.1**	**1.1**	**0.54**	**0.14**
Algeria	14	14	15	5.95	0.90	0.4	0.4	0.4	4.17	0.54
Egypt	169	175	198	2.08	1.44	2.3	2.3	2.2	0.26	−0.17
SUB-SAHARAN AFRICA	**92**	**95**	**112**	**2.05**	**1.88**	**0.1**	**0.1**	**0.1**	**−0.52**	**−0.51**
LATIN AMERICA and CARIBBEAN	**221**	**225**	**258**	**0.26**	**1.42**	**0.4**	**0.4**	**0.4**	**−1.02**	**0.28**
Argentina	34	34	21	−3.76	−5.10	0.9	0.9	0.5	−4.75	−6.00
Brazil	77	79	112	−0.86	3.56	0.4	0.4	0.5	−2.23	2.40
Chile	17	18	24	5.50	2.98	1.1	1.1	1.3	4.38	2.08
Mexico	19	19	20	3.69	0.35	0.2	0.2	0.2	2.83	−0.63
Uruguay	8	8	9	12.70	1.76	2.4	2.3	2.7	12.57	1.42
ASIA and PACIFIC	**4 562**	**5 327**	**6 991**	**5.91**	**2.99**	**1.2**	**1.4**	**1.6**	**4.64**	**1.88**
Bangladesh	20	22	21	1.50	−0.18	0.1	0.1	0.1	−0.38	−1.73
China[c]	152	176	246	6.49	3.70	0.1	0.1	0.2	5.83	3.04
India	3 181	3 883	5 225	7.52	3.24	2.8	3.3	3.9	5.89	1.94
Indonesia	12	12	17	4.36	3.44	0.1	0.1	0.1	3.06	2.46
Iran, Islamic Republic of	191	194	230	2.96	1.95	2.7	2.7	2.8	1.93	0.62
Korea	6	5	6	7.78	1.22	0.1	0.1	0.1	7.27	1.03
Malaysia	11	11	12	3.77	1.22	0.4	0.4	0.4	1.80	−0.25
Pakistan	590	608	778	3.01	2.87	3.7	3.6	3.9	1.13	0.98
Saudi Arabia	17	20	20	−5.07	0.07	0.7	0.8	0.7	−7.59	−1.97
Turkey	129	144	151	0.98	0.50	1.8	1.9	1.8	−0.41	−0.60
LEAST DEVELOPED COUNTRIES (LDC)	**169**	**167**	**189**	**1.39**	**1.43**	**0.2**	**0.2**	**0.2**	**−1.01**	**−0.81**
OECD	**3 134**	**3 189**	**3 138**	**0.06**	**−0.15**	**2.6**	**2.6**	**2.5**	**−0.55**	**−0.61**
NON-OECD	**5 597**	**6 386**	**8 323**	**4.85**	**2.92**	**1.0**	**1.2**	**1.3**	**3.48**	**1.66**

a) Year ending 30 June for Australia and 31 May for New Zealand.
b) Least-squares growth rate (see glossary).
c) Refers to mainland only. The economies of Chinese Taipei, Hong Kong (China) and Macau (China) are included in the Other Asia Pacific aggregate.
est.: estimate.
Source: OECD and FAO Secretariats.

StatLink http://dx.doi.org/10.1787/384560706230

Table A.27. **Cheese projections**

Calendar year[a]	PRODUCTION (kt)			Growth[b] (%)		IMPORTS (kt)			Growth[b] (%)		EXPORTS (kt)			Growth[b] (%)	
	Average 2005-07 est.	2008	2017	1998-2007	2008-17	Average 2005-07 est.	2008	2017	1998-2007	2008-17	Average 2005-07 est.	2008	2017	1998-2007	2008-17
WORLD	18 977	19 752	22 325	2.42	1.33	1 503	1 623	2 113	4.07	2.86	1 558	1 623	2 113	4.10	2.86
DEVELOPED	15 560	16 168	18 064	2.37	1.18	904	997	1 218	4.38	2.24	1 325	1 335	1 587	2.75	1.70
NORTH AMERICA	4 637	4 811	5 299	2.49	1.06	225	234	289	1.87	2.36	48	45	41	-3.60	-0.82
Canada	358	358	400	1.11	1.25	21	19	19	-0.97	2.36	10	7	8	-11.89	1.96
United States	4 280	4 454	4 900	2.61	1.04	204	215	271	2.19	2.55	38	38	33	-0.33	-1.45
EUROPE	9 145	9 591	10 432	1.89	0.88	164	169	189	-2.38	1.27	656	710	595	2.36	-1.95
EU(27)	8 811	9 256	10 096	1.93	0.91	99	101	119	-5.64	1.82	586	643	530	3.00	-2.12
CIS	1 030	1 036	1 342	8.47	2.74	253	321	410	22.77	2.67	134	109	265	22.30	8.68
Russian Federation	597	602	705	6.29	1.69	239	304	376	23.25	2.32	5	5	5	11.53	0.00
Ukraine	247	214	350	17.03	4.64	8	11	22	19.36	7.38	75	30	131	33.18	11.97
OCEANIA DEVELOPED	669	645	895	1.56	3.37	49	54	59	5.11	1.23	485	457	684	2.08	4.14
Australia	375	344	446	1.52	2.47	49	54	59	6.16	1.23	214	178	264	2.39	3.56
New Zealand	294	301	448	1.63	4.36	0	0	0	-12.36	0.00	272	279	420	1.87	4.53
OTHER DEVELOPED	79	84	96	1.11	2.29	214	219	270	1.47	2.41	2	13	2	3.87	-23.20
Japan	40	40	38	1.55	-0.74	210	214	266	1.39	2.52	0	0	0	12.07	0.00
South Africa	39	44	58	0.69	4.47	4	5	4	5.56	-4.59	2	13	2	2.81	-23.20
DEVELOPING	3 417	3 585	4 260	2.69	1.99	598	626	896	4.47	3.78	232	289	527	15.32	7.42
AFRICA	874	901	1 088	4.19	2.27	86	90	199	5.35	8.27	42	66	94	18.34	5.11
NORTH AFRICA	681	698	858	5.14	2.49	71	76	175	6.92	8.72	42	65	93	18.51	5.19
Algeria	2	2	2	1.97	0.00	27	28	41	6.39	3.86	0	0	1	10.44	9.04
Egypt	640	656	800	5.17	2.40	21	25	86	4.76	13.37	18	37	45	26.94	5.15
SUB-SAHARAN AFRICA	193	204	230	1.27	1.49	15	14	24	-0.14	5.50	0	1	1	6.76	-1.97
LATIN AMERICA and CARIBBEAN	1 498	1 565	1 901	1.68	2.16	176	188	257	3.67	3.40	138	159	316	13.57	8.29
Argentina	438	454	573	-0.41	2.51	2	0	0	-15.60	0.00	54	59	126	12.92	10.74
Brazil	493	514	616	1.81	2.06	5	5	6	-18.01	0.45	8	12	20	26.53	4.81
Chile	74	76	117	4.61	4.78	4	2	0	-3.80	4.25	16	21	54	40.81	10.90
Mexico	145	153	163	1.96	0.79	86	101	157	10.92	4.83	2	2	2	17.70	-0.18
Uruguay	41	43	59	7.23	3.45	0	0	0	-24.97	21.57	31	35	51	8.63	4.10
ASIA and PACIFIC	1 045	1 118	1 271	2.96	1.52	337	349	440	4.69	2.45	52	63	117	18.54	7.19
Bangladesh	1	1	1	0.00	0.92	0	0	0	0.96	24.19	0	0	0	0.00	0.00
China[c]	327	376	429	7.88	1.45	33	35	48	17.67	3.62	1	1	1	8.36	1.66
India	1	1	1	6.32	0.00	1	1	1	11.84	0.00	1	1	1	40.03	0.00
Indonesia	0	0	0	0.00	-3.20	4	4	8	-5.11	6.35	0	0	1	27.87	8.02
Iran, Islamic Republic of	221	235	255	0.75	1.14	0	0	0	12.56	-15.21	1	7	4	35.47	1.64
Korea	30	34	69	12.13	7.67	45	46	55	11.41	2.07	0	0	0	7.05	0.00
Malaysia	0	0	0	0.00	0.85	8	8	10	9.08	1.98	0	0	0	-20.47	28.06
Pakistan	0	0	0	0.00	0.00	1	1	1	13.11	4.86	0	1	1	0.00	4.86
Saudi Arabia	0	0	0	0.00	0.00	70	78	103	0.49	3.16	32	38	78	35.02	8.07
Turkey	127	129	156	-0.16	2.16	3	3	5	-2.93	8.49	1	0	0	-21.34	7.79
LEAST DEVELOPED COUNTRIES (LDC)	248	259	276	0.90	0.96	19	14	40	7.32	8.65	0	0	0	15.75	4.38
OECD	14 722	15 332	16 980	1.99	1.09	755	792	994	1.15	2.55	1 192	1 213	1 320	1.55	0.82
NON-OECD	4 255	4 420	5 345	3.93	2.15	748	831	1 120	7.24	3.15	366	410	793	17.67	7.43

For notes, see end of the table.

OECD-FAO AGRICULTURAL OUTLOOK 2008-2017 – ISBN 978-92-64-04590-3 – © OECD/FAO 2008

Table A.27. **Cheese projections** (cont.)

Calendar year[a]	CONSUMPTION (kt)			Growth[b] (%)		PER CAPITA (kg)			Growth[b] (%)	
	Average 2005-07 est.	2008	2017	1998-2007	2008-17	Average 2005-07 est.	2008	2017	1998-2007	2008-17
WORLD	**18 936**	**19 767**	**22 326**	**2.43**	**1.33**	**2.9**	**2.9**	**3.0**	**1.21**	**0.21**
DEVELOPED	**15 149**	**15 837**	**17 689**	**2.47**	**1.20**	**11.3**	**11.8**	**12.8**	**2.08**	**0.94**
NORTH AMERICA	**4 801**	**5 002**	**5 542**	**2.62**	**1.13**	**14.5**	**14.8**	**15.1**	**1.61**	**0.25**
Canada	366	368	410	1.53	1.19	11.2	11.1	11.4	0.54	0.36
United States	4 435	4 633	5 132	2.71	1.13	14.8	15.2	15.5	1.70	0.24
EUROPE	**8 655**	**9 049**	**10 026**	**1.74**	**1.08**	**16.4**	**17.1**	**18.7**	**1.43**	**0.98**
EU(27)	8 323	8 714	9 685	1.75	1.11	16.9	17.6	19.4	1.43	1.02
CIS	**1 149**	**1 249**	**1 487**	**9.24**	**1.94**	**4.1**	**4.5**	**5.4**	**9.44**	**2.05**
Russian Federation	832	902	1 076	9.13	1.92	5.8	6.4	8.0	9.58	2.41
Ukraine	179	196	241	13.77	2.48	3.9	4.3	5.6	14.59	3.27
OCEANIA DEVELOPED	**253**	**248**	**269**	**1.73**	**0.99**	**10.2**	**9.8**	**9.8**	**0.55**	**0.07**
Australia	225	220	241	1.96	1.11	10.9	10.4	10.5	0.76	0.16
New Zealand	28	28	28	0.00	−0.01	6.8	6.7	6.2	−1.10	−0.79
OTHER DEVELOPED	**291**	**290**	**364**	**1.36**	**2.86**	**1.7**	**1 6**	**2.1**	**0.98**	**2.88**
Japan	249	254	304	1.41	2.06	2.0	2.0	2.4	1.29	2.25
South Africa	42	36	61	1.07	7.26	0.9	0.7	1.2	−0.02	6.85
DEVELOPING	**3 787**	**3 930**	**4 637**	**2.50**	**1.82**	**0.7**	**0.7**	**0.8**	**1.04**	**0.51**
AFRICA	**918**	**925**	**1 193**	**3.88**	**2.86**	**1.0**	**1.0**	**1.0**	**1.49**	**0.63**
NORTH AFRICA	**709**	**709**	**940**	**4.79**	**3.16**	**3.0**	**2.9**	**3.3**	**2.88**	**1.37**
Algeria	28	29	41	6.13	3.62	0.8	0.8	1.1	4.65	2.17
Egypt	643	643	841	4.86	3.01	8.7	8.4	9.5	3.05	1.40
SUB-SAHARAN AFRICA	**208**	**216**	**253**	**1.15**	**1.83**	**0.3**	**0.3**	**0.3**	**−1.42**	**−0.55**
LATIN AMERICA and CARIBBEAN	**1 543**	**1 601**	**1 849**	**1.32**	**1.53**	**2.7**	**2.8**	**2.9**	**0.04**	**0.38**
Argentina	387	395	447	−1.57	1.01	9.9	9.9	10.4	−2.55	0.10
Brazil	490	508	602	1.15	1.97	2.6	2.6	2.8	−0.22	0.81
Chile	62	56	63	1.10	1.09	3.8	3.4	3.5	−0.02	0.19
Mexico	220	251	310	4.61	2.02	2.2	2.4	2.8	3.75	1.64
Uruguay	10	8	8	0.64	−0.08	3.0	2.4	2.3	0.52	−0.43
ASIA and PACIFIC	**1 326**	**1 404**	**1 594**	**3.00**	**1.43**	**0.3**	**0.4**	**0.4**	**1.73**	**0.32**
Bangladesh	1	1	2	−0.96	2.70	0.0	0.0	0.0	−2.84	1.15
China[c]	359	411	477	8.55	1.65	0.3	0.3	0.3	7.88	0.99
India	1	1	1	−2.43	0.00	0.0	0.0	0.0	−4.06	−1.31
Indonesia	4	4	7	−5.82	6.21	0.0	0.0	0.0	−7.13	5.23
Iran, Islamic Republic of	220	229	251	0.70	1.07	3.1	3.2	3.1	0.33	0.26
Korea	75	80	124	11.64	4.82	1.6	1.7	2.5	11.13	4.64
Malaysia	8	8	10	9.48	2.12	0.3	0.3	0.3	7.51	0.65
Pakistan	1	0	0	19.56	0.00	0.0	0.0	0.0	67.05	0.00
Saudi Arabia	38	40	25	−7.59	−5.23	1.6	1.6	0.8	−10.11	−7.28
Turkey	130	132	162	0.24	2.32	1.8	1.7	1.9	−1.14	1.22
LEAST DEVELOPED COUNTRIES (LDC)	**267**	**273**	**315**	**1.27**	**1.64**	**0.4**	**0.4**	**0.3**	**−1.12**	**−0.60**
OECD	**14 297**	**14 919**	**16 649**	**2.00**	**1.18**	**11.8**	**12.2**	**13.0**	**1.39**	**0.73**
NON-OECD	**4 639**	**4 848**	**5 678**	**3.76**	**1.76**	**0.9**	**0.9**	**0.9**	**2.38**	**0.50**

a) Year ending 30 June for Australia and 31 May for New Zealand.
b) Least-squares growth rate (see glossary).
c) Refers to mainland only. The economies of Chinese Taipei, Hong Kong (China) and Macau (China) are included in the Other Asia Pacific aggregate.
est.: estimate.
Source: OECD and FAO Secretariats.

StatLink ⬛☶⬛ http://dx.doi.org/10.1787/384632178228

Table A.28. **Skim milk powder projections**

Calendar year[a]	PRODUCTION (kt)			Growth[b] (%)		IMPORTS (kt)			Growth[b] (%)		EXPORTS (kt)			Growth[b] (%)	
	Average 2005-07 est.	2008	2017	1998-2007	2008-17	Average 2005-07 est.	2008	2017	1998-2007	2008-17	Average 2005-07 est.	2008	2017	1998-2007	2008-17
WORLD	3 214	3 362	3 833	−1.35	1.52	1 204	1 192	1 549	0.05	3.08	1 093	1 192	1 549	−1.33	3.08
DEVELOPED	2 733	2 844	3 097	−1.92	1.05	143	154	153	−3.73	0.24	971	1 051	1 279	−1.82	2.51
NORTH AMERICA	769	852	1 062	2.08	2.61	4	3	3	−5.86	0.00	259	322	415	5.91	3.51
Canada	74	87	94	0.19	0.75	3	3	3	28.88	0.00	13	15	10	−14.98	−2.85
United States	695	765	968	2.30	2.81	1	0	0	−24.43	0.00	247	308	405	8.66	3.73
EUROPE	955	955	825	−4.28	−1.53	25	25	15	−8.42	−4.88	164	139	53	−13.50	−10.28
EU(27)	924	926	796	−4.37	−1.59	19	20	10	−11.12	−6.72	148	122	36	−14.78	−13.15
CIS	252	252	279	−6.92	1.08	71	76	99	5.31	3.48	106	116	148	8.21	2.62
Russian Federation	81	80	93	−16.36	1.58	49	50	58	3.14	2.43	1	1	1	−35.82	0.00
Ukraine	130	132	145	1.69	1.09	0	0	1	−17.70	7.99	64	70	76	11.31	0.76
OCEANIA DEVELOPED	564	547	669	2.70	2.18	4	4	5	0.74	2.01	441	419	585	1.12	3.54
Australia	195	162	231	−3.05	3.68	4	4	5	4.22	2.01	162	129	197	−3.16	4.23
New Zealand	369	385	439	6.86	1.46	0	0	0	5.00	0.00	279	291	388	4.18	3.21
OTHER DEVELOPED	193	238	261	−0.95	1.52	39	46	31	−5.98	−4.51	1	55	78	−11.19	5.02
Japan	180	173	174	−1.09	0.04	33	42	29	−7.21	−3.96	0	0	0	0.00	0.00
South Africa	13	65	87	2.68	4.38	6	5	2	12.48	−10.75	1	55	78	−11.19	5.02
DEVELOPING	480	518	736	3.10	3.76	1 061	1 038	1 395	1.19	3.44	122	140	269	6.34	6.31
AFRICA	3	3	3	−0.17	0.00	157	156	211	−1.44	3.33	2	2	2	−5.10	−2.01
NORTH AFRICA	0	0	0	0.00	0.00	114	109	138	−0.67	2.63	1	1	0	−5.71	−13.36
Algeria	0	0	0	0.00	0.00	51	49	62	−7.30	2.76	0	0	0	−5.43	0.00
Egypt	0	0	0	0.00	0.00	28	35	30	5.16	−1.48	0	1	0	−24.34	−25.77
SUB-SAHARAN AFRICA	3	3	3	−0.17	0.00	43	47	72	−3.30	4.82	1	2	2	−4.61	1.08
LATIN AMERICA and CARIBBEAN	229	240	355	5.02	4.39	198	200	253	−4.08	2.60	30	42	125	−2.75	10.63
Argentina	29	33	39	−5.13	2.01	0	0	0	−14.68	0.00	17	22	31	−1.78	3.46
Brazil	118	129	151	9.78	1.82	8	4	7	−22.62	2.27	4	4	12	19.25	4.32
Chile	16	22	60	6.88	10.99	4	1	0	−15.44	4.92	0	1	24	27.62	33.77
Mexico	32	32	35	2.82	1.19	126	135	175	2.18	2.90	0	0	0	−11.10	−0.26
Uruguay	12	18	63	−3.86	13.12	0	0	0	−31.93	33.68	7	13	57	−9.73	15.13
ASIA and PACIFIC	249	275	378	1.57	3.23	706	682	932	3.92	3.70	90	96	143	13.13	3.70
Bangladesh	0	0	0	0.00	0.00	7	3	6	−9.92	6.12	0	0	0	34.70	0.00
China[c]	57	57	111	2.28	7.25	53	40	88	16.02	9.01	2	5	5	5.04	0.00
India	161	179	209	1.26	1.31	0	0	0	−33.64	0.00	44	50	70	37.66	2.49
Indonesia	0	0	0	0.00	0.00	87	89	111	5.08	2.32	3	0	0	18.39	0.00
Iran, Islamic Republic of	0	0	0	0.00	0.00	7	9	14	6.45	4.05	0	1	0	−21.66	−6.59
Korea	21	23	42	4.00	6.65	6	6	2	9.63	−10.76	0	0	0	0.40	0.00
Malaysia	0	0	0	0.00	0.00	70	67	89	1.51	3.70	7	7	14	27.15	8.03
Pakistan	0	0	0	0.00	0.00	5	6	9	13.59	3.94	0	0	1	−9.98	8.35
Saudi Arabia	0	0	0	0.00	0.00	95	88	120	18.54	3.98	3	1	0	−1.50	0.97
Turkey	0	0	0	0.00	0.00	4	3	5	1.36	4.99	0	0	0	−30.23	0.00
LEAST DEVELOPED COUNTRIES (LDC)	0	0	0	0.00	0.00	35	32	49	−11.05	4.71	1	1	1	−5.79	1.17
OECD	2 520	2 581	2 808	−1.20	1.00	197	213	230	−2.73	0.91	864	881	1 053	−2.36	2.27
NON-OECD	693	781	1 025	−1.44	3.04	1 007	979	1 319	1.24	3.50	229	311	496	6.97	4.92

For notes, see end of the table.

Table A.28. **Skim milk powder projections** (cont.)

Calendar year[a]	CONSUMPTION (kt)			Growth[b] (%)		PER CAPITA (kg)			Growth[b] (%)	
	Average 2005-07 est.	2008	2017	1998-2007	2008-17	Average 2005-07 est.	2008	2017	1998-2007	2008-17
WORLD	**3 330**	**3 297**	**3 817**	**−14.13**	**1.69**	**0.5**	**0.5**	**0.5**	**−0.73**	**0.57**
DEVELOPED	**1 915**	**1 885**	**1 956**	**−14.19**	**0.40**	**1.4**	**1.4**	**1.4**	**−2.59**	**0.14**
NORTH AMERICA	**569**	**529**	**650**	**4.32**	**2.13**	**1.7**	**1.6**	**1.8**	**3.31**	**1.25**
Canada	71	75	87	8.13	1.38	2.2	2.2	2.4	7.14	0.54
United States	498	455	564	3.80	2.25	1.7	1.5	1.7	2.79	1.37
EUROPE	**833**	**842**	**787**	**−13.50**	**−0.74**	**1.6**	**1.6**	**1.5**	**−3.37**	**−0.84**
EU(27)	812	824	769	−2.21	−0.75	1.7	1.7	1.5	−2.52	−0.85
CIS	**217**	**212**	**230**	**−8.65**	**1.09**	**0.8**	**0.8**	**0.8**	**−8.45**	**1.20**
Russian Federation	129	129	150	−11.30	1.91	0.9	0.9	1.1	−10.85	2.41
Ukraine	66	62	70	−2.92	1.53	1.4	1.3	1.6	−2.10	2.31
OCEANIA DEVELOPED	**64**	**72**	**75**	**−0.56**	**0.60**	**2.6**	**2.9**	**2.7**	**−1.74**	**−0.31**
Australia	29	37	40	−5.50	1.13	1.4	1.8	1.7	−6.70	0.18
New Zealand	35	35	35	6.74	0.05	8.5	8.3	7.8	5.64	−0.74
OTHER DEVELOPED	**232**	**230**	**214**	**−1.90**	**−0.79**	**1.3**	**1.3**	**1.2**	**−2.28**	**−0.78**
Japan	214	215	203	−2.28	−0.64	1.7	1.7	1.6	−2.40	−0.46
South Africa	18	15	11	7.24	−3.32	0.4	0.3	0.2	6.15	−3.72
DEVELOPING	**1 415**	**1 413**	**1 860**	**1.34**	**3.22**	**0.3**	**0.3**	**0.3**	**−0.11**	**1.90**
AFRICA	**157**	**156**	**211**	**−1.39**	**3.35**	**0.2**	**0.2**	**0.2**	**−3.78**	**1.12**
NORTH AFRICA	**113**	**108**	**138**	**−0.60**	**2.69**	**0.5**	**0.4**	**0.5**	**−2.51**	**0.90**
Algeria	51	49	62	−7.30	2.76	1.5	1.4	1.6	−8.78	1.32
Egypt	27	34	30	5.44	−1.30	0.4	0.4	0.3	3.63	−2.91
SUB-SAHARAN AFRICA	**44**	**48**	**73**	**−3.19**	**4.69**	**0.1**	**0.1**	**0.1**	**−5.76**	**2.31**
LATIN AMERICA and CARIBBEAN	**396**	**399**	**484**	**0.10**	**2.40**	**0.7**	**0.7**	**0.8**	**−1.18**	**1.26**
Argentina	12	11	0	9.00	−2.24	0.3	0.3	0.2	−10.84	−3.15
Brazil	122	129	146	2.74	1.79	0.6	0.7	0.7	1.38	0.63
Chile	19	22	36	0.00	5.66	1.1	1.3	2.0	−1.12	4.76
Mexico	150	100	210	2.18	2.72	1.5	1.6	1.8	1.32	1.75
Uruguay	5	5	6	9.25	2.76	1.5	1.5	1.8	9.13	2.41
ASIA and PACIFIC	**862**	**858**	**1 165**	**2.57**	**3.55**	**0.2**	**0.2**	**0.3**	**1.30**	**2.44**
Bangladesh	7	3	6	−9.90	6.12	0.0	0.0	0.0	−11.78	4.57
China[c]	108	92	194	7.25	8.30	0.1	0.1	0.1	6.58	7.63
India	117	129	139	−2.95	0.79	0.1	0.1	0.1	−4.57	−0.52
Indonesia	84	89	111	6.19	2.32	0.4	0.4	0.4	4.88	1.34
Iran, Islamic Republic of	7	9	14	8.87	4.78	0.1	0.1	0.2	7.84	3.45
Korea	26	29	44	3.95	4.82	0.5	0.6	0.9	3.45	4.63
Malaysia	63	60	75	0.34	3.05	2.4	2.2	2.4	−1.63	1.58
Pakistan	5	6	8	12.73	3.51	0.0	0.0	0.0	10.85	1.62
Saudi Arabia	92	87	120	21.37	4.03	3.8	3.5	4.0	18.84	1.98
Turkey	4	3	5	2.42	4.99	0.1	0.0	0.1	1.03	3.89
LEAST DEVELOPED COUNTRIES (LDC)	**34**	**31**	**48**	**−11.14**	**4.78**	**0.0**	**0.0**	**0.1**	**−13.53**	**2.54**
OECD	**1 862**	**1 850**	**1 970**	**−0.09**	**0.67**	**1.5**	**1.5**	**1.5**	**−0.70**	**0.21**
NON-OECD	**1 469**	**1 447**	**1 846**	**−14.04**	**2.89**	**0.3**	**0.3**	**0.3**	**0.16**	**1.63**

a) Year ending 30 June for Australia and 31 May for New Zealand.
b) Least-squares growth rate (see glossary).
c) Refers to mainland only. The economies of Chinese Taipei, Hong Kong (China) and Macau (China) are included in the Other Asia Pacific aggregate.
est.: estimate.
Source: OECD and FAO Secretariats.

StatLink ᴍsᴘ http://dx.doi.org/10.1787/384680338357

Table A.29. **Whole milk powder projections**

Calendar year[a]	PRODUCTION (kt)			Growth[b] (%)		IMPORTS (kt)			Growth[b] (%)		EXPORTS (kt)			Growth[b] (%)	
	Average 2005-07 est.	2008	2017	1998-2007	2008-17	Average 2005-07 est.	2008	2017	1998-2007	2008-17	Average 2005-07 est.	2008	2017	1998-2007	2008-17
WORLD	3 985	4 069	4 897	4.06	2.08	1 421	1 625	2 197	1.75	3.43	1 717	1 624	2 196	2.33	3.43
DEVELOPED	1 854	1 655	1 844	0.76	1.22	75	79	90	3.41	1.06	1 229	1 079	1 267	0.39	1.80
NORTH AMERICA	29	29	33	−12.30	1.40	23	20	20	9.50	0.00	1	1	1	−41.45	−0.64
Canada	15	14	11	−1.82	−2.81	21	18	18	12.02	0.00	0	0	0	−41.37	−4.25
United States	14	15	22	−18.01	4.22	2	2	2	−3.65	0.00	1	1	1	−27.50	0.00
EUROPE	866	718	557	−2.53	−2.73	7	7	7	−8.19	−0.81	454	334	212	−5.84	−4.82
EU(27)	842	696	534	−2.67	−2.83	2	2	1	−16.45	−3.50	452	331	209	−5.91	−4.88
CIS	136	141	176	3.65	2.50	37	43	57	2.37	2.97	38	46	59	17.81	2.77
Russian Federation	76	69	81	1.72	1.76	29	35	36	3.03	0.35	5	5	5	3.90	0.00
Ukraine	30	31	49	16.02	4.68	0	0	1	−31.79	8.58	21	21	35	36.01	5.51
OCEANIA DEVELOPED	795	740	1 049	5.64	3.79	8	7	5	3.60	−4.63	733	697	994	5.69	3.85
Australia	161	120	201	0.42	5.51	8	7	5	6.62	−4.63	103	81	149	−2.54	6.50
New Zealand	634	619	848	7.33	3.41	0	0	0	−1.46	0.00	630	616	845	7.70	3.43
OTHER DEVELOPED	28	27	29	−0.44	1.48	1	2	1	7.04	−9.03	2	0	0	−23.62	−6.85
Japan	14	14	12	−3.73	−1.31	0	0	0	7.25	0.00	0	0	0	0.00	0.00
South Africa	14	13	17	3.76	3.86	1	2	1	6.09	−9.03	2	0	0	−23.62	−6.85
DEVELOPING	2 132	2 414	3 053	7.65	2.64	1 346	1 545	2 107	1.90	3.54	488	545	929	9.66	6.13
AFRICA	6	7	6	−4.63	0.29	345	369	533	6.13	4.02	8	8	10	−3.00	3.27
NORTH AFRICA	0	0	0	0.00	0.00	147	156	215	2.86	3.55	0	0	0	7.67	−8.14
Algeria	0	0	0	0.00	0.00	126	132	170	2.58	2.86	0	0	0	−59.55	9.04
Egypt	0	0	0	0.00	0.00	14	17	32	5.03	6.56	0	0	0	3.69	−11.33
SUB-SAHARAN AFRICA	6	7	6	−4.63	0.29	198	213	318	9.21	4.36	8	8	10	−2.75	3.45
LATIN AMERICA and CARIBBEAN	1 067	1 131	1 443	4.30	2.84	262	289	311	−5.27	0.74	245	259	501	5.91	7.35
Argentina	244	268	458	1.65	5.92	2	0	0	−1.79	0.00	163	171	364	4.31	8.41
Brazil	463	496	565	8.63	1.76	27	36	40	−21.69	1.34	20	20	19	54.38	−0.35
Chile	54	56	68	−2.18	2.07	3	0	0	−13.07	0.00	9	9	15	5.93	6.47
Mexico	184	187	189	4.65	0.07	42	41	42	0.08	0.09	10	10	10	2.21	0.09
Uruguay	21	24	39	2.71	5.69	0	0	0	−22.61	28.90	17	19	33	2.48	5.99
ASIA and PACIFIC	1 058	1 276	1 604	12.29	2.47	739	887	1 263	3.62	4.14	234	279	418	16.17	4.89
Bangladesh	0	0	0	0.00	0.00	22	25	67	3.14	10.42	0	0	0	0.00	0.00
China[c]	1 033	1 244	1 561	12.15	2.44	65	97	164	3.99	8.32	43	75	48	27.95	−3.37
India	15	10	10	35.93	0.00	0	0	0	−2.10	0.00	15	10	10	67.42	0.00
Indonesia	0	0	0	0.00	−1.85	45	59	98	22.07	5.63	17	19	41	26.41	8.28
Iran, Islamic Republic of	1	1	1	1.82	−0.58	3	11	19	32.83	5.16	0	0	0	3.96	7.98
Korea	4	6	17	−0.37	12.51	2	2	3	22.49	3.20	0	0	0	13.60	0.00
Malaysia	0	0	0	0.00	1.15	41	43	50	−2.86	1.66	16	18	25	6.13	3.87
Pakistan	0	0	0	0.00	0.00	1	2	3	−27.95	5.94	0	0	1	−15.33	8.45
Saudi Arabia	0	0	0	0.00	0.00	74	88	151	5.84	6.03	31	37	81	63.83	8.64
Turkey	0	0	0	0.00	0.00	5	4	7	7.44	5.39	1	1	1	46.16	8.12
LEAST DEVELOPED COUNTRIES (LDC)	0	0	0	0.00	0.00	141	153	259	10.80	5.72	4	4	9	27.45	8.37
OECD	1 888	1 690	1 854	0.88	1.03	82	77	79	1.07	0.12	1 200	1 043	1 219	0.13	1.74
NON-OECD	2 097	2 379	3 043	7.59	2.78	1 339	1 547	2 118	1.89	3.58	517	581	977	9.75	5.99

For notes, see end of the table.

OECD-FAO AGRICULTURAL OUTLOOK 2008-2017 – ISBN 978-92-64-04590-3 – © OECD/FAO 2008

Table A.29. **Whole milk powder projections** (cont.)

Calendar year[a]	CONSUMPTION (kt)			Growth[b] (%)		PER CAPITA (kg)			Growth[b] (%)	
	Average 2005-07 est.	2008	2017	1998-2007	2008-17	Average 2005-07 est.	2008	2017	1998-2007	2008-17
WORLD	**3 693**	**4 071**	**4 899**	**3.97**	**2.08**	**0.6**	**0.6**	**0.7**	**2.75**	**0.97**
DEVELOPED	**700**	**654**	**666**	**1.70**	**0.19**	**0.5**	**0.5**	**0.5**	**1.31**	**−0.07**
NORTH AMERICA	**51**	**49**	**52**	**−4.61**	**0.88**	**0.2**	**0.1**	**0.1**	**−5.62**	**0.00**
Canada	35	32	29	6.22	−1.11	1.1	1.0	0.8	5.23	−1.94
United States	15	16	23	−15.38	4.01	0.1	0.1	0.1	−16.39	3.12
EUROPE	**418**	**390**	**350**	**1.73**	**−1.19**	**0.8**	**0.7**	**0.7**	**1.42**	**−1.29**
EU(27)	393	366	326	1.76	−1.27	0.8	0.7	0.7	1.44	−1.37
CIS	**134**	**138**	**174**	**0.49**	**2.55**	**0.5**	**0.5**	**0.6**	**0.69**	**2.66**
Russian Federation	101	99	112	0.74	1.37	0.7	0.7	0.8	1.19	1.87
Ukraine	10	11	15	2.05	3.11	0.2	0.2	0.3	2.87	3.89
OCEANIA DEVELOPED	**69**	**50**	**59**	**4.86**	**2.02**	**2.8**	**2.0**	**2.2**	**3.68**	**1.10**
Australia	65	46	56	8.23	2.16	3.2	2.2	2.4	7.04	1.22
New Zealand	4	4	4	−11.25	0.00	0.9	0.9	0.8	−12.35	−0.78
OTHER DEVELOPED	**28**	**29**	**30**	**4.42**	**0.53**	**0.2**	**0.2**	**0.2**	**4.04**	**0.55**
Japan	14	14	12	−3.68	−1.31	0.1	0.1	0.1	3.80	1.13
South Africa	14	15	18	24.97	2.02	0.3	0.3	0.3	7.75	1.62
DEVELOPING	**2 993**	**3 416**	**4 233**	**4.64**	**2.41**	**0.6**	**0.6**	**0.7**	**3.19**	**1.09**
AFRICA	**342**	**367**	**529**	**6.19**	**3.99**	**0.4**	**0.4**	**0.5**	**3.79**	**1.76**
NORTH AFRICA	**147**	**156**	**215**	**2.93**	**3.56**	**0.6**	**0.6**	**0.7**	**1.02**	**1.77**
Algeria	126	132	170	2.58	2.86	3.8	3.8	4.3	1.10	1.41
Egypt	14	17	32	5.63	6.62	0.2	0.2	0.4	3.81	5.01
SUB-SAHARAN AFRICA	**195**	**211**	**314**	**9.25**	**4.30**	**0.3**	**0.3**	**0.4**	**6.68**	**1.92**
LATIN AMERICA and CARIBBEAN	**1 089**	**1 165**	**1 255**	**1.30**	**0.94**	**1.9**	**2.0**	**2.0**	**0.02**	**−0.20**
Argentina	83	98	94	−3.39	−0.53	2.1	2.5	2.2	−4.38	−1.43
Brazil	474	512	586	3.69	1.81	2.5	2.7	2.7	2.32	0.65
Chile	48	47	53	−3.59	1.07	2.9	2.8	2.9	−4.71	0.17
Mexico	210	210	220	3.77	0.07	2.1	2.1	1.9	2.91	−0.90
Uruguay	7	7	9	10.95	2.73	2.1	2.2	2.7	10.83	2.38
ASIA and PACIFIC	**1 562**	**1 884**	**2 449**	**7.21**	**2.91**	**0.4**	**0.5**	**0.6**	**5.94**	**1.80**
Bangladesh	22	25	67	3.14	10.42	0.1	0.2	0.4	1.27	8.87
China[c]	1 055	1 266	1 678	11.21	3.13	0.8	0.9	1.2	10.54	2.46
India	0	0	0	2.17	0.00	0.0	0.0	0.0	0.54	−1.31
Indonesia	28	40	57	22.54	4.00	0.1	0.2	0.2	21.23	3.02
Iran, Islamic Republic of	4	12	20	18.84	4.69	0.1	0.2	0.2	17.81	3.06
Korea	6	8	20	4.03	10.59	0.1	0.2	0.4	3.53	10.41
Malaysia	25	26	25	−6.43	−0.20	1.0	0.9	0.8	−8.40	−1.67
Pakistan	1	1	2	−31.57	4.85	0.0	0.0	0.0	−33.45	2.96
Saudi Arabia	43	51	70	−1.55	3.58	1.8	2.0	2.3	−4.08	1.53
Turkey	4	4	6	5.90	4.92	0.1	0.1	0.1	4.51	3.81
LEAST DEVELOPED COUNTRIES (LDC)	**136**	**148**	**248**	**10.30**	**5.66**	**0.2**	**0.2**	**0.3**	**7.91**	**3.42**
OECD	**770**	**724**	**713**	**2.12**	**−0.18**	**0.6**	**0.6**	**0.6**	**1.51**	**−0.63**
NON-OECD	**2 923**	**3 347**	**4 186**	**4.51**	**2.52**	**0.5**	**0.6**	**0.7**	**3.13**	**1.26**

a) Year ending 30 June for Australia and 31 May for New Zealand.
b) Least-squares growth rate (see glossary).
c) Refers to mainland only. The economies of Chinese Taipei, Hong Kong (China) and Macau (China) are included in the Other Asia Pacific aggregate.
est.: estimate.
Source: OECD and FAO Secretariats.

StatLink 🔗 http://dx.doi.org/10.1787/384685456054

Table A.30. **Milk projections**

Calendar year[a]	PRODUCTION (kt)			Growth[b] (%)		INVENTORIES ('000 hd)			Growth[b] (%)		YIELD (ton/hd)			Growth[b] (%)	
	Average 2005-07 est.	2008	2017	1998-2007	2008-17	Average 2005-07 est.	2008	2017	1998-2007	2008-17	Average 2005-07 est.	2008	2017	1998-2007	2008-17
WORLD	652 424	682 767	802 633	2.06	1.80	557 701	585 419	649 927	1.21	1.26	1.2	1.2	1.2	0.85	0.55
DEVELOPED	350 781	357 174	388 850	0.48	0.92	80 027	80 665	82 682	−0.79	0.28	4.4	4.4	4.7	1.27	0.64
NORTH AMERICA	90 509	94 527	102 113	1.44	0.84	10 111	10 212	9 907	−0.24	−0.37	9.0	9.3	10.3	1.69	1.22
Canada	8 208	8 355	8 822	−0.01	0.57	1 009	998	994	−1.46	−0.07	8.1	8.4	8.9	1.45	0.64
United States	82 301	86 172	93 290	1.60	0.87	9 102	9 214	8 913	−0.10	−0.41	9.0	9.4	10.5	1.70	1.28
EUROPE	157 968	159 251	159 394	−0.30	0.00	31 285	30 700	28 384	−1.66	−0.86	5.1	5.2	5.6	1.36	0.86
EU(27)	147 846	149 222	149 352	−0.32	0.00	24 351	23 886	21 682	−2.00	−1.06	6.1	6.2	6.9	1.69	1.06
CIS	66 953	68 515	85 239	0.94	2.41	30 730	31 885	35 719	−0.59	1.32	2.2	2.1	2.4	1.53	1.09
Russian Federation	32 188	31 230	35 732	−0.09	1.46	10 556	10 498	11 176	−3.30	0.80	3.0	3.0	3.2	3.21	0.65
Ukraine	13 328	13 758	18 015	−0.08	2.90	5 516	5 466	6 133	−2.23	1.19	2.4	2.5	2.9	2.16	1.72
OCEANIA DEVELOPED	24 339	23 728	30 869	1.48	2.86	5 995	5 920	6 910	1.06	1.72	4.1	4.0	4.5	0.42	1.14
Australia	10 241	9 344	11 620	−0.30	2.57	1 874	1 777	2 147	−1.79	2.18	5.5	5.3	5.4	1.49	0.39
New Zealand	14 098	14 385	19 249	2.92	3.05	4 120	4 143	4 763	2.58	1.52	3.4	3.5	4.0	0.34	1.53
OTHER DEVELOPED	11 013	11 153	11 234	−0.33	−0.20	1 907	1 947	1 762	−1.44	−1.68	5.8	5.7	6.4	1.11	1.48
Japan	8 133	7 952	7 905	−0.63	−0.06	1 102	1 066	954	−1.85	−1.22	7.4	7.5	8.3	1.22	1.16
South Africa	2 881	3 201	3 330	0.56	−0.48	805	881	808	−0.79	−2.16	3.6	3.6	4.1	1.35	1.68
DEVELOPING	301 643	325 593	413 784	4.06	2.70	477 674	504 754	567 245	1.56	1.40	0.6	0.6	0.7	2.50	1.30
AFRICA	28 780	31 119	40 683	2.30	3.09	178 937	186 417	217 255	1.71	1.83	0.2	0.2	0.2	0.59	1.26
NORTH AFRICA	10 052	10 725	13 690	2.36	2.81	31 613	33 683	35 247	2.36	0.62	0.3	0.3	0.4	0.00	2.19
Algeria	1 735	2 032	2 468	2.85	2.26	9 196	10 261	10 365	2.50	0.26	0.2	0.2	0.2	0.35	2.00
Egypt	3 836	3 924	4 869	0.94	2.52	5 080	5 290	5 261	−1.95	0.12	0.8	0.7	0.9	2.90	2.40
SUB-SAHARAN AFRICA	18 727	20 394	26 993	2.26	3.23	147 324	152 734	182 008	1.58	2.07	0.1	0.1	0.1	0.68	1.15
LATIN AMERICA and CARIBBEAN	70 262	72 582	87 506	2.67	2.11	51 497	52 977	57 739	1.99	1.06	1.4	1.4	1.5	0.68	1.05
Argentina	9 668	9 817	12 951	−0.39	3.05	2 107	2 149	2 377	−2.38	1.08	4.6	4.6	5.4	1.99	1.96
Brazil	26 317	27 141	31 699	4.01	1.82	21 440	22 114	23 867	2.87	1.14	1.2	1.2	1.3	1.14	0.68
Chile	2 413	2 565	3 405	2.16	3.09	2 132	2 239	2 899	2.16	2.74	1.1	1.1	1.2	0.00	0.35
Mexico	10 047	10 191	10 492	1.91	0.33	6 870	6 874	6 843	0.36	−0.05	1.5	1.5	1.5	1.54	0.38
Uruguay	1 787	1 896	2 655	2.74	3.74	1 042	1 057	1 269	2.88	2.04	1.7	1.8	2.1	−0.15	1.70
ASIA and PACIFIC	202 601	221 892	285 595	4.84	2.83	247 240	265 360	292 251	1.36	1.17	0.8	0.8	1.0	3.49	1.67
Bangladesh	2 316	2 683	3 615	1.38	3.52	21 394	24 653	30 789	0.74	2.71	0.1	0.1	0.1	0.64	0.81
China[c]	35 406	42 758	62 197	17.56	4.11	17 823	19 274	20 176	7.73	0.50	2.0	2.2	3.1	9.83	3.61
India	98 293	104 234	128 541	3.33	2.36	74 861	76 794	84 581	1.98	1.15	1.3	1.4	1.5	1.35	1.22
Indonesia	881	943	1 270	2.88	3.28	9 018	9 251	11 258	1.02	2.15	0.1	0.1	0.1	1.86	1.12
Iran, Islamic Republic of	7 678	8 397	10 402	4.81	2.52	41 209	46 774	45 265	−0.50	−0.13	0.2	0.2	0.2	5.31	2.66
Korea	2 355	2 440	2 951	1.10	2.08	301	310	340	−0.45	1.06	7.8	7.9	8.7	1.55	1.02
Malaysia	46	49	59	3.03	2.08	96	100	120	1.07	1.98	0.5	0.5	0.5	1.96	0.11
Pakistan	31 139	33 306	41 780	3.21	2.58	27 673	29 451	34 734	2.87	1.86	1.1	1.1	1.2	0.34	0.72
Saudi Arabia	1 221	1 328	1 859	4.93	3.65	4 725	5 032	5 752	2.84	1.41	0.3	0.3	0.3	2.09	2.24
Turkey	11 598	13 392	17 556	2.38	2.98	22 626	25 612	28 073	−1.98	0.94	0.5	0.5	0.6	4.36	2.04
LEAST DEVELOPED COUNTRIES (LDC)	21 687	23 477	30 844	2.12	3.14	147 393	154 888	184 596	1.64	2.09	0.1	0.2	0.2	0.48	1.05
OECD	300 300	306 914	326 702	0.45	0.68	72 363	74 871	75 576	−1.17	0.08	4.1	4.1	4.3	1.63	0.60
NON-OECD	352 124	375 853	475 932	3.46	2.64	485 338	510 548	574 351	1.58	1.42	0.7	0.7	0.8	1.88	1.23

a) Year ending 30 June for Australia and 31 May for New Zealand.
b) Least-squares growth rate (see glossary).
c) Refers to mainland only. The economies of Chinese Taipei, Hong Kong (China) and Macau (China) are included in the Other Asia Pacific aggregate.
est.: estimate.
Source: OECD and FAO Secretariats.

StatLink ᵐˢ⥥ http://dx.doi.org/10.1787/384733611086

Table A.31. **Whey powder and casein projections**

Calendar year[a]		Average			Growth[b] (%)	
		2005-07 est.	2008	2017	1997-2006[b]	2008-17
AUSTRALIA						
Net trade, whey	kt pw	78.8	87.7	89.0	11.83	0.05
Exports, casein	kt pw	10.9	7.2	10.5	0.19	3.51
CANADA						
Net trade, whey	kt pw	6.8	10.5	1.0	9.88	−30.97
EU(27)						
Net trade, whey	kt pw	235.0	343.2	380.7	2.81	1.16
Casein EU(15)						
production	kt pw	141.0	146.9	191.6	−2.63	2.91
consumption	kt pw	117.0	104.9	126.5	−6.85	1.91
net trade	kt pw	24.0	42.0	65.1	11.82	5.15
JAPAN						
Net trade, whey	kt pw	−57.0	−60.7	−69.7	2.75	1.56
Imports, casein	kt pw	17.1	16.1	13.9	−0.63	−1.69
KOREA						
Net trade, whey	kt pw	−37.8	−37.0	−39.9	3.09	0.84
MEXICO						
Net trade, whey	kt pw	−51.3	−53.4	−49.2	−1.34	−0.93
NEW ZEALAND						
Net trade, whey	kt pw	5.6	6.2	9.1	1.45	4.16
Exports, casein	kt pw	161.0	154.2	212.9	6.21	3.36
UNITED STATES						
Whey						
production	kt pw	492.6	523.8	465.5	−0.95	−1.23
consumption	kt pw	274.2	257.1	209.0	−5.67	−2.53
exports	kt pw	227.0	275.3	265.0	8.63	−0.04
Imports, casein	kt pw	69.1	66.8	64.0	−0.28	−0.55
ARGENTINA						
Net trade, whey	kt pw	12.8	33.2	54.0	27.94	5.13
BRAZIL						
Net trade, whey	kt pw	−28.1	−29.1	−32.9	−3.49	1.65
CHINA[c]						
Net trade, whey	kt pw	−202.0	−218.1	−320.8	12.05	4.16
RUSSIA						
Net trade, whey	kt pw	−47.7	−50.4	−62.4	37.58	2.37

a) Year ending 30 June for Australia and 31 May for New Zealand.
b) Least squares growth rate (see glossary).
c) Refers to mainland only.
d) est.: estimate.
Source: OECD and FAO Secretariats.

StatLink http://dx.doi.org/10.1787/384752311164

Table A.32. **Main policy assumptions for biofuel markets**

		06/07	07/08 est.	08/09	09/10	10/11	11/12	12/13	13/14	14/15	15/16	16/17	17/18
BRAZIL													
Ethanol													
Import tariffs	%	20.00	20.00	20.00	20.00	20.00	20.00	20.00	20.00	20.00	20.00	20.00	20.00
Incorporation mandate[a]	%	15.28	17.46	18.26	18.26	18.26	18.26	18.26	18.26	18.26	18.26	18.26	18.26
Biodiesel													
Tax concessions[b]	BRL/hl	7	7	6	6	5	4	4	3	2	1	1	0
Import tariffs	%	4.60	4.60	4.60	4.60	4.60	4.60	4.60	4.60	4.60	4.60	4.60	4.60
CANADA													
Ethanol													
Tax concessions[b]	CAD/hl	28	21	17	17	17	17	17	16	16	16	16	16
Import tariffs	CAD/hl	5.00	5.00	5.00	5.00	5.00	5.00	5.00	5.00	5.00	5.00	5.00	5.00
Incorporation mandate[a]	%	0.00	0.16	0.16	0.16	3.33	3.33	4.07	4.07	4.07	4.07	4.07	4.07
Direct support	CAD/hl	0.00	0.00	10.00	10.00	10.00	8.00	7.00	6.00	5.00	4.00	4.00	4.00
Biodiesel													
Tax concessions[b]	CAD/hl	23	23	19	19	19	19	19	19	19	19	19	19
Incorporation mandate[a]	%	0.00	0.00	0.00	0.00	0.00	0.00	1.61	1.61	1.61	1.61	1.61	1.61
Direct support	CAD/hl	0.00	0.00	20.00	20.00	20.00	16.00	14.00	12.00	10.00	8.00	6.00	6.00
COLOMBIA													
Ethanol													
Import tariffs	%	9.65	9.65	9.65	9.65	9.65	9.65	9.65	9.65	9.65	9.65	9.65	9.65
Blending target[c]	%	10.00	10.00	10.00	10.00	10.00	10.00	10.00	10.00	10.00	10.00	10.00	10.00
Biodiesel													
Blending target	%	0.00	0.00	5.00	5.00	5.00	5.00	5.00	5.00	5.00	5.00	5.00	5.00
EU													
Ethanol													
Tax concessions[b]	EUR/hl	30	30	30	30	30	30	30	30	30	30	30	30
Import tariffs	EUR/hl	19.20	19.20	19.20	19.20	19.20	19.20	19.20	19.20	19.20	19.20	19.20	19.20
Incorporation mandate[a, d]	%	0.15	0.56	1.13	2.19	2.63	2.69	2.76	2.83	2.91	2.98	2.98	2.98
Biodiesel													
Tax concessions[b]	EUR/hl	48	34	34	34	34	34	34	34	34	34	34	34
Import tariffs	%	6.50	6.50	6.50	6.50	6.50	6.50	6.50	6.50	6.50	6.50	6.50	6.50
Incorporation mandate[a, d]	%	0.15	0.94	1.85	3.44	3.97	4.00	4.03	4.06	4.08	4.11	4.11	4.11
INDONESIA													
Ethanol													
Import tariffs	%	26.31	26.31	26.31	26.31	26.31	26.31	26.31	26.31	26.31	26.31	26.31	26.31
Blending target	%	0.00	0.00	2.00	4.00	6.00	8.00	10.00	10.00	10.00	10.00	10.00	10.00
Biodiesel													
Blending target	%	0.00	2.50	5.00	7.50	10.00	10.00	10.00	10.00	10.00	10.00	10.00	10.00
MALAYSIA													
Ethanol													
Import tariffs	%	0.00	0.00	0.00	0.00	0.00	0.00	0.00	0.00	0.00	0.00	0.00	0.00
Blending target	%	0.00	0.00	0.00	0.00	0.00	0.00	0.00	0.00	0.00	0.00	0.00	0.00
Biodiesel													
Blending target	%	0.00	0.00	1.67	3.33	5.00	5.00	5.00	5.00	5.00	5.00	5.00	5.00
SOUTH AFRICA													
Ethanol													
Import tariffs	%	0.00	0.00	0.00	0.00	0.00	0.00	0.00	0.00	0.00	0.00	0.00	0.00
Blending target	%	0.00	0.00	0.00	0.00	0.50	1.00	1.50	2.00	2.00	2.00	2.00	2.00
Biodiesel													
Import tariffs	%	0.00	0.00	0.00	0.00	0.00	0.00	0.00	0.00	0.00	0.00	0.00	0.00
Blending target	%	0.00	0.00	0.00	0.00	0.00	0.00	0.00	0.00	0.00	0.00	0.00	0.00

For notes, see end of the table.

OECD-FAO AGRICULTURAL OUTLOOK 2008-2017 – ISBN 978-92-64-04590-3 – © OECD/FAO 2008

Table A.32. **Main policy assumptions for biofuel markets** (*cont.*)

		06/07	07/08 est.	08/09	09/10	10/11	11/12	12/13	13/14	14/15	15/16	16/17	17/18
THAILAND													
Ethanol													
Import tariffs	%	0.00	0.00	0.00	0.00	0.00	0.00	0.00	0.00	0.00	0.00	0.00	0.00
Blending target	%	0.00	0.00	2.00	4.00	6.00	8.00	10.00	10.00	10.00	10.00	10.00	10.00
Biodiesel													
Blending target	%	0.00	0.00	0.00	0.00	0.00	0.00	0.00	0.00	0.00	0.00	0.00	0.00
UNITED STATES													
Ethanol													
Import tariffs	USD/hl	14.27	14.27	14.27	14.27	14.27	14.27	14.27	14.27	14.27	14.27	14.27	14.27
Import tariffs	%	2.50	2.50	2.50	2.50	2.50	2.50	2.50	2.50	2.50	2.50	2.50	2.50
Blenders tax credit	USD/hl	13.47	13.47	13.47	13.47	13.47	13.47	13.47	13.47	13.47	13.47	13.47	13.47
Biodiesel													
Import tariffs	%	4.60	4.60	4.60	4.60	4.60	4.60	4.60	4.60	4.60	4.60	4.60	4.60
Blenders tax credit	USD/hl	26.42	26.42	26.42	26.42	26.42	26.42	26.42	26.42	26.42	26.42	26.42	26.42

a) Difference between tax rates applying to fossil and biogen fuels.
b) Share in respective fuel type, energy equivalent.
c) Applies to cities with more than 500 000 inhabitants.
d) Note that for many countries, shares for ethanol and biodiesel are not specified individually in the legislation.
est: estimate.
Source: OECD and FAO Secretariats.

StatLink http://dx.doi.org/10.1787/384772733703

Table A.33. Biofuel projections: ethanol

	Production (mn l)				Domestic use (mn l)				Fuel use (mn l)				Share in gazoline type fuel use (%)					Net trade (mn l)			
													Energy shares				Volume shares 2017				
	Average 2005-07 est.	2008	2017	Growth[a] (%) 2008-17	Average 2005-07 est.	2008	2017	Growth[a] (%) 2008-17	Average 2005-07 est.	2008	2017	Growth[a] (%) 2008-17	Average 2005-07 est.	2008	2017	Growth[a] (%) 2008-17		Average 2005-07 est.	2008	2017	Growth[a] (%) 2008-17
North America																					
Canada	762	1 383	2 730	5.05	939	1 608	2 983	5.83	735	1 400	2 757	6.34	1.26	2.34	4.07[b]	4.98	5.96	-178	-224	-253	-24.50
United States	21 478	38 394	52 444	3.06	22 713	38 880	57 544	3.79	21 094	37 228	55 827	3.91	2.63	4.55	6.03	2.55	8.74	-1 235	-486	-5 100	0.00
Western Europe																					
EU27	2 049	4 402	11 883	10.53	4 649	7 297	14 707	7.37	2 127	4 748	11 962	9.58	1.00	2.19	4.88	8.22	7.11	-1 783	-2 895	-2 824	0.00
Oceania developed																					
Australia	63	156	1 004	12.52	63	156	1 004	12.52	63	156	1 004	12.52	0.22	0.54	3.30	11.82	4.84	0	0	0	0.00
Other developed																					
Japan	n.a.	n.a.	n.a.	n.a.	n.a.	n.a.	n.a.	n.a.	n.a.	n.a.	n.a.	n.a.	n.a.	n.a.	n.a.	n.a.	n.a.	-568	-825	-1 475	0.00
South Africa	410	369	683	6.32	99	134	527	8.32	0	0	367	32.98	0.00	0.00	1.87	-21.92	2.77	310	235	156	26.72
Sub-Saharian Africa																					
Ethiopia	33	38	74	8.27	33	34	39	1.32	0	1	6	13.36	0.00	0.34	0.67	5.01	1.00	4	4	35	28.25
Mozambique	21	24	28	2.00	22	23	28	2.46	0	1	5	22.20	0.00	0.34	1.86	17.89	2.75	-1	1	0	-1.39
Tanzania	26	29	43	4.28	30	35	51	4.07	0	5	18	14.96	0.00	1.01	2.54	10.07	3.75	-4	-6	-8	1.27
Latin America and Caribbean																					
Brazil	17 396	22 110	40 511	6.36	14 595	18 806	31 694	5.90	13 499	17 641	30 289	6.11	32.31	40.43	56.62	3.83	66.08	2 801	3 304	8 816	8.45
Columbia	272	497	796	5.58	303	472	506	0.79	268	435	460	0.65	3.34	5.21	4.99	-0.43	7.27	-31	25	290	28.67
Peru	16	22	40	5.29	11	14	19	3.77	0	2	2	0.37	0.00	0.16	0.19	2.33	0.29	5	8	21	7.25
Asia and Pacific																					
China	5 564	6 686	10 210	4.29	4 998	5 775	10 792	6.44	1 565	2 139	6 211	10.71	1.66	1.98	4.03	6.90	5.89	566	910	-583	-71.15
India	1 411	1 909	3 574	7.32	1 678	1 958	3 192	5.59	267	416	1 059	10.86	1.73	2.65	5.61	8.83	8.15	-267	-49	383	55.91
Indonesia	177	212	227	0.70	147	153	171	1.27	0	4	5	1.30	0.00	0.02	0.01	-2.69	0.02	30	59	56	-0.92
Malaysia	63	70	84	2.15	97	84	105	2.47	0	4	7	5.53	0.00	0.02	0.02	-0.78	0.03	-34	-14	-20	0.00
Philippines	62	105	126	1.98	109	147	170	1.58	17	50	50	0.00	0.24	0.70	0.53	-3.06	0.79	-47	-42	-44	0.00
Thailand	285	408	1 790	18.90	266	366	1 530	15.96	134	229	1 374	19.80	1.26	2.08	11.70	19.09	16.51	19	42	260	37.81
Turkey	55	77	81	0.39	103	119	128	0.85	43	58	63	0.94	0.62	0.87	1.15	3.17	1.70	-48	-42	-48	0.00
Vietnam	140	164	532	13.90	134	139	164	1.85	0	0	0	0.70	0.00	0.00	0.00	-10.52	0.00	6	25	368	28.01
TOTAL	50 284	77 054	126 860	5.12	50 991	76 200	125 355	5.11	39 811	64 517	111 467	5.58	3.78	5.46	7.63	3.30	10.98	-454	30	30	0.00

StatLink http://dx.doi.org/10.1787/384788645556

a) Least-squares growth rate.
b) Correspond to 5% of net-sale for on-road motor vehicles.
For notes, see end of the table.
est.: estimate, n.a.: Not available.
Source: OECD and FAO Secretariats.

OECD-FAO AGRICULTURAL OUTLOOK 2008-2017 – ISBN 978-92-64-04590-3 – © OECD/FAO 2008

Table A.34. Biofuel projections: biodiesel

	Production (mn l)				Domestic use (mn l)				Share in diesel type fuel use (%)					Net trade (mn l)			
									Energy shares				Volume shares 2017				
	Average 2005-07 est.	2008	2017	Growth[a] (%) 2008-17	Average 2005-07 est.	2008	2017	Growth[a] (%) 2008-17	Average 2005-07 est.	2008	2017	Growth[a] (%) 2008-17		Average 2005-07 est.	2008	2017	Growth[a] (%) 2008-17
North America																	
Canada	46	207	660	11.41	46	223	664	12.36	0.22	1.05	2.73	11.00	3.45	0	-15	-4	-5.66
United States	1 429	2 017	1 731	-2.22	852	1 476	1 638	1.67	0.28	0.47	0.45	0.31	0.58	577	541	93	-23.29
Western Europe																	
EU27	5 095	6 580	13 271	6.64	5 436	7 825	14 843	5.57	2.12	2.98	4.99	4.21	6.17	-341	-1 245	-1 572	0.00
Oceania developed																	
Australia	199	911	994	0.96	199	911	994	0.96	1.82	8.21	5.15	-0.08	0.00	0	0	0	0.00
Other developed																	
South Africa	0	0	0	-0.11	0	0	0	0.00	0.00	0.00	0.00	0.00	0.00	0	0	0	-0.11
Sub-Saharian Africa																	
Ethiopia	2	6	36	18.50	2	2	23	22.41	0.00	0.16	0.80	14.07	1.00	0	4	13	13.92
Mozambique	1	3	34	24.72	1	2	14	22.20	0.00	0.40	2.21	17.86	2.75	0	1	19	26.93
Tanzania	4	10	53	17.86	4	8	36	16.86	0.15	0.80	2.62	12.75	3.25	0	2	17	20.41
Latin America and Caribbean																	
Brazil	158	760	2 519	10.80	158	650	2 603	15.25	0.29	1.15	3.61	12.54	4.47	0	110	-84	-80.04
Columbia	10	218	388	6.09	0	159	229	4.02	0.00	4.04	5.29	2.99	6.52	0	59	160	9.76
Peru	0	0	0	-0.12	0	0	0	0.00	0.00	0.00	0.00	0.00	0.00	0	0	0	-0.12
Asia and Pacific																	
India	277	317	385	2.14	277	318	388	2.21	0.59	0.88	0.88	0.00	1.10	0	0	-3	0.00
Indonesia	241	753	2 984	15.45	47	129	2 169	32.30	0.28	0.66	7.88	28.52	9.66	168	624	815	1.84
Malaysia	148	443	1 137	10.15	0	43	143	13.16	0.40	0.43	0.80	6.87	1.00	148	400	994	9.80
Philippines	0	0	85	51.42	0	7	88	25.10	0.00	0.08	0.80	23.06	1.00	0	-7	-3	0.52
Thailand	0	48	75	2.30	0	0	0	0.00	0.00	0.00	0.00	0.00	0.00	0	48	75	2.30
Turkey	0	0	0	-0.14	0	0	0	0.00	0.00	0.00	0.00	0.00	0.00	0	0	0	-0.14
Vietnam	0	0	5	30.43	0	2	3	4.67	0.00	0.02	0.02	-6.55	0.02	0	-2	1	9.81
TOTAL	7 610	12 274	24 357	6.66	7 023	11 753	23 836	6.86	0.93	1.50	2.59	5.03	3.21	552	521	521	0.00

a) Least-squares growth rate.

est.: estimate.

Source: OECD and FAO Secretariats.

StatLink ⟹ http://dx.doi.org/10.1787/384836251405

ANNEX B

Glossary of Terms

AMAD

Agricultural Market Access database. A co-operative effort between Agriculture and Agri-food Canada, EU Commission-Agriculture Directorate-General, FAO, OECD, The World Bank, UNCTAD and the United States Department of Agriculture, Economic Research Service. Data in the database is obtained from countries' schedules and notifications submitted to the WTO.

Australia-US Free Trade Agreement (AUSFTA)

A Bilateral Agreement negotiated between the United States and Australia that came into force on 1 January 2005. AUSFTA covers goods, services, investment, financial services, government procurement, standards and technical regulations, telecommunications, competition-related matters, electronic commerce, intellectual property rights, labour and the environment.

Avian influenza

Avian influenza is an infectious disease of birds caused by type A strains of the influenza virus. The disease, which was first identified in Italy more than 100 years ago, occurs worldwide. The quarantine of infected farms, destruction of infected or potentially exposed flocks, and recently inoculation are standard control measures.

Atlantic beef/pigmeat market

Beef/pigmeat trade between countries in the Atlantic Rim.

Baseline

The set of market projections used for the outlook analysis in this report and as a benchmark for the analysis of the impact of different economic and policy scenarios. A detailed description of the generation of the baseline is provided in the chapter on Methodology in this report.

Biofuels

In the wider sense defined as all solid, fluid or gaseous fuels produced from biomass. More narrowly, the term biofuels comprises those that replace petroleum-based road-transport fuels, *i.e.* bioethanol produced from sugar crops, cereals and other starchy crops that can be used as an additive to, in a blend with or as a replacement of gasoline, and biodiesel produced mostly from vegetable oils, but also from waste oils and animal fats, that can be used in blends with or as a replacement of petroleum-based diesel.

Biomass

Biomass is defined as any plant matter used directly as fuel or converted into other forms before combustion. Included are wood, vegetal waste (including wood waste and crops used for energy production), animal materials/wastes and industrial and urban wastes, used as feedstocks for producing bioproducts.

Bovine Spongiform Encephalopathy (BSE)

A fatal disease of the central nervous system of cattle, first identified in the United Kingdom in 1986. On 20 March 1996 the UK Spongiform Encephalopathy Advisory Committee (SEAC) announced the discovery of a new variant of Creutzfeldt-Jacob Disease (vCJD), a fatal disease of the central nervous system in humans, which might be linked to consumption of beef affected by exposure to BSE.

Cereals

Defined as wheat, coarse grains and rice.

CAFTA

CAFTA is a comprehensive trade agreement between Costa Rica, the Dominican Republic, El Salvador, Guatemala, Honduras, Nicaragua, and the United States

Common Agricultural Policy (CAP)

The European Union's agricultural policy, first defined in Article 39 of the Treaty of Rome signed in 1957.

CAP reform

The EU Commission has published a Communication on the Mid-Term Review on the Common Agricultural Policy in July 2002, in January 2003 the Commission adopted a formal proposal. A formal decision on the "CAP reform a long-term perspective for sustainable agriculture" was taken by the EU farm ministers. The reform includes far-reaching amendments of current policies, including further reductions in support prices, partly offset by direct payments, and a further decoupling of most direct payments from current production.

Coarse grains

Defined as barley, maize, oats, sorghum and other coarse grains in all countries except Australia, where it includes triticale and in the European Union where it includes rye and other mixed grains.

Conservation Reserve Program (CRP)

A major provision of the United States' Food Security Act of 1985 and extended under the Food and Agriculture Conservation and Trade Act of 1990, the Food and Agriculture Improvement and Reform Act of 1996, and the Farm Security and Rural Investment Act of 2002 is designed to reduce erosion on 40 to 45 million acres (16 to 18 million hectares) of farm land. Under the programme, producers who sign contracts agree to convert erodable crop land to approved conservation uses for ten years. Participating producers receive annual rental payments and cash or payment in kind to share up to 50% of the cost of establishing permanent vegetative cover. The CRP is part of the *Environmental Conservation Acreage Reserve Program*. The 1996 FAIR Act authorised a 36.4 million acre (14.7 million hectares) maximum under CRP, its 1995 level. The maximum area enrolled in the CRP was increased to 39.2 million acres in the 2002 FSRI Act.

Commonwealth of Independent States (CIS)

The heads of twelve sovereign states (except the Baltic states) have signed the Treaty on establishment of the Economic Union, in which they stressed that the Azerbaijan Republic, Republic of Armenia, Republic of Belarus, Republic of Georgia, Republic of Kazakhstan, Kyrgyz Republic, Republic of Moldova, Russian Federation, Republic of Tajikistan, Turkmenistan, Republic of Uzbekistan and Ukraine on equality basis established the Commonwealth of Independent States.

Common Market Organisation (CMO) for sugar

The common organisation of the sugar market (CMO) in the European Union was established in 1968 to ensure a fair income to community sugar producers and self-supply of the Community market. At present the CMO is governed by Council Regulation (EC) No. 318/2006 (the basic regulation) which establishes a restructuring fund financed by sugar producers to assist the restructuring process needed to render the industry more competitive.

Crop year, coarse grains

Refers to the crop marketing year beginning 1 April for Japan, 1 July for the European Union and New Zealand, 1 August for Canada and 1 October for Australia. The US crop year begins 1 June for barley and oats and 1 September for maize and sorghum.

Crop year, oilseeds

Refers to the crop marketing year beginning 1 April for Japan, 1 July for the European Union and New Zealand, 1 August for Canada and 1 October for Australia. The US crop year begins 1 June for rapeseed, 1 September for soyabeans and for sunflower seed.

Crop year, rice

Refers to the crop marketing year beginning 1 April for Japan, Australia, 1 August for the United States, 1 September for the European Union, 1 October for Mexico, 1 November for Korea and 1 January for other countries.

Crop year, sugar

A common crop marketing year beginning 1 October and extending to 31 September, used by FO Licht.

Crop year, wheat

Refers to the crop marketing year beginning 1 April for Japan, 1 June for the United States, 1 July for the European Union and New Zealand, 1 August for Canada and 1 October for Australia.

Decoupled payments

Budgetary payments paid to eligible recipients who are not linked to current production of specific commodities or livestock numbers or the use of specific factors of production.

Direct payments

Payments made directly by governments to producers.

Doha Development Agenda

The current round of multilateral trade negotiations in the World Trade Organisation that were initiated in November 2001, in Doha, Qatar

Domestic support

Refers to the annual level of support, expressed in monetary terms, provided to agricultural production. It is one of the three pillars of the Uruguay Round Agreement on Agriculture targeted for reduction.

Economic Partnership Agreements (EPAs)

Free trade agreementss currently being negotiated between the EU and the African, Caribbean Pacific (ACP) group of developing countries to replace the Cotonou Agreement which expired in 2007.

Energy Independence and Security Act (EISA) 2007

US legislation passed in December 2007 that is designed to increase US energy security by lessening dependence on imported oil, to improve energy conservation and efficiency, expand the production of renewable fuels, and to make America's air cleaner for future generations.

Ethanol

A bio-fuel that can be used as a fuel substitute (hydrous ethanol) or a fuel extender (anhydrous ethanol) in mixes with petroleum, and which is produced from agricultural feed-stocks such as sugar cane and maize.

Everything-But-Arms (EBA)

The Everything-But-Arms (EBA) Initiative eliminates EU import tariffs for numerous goods, including agricultural products, from the least developed countries. The tariff elimination is scheduled in four steps from 2006/07 to 2009/10.

Export credits (with official support)

Government financial support, direct financing, guarantees, insurance or interest rate support provided to foreign buyers to assist in the financing of the purchase of goods from national exporters.

Export restitutions (refunds)

EU export subsidies provided to cover the difference between internal prices and world market prices for particular commodities.

Export subsidies

Subsidies given to traders to cover the difference between internal market prices and world market prices, such as for example the EU *export restitutions*. Export subsidies are now subject to value and volume restrictions under the *Uruguay Round Agreement on Agriculture*.

Foot and Mouth Disease (FMD)

Foot and mouth disease is a highly contagious disease, which chiefly affects cloven-hoofed animal species (cattle, sheep, goats and pigs). Its symptoms are the appearance of vesicles (aphthae) on the animals' mouths (with a consequent reduction in appetite) and feet. It is caused by a virus which may be found in the animals' blood, saliva and milk. The virus is transmitted in a number of ways, via humans, insects, most meat products, urine and faeces, feed, water or soil. Although the mortality rate in adult animals from this disease is generally low and the disease presents no risk for humans, because it is highly contagious, infected animals in a given country are generally put down and other countries place an embargo on imports of live animals and fresh, chilled or frozen meat from the country of infection; in that case, only smoked, salted or dried meat and meat preserves may be imported from the country concerned. In addition, given the possibility of contagion between different species of cloven-hoofed animals, when foot and mouth disease breaks out in one species in a given country, exports of meat from all four types of animal are suspended

FSRI Act, 2002

Officially known as the Farm Security and Rural Investment Act of 2002. This US farm legislation replaces the FAIR Act of 1996, covering a wide range of commodity programs and policies for US agriculture for the period 2002-2007.

Gur, jaggery, khandasari

Semi-processed sugars (plantation whites) extracted from sugarcane in India.

Industrial oilseeds

A category of oilseed production in the European Union for industrial use (*i.e.* biofuels).

Intervention purchases

Purchases by the EC Commission of certain commodities to support internal market prices.

Intervention purchase price

Price at which the European Commission will purchase produce to support internal market prices. It usually is below 100% of the intervention price, which is an annually decided policy price.

Intervention stocks

Stocks held by national intervention agencies in the European Union as a result of *intervention* buying of commodities subject to market price support. Intervention stocks may be released onto the internal markets if internal prices exceed intervention prices; otherwise, they may be sold on the world market with the aid of *export restitutions*.

Inulin

Inulin syrups are extracted from chicory through a process commercially developed in the 1980s. They usually contain 83 per cent fructose. Inulin syrup production in the European Union is covered by the sugar regime and subject to a production quota.

Isoglucose

Isoglucose is a starch-based fructose sweetener, produced by the action of glucose isomerase enzyme on dextrose. This isomerisation process can be used to produce glucose/fructose blends containing up to 42% fructose. Application of a further process can raise the fructose content to 55%. Where the fructose content is 42%, isoglucose is equivalent in sweetness to sugar. Isoglucose production in the European Union is covered by the sugar regime and subject to a production quota.

Least squares growth rate

The **least-squares growth rate**, r, is estimated by fitting a linear regression trend line to the logarithmic annual values of the variable in the relevant period, as follows : $Ln(xt) = a + r^{*} t$.

Loan rate

The commodity price at which the *Commodity Credit Corporation* (CCC) offers *non-recourse loans* to participating farmers. The crops covered by the programme are used as collateral for these loans. The loan rate serves as a floor price, with the effective level lying somewhat above the announced rate, for participating farmers in the sense that they can default on their loan and forfeit their crop to the CCC rather than sell it in the open market at a lower price.

Market access

Governed by provisions of the *Uruguay Round Agreement* on *Agriculture* which refer to concessions contained in the country schedules with respect to bindings and reductions of tariffs and to other minimum import commitments.

Marketing allotments (US sugar program)

Marketing allotments designate how much sugar can be sold by sugar millers and processors on the US internal market and were established by the 2002 FSRI Act as a way to guarantee the US sugar loan program operates at no cost to the Federal Government.

Marketing year, oilseed meals

Refers to the marketing year beginning 1 October.

Marketing year, oilseed oils

Refers to the marketing year beginning 1 October.

MERCOSUR

A multilateral agreement on trade, including agricultural trade between Argentina, Brazil, Paraguay and Uruguay. The agreement was signed in 1991 and came into effect on 1 January 1995. Its main goal is to create a customs union between the four countries by 2006.

Market Price Support (MPS) Payment

Indicator of the annual monetary value of gross transfers from consumers and taxpayers to agricultural producers arising from policy measures creating a gap between domestic market prices and *border prices* of a specific agricultural commodity, measured at the farm gate level. Conditional on the production of a specific commodity, MPS includes the transfer to producers associated with both production for domestic use and exports, and is measured by the price gap applied to current production. The MPS is net of financial contributions from individual producers through producer levies on sales of the specific commodity or penalties for not respecting regulations such as production quotas (*Price levies*), and in the case of livestock production is net of the market price support on domestically produced coarse grains and oilseeds used as animal feed (*Excess feed cost*).

Methyl Tertiary Butyl Ether (MTBE)

A chemical gasoline additive that can be used to boost the octane number and oxygen content of the fuel, but can render contaminated water undrinkable.

Milk quota scheme

A supply control measure to limit the volume of milk produced or supplied. Quantities up to a specified quota amount benefit from full *market price support*. Over-quota volumes may be penalised by a levy (as in the European Union, where the "super levy" is 115% of the target price) or may receive a lower price. Allocations are usually fixed at individual producer level. Other features, including arrangements for quota reallocation, differ according to scheme.

North American Free Trade Agreement (NAFTA)

A trilateral agreement on trade, including agricultural trade, between Canada, Mexico and the United States, phasing out tariffs and revising other trade rules between the three countries over a 15-year period. The agreement was signed in December 1992 and came into effect on 1 January 1994.

Oilseed meal

Defined as rapeseed meal (canola), soyabean meal, and sunflower meal in all countries, except in Japan where it excludes sunflower meal.

OECD-FAO AGRICULTURAL OUTLOOK 2008-2017 – ISBN 978-92-64-04590-3 – © OECD/FAO 2008

Oilseeds

Defined as rapeseed (canola), soyabeans, and sunflower seed in all countries, except in Japan where it excludes sunflower seed.

Pacific beef/pigmeat market

Beef/pigmeat trade between countries in the Pacific Rim where foot and mouth disease is not endemic.

Payment-In-Kind (PIK)

A programme used in the US to help dispose of public stocks of commodities. Under PIK, government payments in the form of Commodity Credit Corporation (CCC)-owned commodities are given to farmers in return for additional reductions in harvested acreage.

PROCAMPO

A programme of direct support to farmers in Mexico. It provides for direct payments per hectare on a historical basis.

Producer Support Estimate (PSE)

Indicator of the annual monetary value of gross transfers from consumers and taxpayers to agricultural producers, measured at farm gate level, arising from policy measure, regardless of their nature, objectives or impacts on farm production or income. The PSE measure support arising from policies targeted to agriculture relative to a situation without such policies, i.e. when producers are subject only to general policies (including economic, social, environmental and tax policies) of the country. The PSE is a gross notion implying that any costs associated with those policies and incurred by individual producers are not deducted. It is also a nominal assistance notion meaning that increased costs associated with import duties on inputs are not deducted. But it is an indicator net of producer contributions to help finance the policy measure (e.g. producer levies) providing a given transfer to producers. The PSE includes implicit and explicit payments. The percentage PSE is the ration of the PSE to the value of total gross farm receipts, measured by the value of total production (at farm gate prices), plus budgetary support. The nomenclature and definitions of this indicator replaced the former Producer Subsidy Equivalent in 1999.

Purchasing Power Parity (PPP)

Purchasing power parities (PPPs) are the rates of currency conversion that eliminate the differences in price levels between countries. The PPPs are given in national currency units per US dollar.

Non-Recourse loan programme

Programme to be implemented under the US FAIR Act of 1996 for butter, non-fat dry milk and cheese after 1999 in which loans must be repaid with interest to processors to assist them in the management of dairy product inventories.

Saccharin

A low calorie, artificial sweetener used as a substitute for sugar mainly in beverage preparations.

Scenario

A model-generated set of market projections based on alternative assumptions than those used in the baseline. Used to provide quantitative information on the impact of changes in assumptions on the outlook.

Set-aside programme

European Union programme for cereal, oilseed and protein crops that both requires and allows producers to set-aside a portion of their historical base acreage from current production. Mandatory set-aside rates for commercial producers are set at 10% until 2006.

Single Farm Payment

With the 2003 CAP reform, the EU introduced a farm-based payment largely independent of current production decisions and market developments, but based on the level of former payments received by farmers. To facilitate land transfers, entitlements are calculated by dividing the reference amount of payment by the number of eligible hectares (incl. forage area) in the reference year. Farmers receiving the new SFP are obliged to keep their land in good agricultural and environmental condition and have the flexibility to produce any commodity on their land except fruits, vegetables and table potatoes.

SPS Agreement

WTO Agreement on Sanitary and Phyto-sanitary measures, including standards used to protect human, animal or plant life and health.

Support price

Prices fixed by government policy makers in order to determine, directly or indirectly, domestic market or producer prices. All administered price schemes set a minimum guaranteed support price or a target price for the commodity, which is maintained by associated policy measures, such as quantitative restrictions on production and imports; taxes, levies and tariffs on imports; export subsidies; and public stockholding.

Tariff-rate quota (TRQ)

Resulted from the Uruguay Round Agreement on Agriculture. Certain countries agreed to provide minimum import opportunities for products previously protected by non-tariff barriers. This import system established a quota and a two-tier tariff regime for affected commodities. Imports within the quota enter at a lower (in-quota) tariff rate while a higher (out-of-quota) tariff rate is used for imports above the concessionary access level.

Uruguay Round Agreement on Agriculture (URAA)

The terms of the URAA are contained in the section entitled the "Agreement on Agriculture" of the Final Act Embodying the Results of the Uruguay Round of Multilateral Trade Negotiations. This text contains commitments in the areas of *market access*, domestic support, and *export subsidies*, and general provisions concerning monitoring and continuation. In addition, each country's schedule is an integral part of its contractual commitment under the URAA. There is a separate agreement entitled the Agreement on the Application of Sanitary and Phyto-sanitary Measures. This agreement seeks establishing a multilateral framework of rules and disciplines to guide the adoption, development and the enforcement of sanitary and phyto-sanitary measures in order to minimise their negative effects on trade. See also *Phyto-sanitary regulations* and *Sanitary regulations*.

Vegetable oil

Defined as rapeseed oil (canola), soyabean oil, sunflower seed oil and palm oil, except in Japan where it excludes sunflower seed oil.

Voluntary Quota Restructuring Scheme

Established as part of the reform of the European Union's Common Market Organisation (CMO) for sugar in February 2006 to apply for four years from 1 July 2006. Under the scheme, sugar producers receive a degressive payment for permanently surrendering sugar production quota, in part or in entirety, over the period 2006-07 to 2009-10.

WTO

World Trade Organisation created by the Uruguay Round agreement.

OECD PUBLICATIONS, 2, rue André-Pascal, 75775 PARIS CEDEX 16
PRINTED IN FRANCE
(51 2008 10 1 P) ISBN 978-92-64-04590-3 – No. 56211 2008